DELIA'S JOURNEY

CAROLINE RUSSELL CLARK

Cover and Interior Design by Petya Tsankova
Publishing Support: Clapham Publishing Services

With much love to my mother Jocelyn Delia
and to the 11 great-grandchildren in whom she delighted
as she neared her end in 2015.

We continue to weave our threads.

DELIA'S JOURNEY

1797-1840

1. Western Door to Halifax Piece Hall (Author 2019)

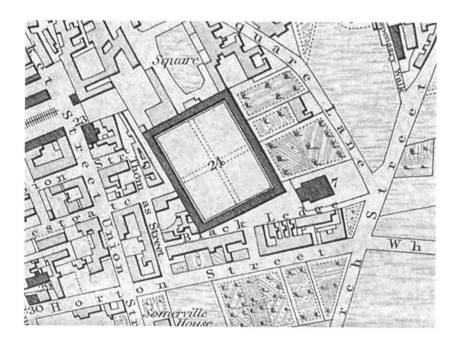

*2. Map of Halifax with Piece Hall 24, Square Chapel 7 and Church
Street on right (Held in Halifax Library)*

Contents

Introduction

This is the story of a family from 1797 until 1840—an ambitious, God-fearing, middling Yorkshire family. At a time of economic upheaval they struggled to overcome political turmoil, survive financial hardship and make their mark on civic society. By 1840 this family of twelve adults and eight children decided to leave their home near Halifax and sail halfway round the world to the unknown land of South Australia; they left behind one married daughter, and all they had ever known. Their 1840 migration was a common story throughout the nineteenth century; it is still a common story in the twenty first. I am a descendant of those people. Here follows my attempt to flesh out the lives of these forebears, driven away by harsh conditions at home and pulled overseas by visions of freedom, independence and prosperity.

I uncovered their story through five years of diligent research in family papers, libraries, museums, on the internet and by walking those same hills and valleys. These people existed; these incidents occurred. Having said that, it is not always possible to place people with absolute certainty in particular places. Many in Calderdale share the surname Mellor, and the Christian names of Thomas, Joseph, Joshua, Hannah, Elizabeth and Mary. Despite obvious confusion I have used the repeated names the Mellor family used. It might have been easier to give them different ones but I wanted to convey life as they had lived it.

Halifax parish in Yorkshire's West Riding, seventeen miles by eleven, was the largest in England and a powerhouse of growth and industry; nevertheless it was a small neighbourhood. In 1821 the census counted 93,000 souls across the parish and 12,000 in the town itself. Mellors, Thorntons, Turners, Walkers and their relatives, dotted the hills and valleys. This Mellor family lived and worked within seven or eight miles of each other, around Halifax and neighbouring Huddersfield. Neighbours had a good knowledge of each other, sharing attitudes and views and meeting regularly at church, chapel, workshop, and marketplace. They left behind a few photographs, a few notes in newspapers, a tiny glimpse of attitudes coming through my grandmother, and three accounts written in south Australia, two by Delia's husband, Daniel George Brock and one by Thomas Mellor's grandson. I trawled church and chapel records, newspapers, journals and historic accounts. I derived thoughts and feelings of the characters by imaginative historical reading, by analyses of historical texts, and by re-reading Charlotte Bronte who was a local contemporary, George Elliot, Elizabeth Gaskell and Charles Dickens, whose father inhabited the adjacent debtor's prison in London at the same time as Thomas Mellor, the father of Delia Mellor. To depict family life of the 1800s I've drawn from today's experiences. While transformed by material differences between the two centuries, human life repeats itself. Raising children, making decisions, adjusting to change, dealing with difficulties—all draw on the same human resources today as then. From records of the times I deduced contemporary attitudes driving emigration. Feelings though are imagined, not factual.

I include illustrations from books, maps, newspaper cuttings and photographs held by Calderdale Library in Halifax and Elland, and by the University of Huddersfield library. The wonderful Myers Map of the Parish of Halifax surveyed in 1834 and 1835 has been a mine of information as to how people moved and lived in this small area of hills, wooded valleys and plentiful streams. I have a few photographs of the individuals mentioned in this story—and my own photographs of the Halifax/Huddersfield of today. I rediscover events in early 1800s and end it in 1840 with the family on the brink of a new Australian life and, as I am unfamiliar with that next chapter—but many others are not, I leave that story to them; this is my story of how the family came to South Australia on 7th July 1840.

The Mellor family is largely unknown to their present descendants; their names, places of birth or occupations. Or why they sailed for three months in a small wooden sailing ship across deep oceans to an unknown world. I hope to show my grandchildren—and others—that there is an inheritance handed on unevenly and unwittingly as families struggle, an inheritance enabled by loving ties across the generations; and that living requires courage and endurance. It is in these stories that we find threads linking us with those who have gone before, threads of ordinary life, daily ambition and familial affection. My daughter Esme Delia was named after my grandmother, who in turn was named after her grandmother Delia Mellor, one of that emigrating family of 1840. The latest Delia was named after her great-grandmother, Jocelyn

Delia. That naming was enabled by the love transferred between eight generations—not because it was the name always handed down but because it was the name of much loved women passed on in their memory, and in honour of the respect with which they were held by their children and grand-children.

3. Northern England

"The Pennine Hills run down central England's northern spine. Liverpool and Manchester lied to the west on lowlands while Newcastle and Hull lie to the east. Halifax, in the Calder valley, and Huddersfield to the south-east in the Colne valley, lie centrally within the Pennine Hills. To their south lies Sheffield while Bradford is 8 miles distant to the north and Leeds is 15 miles northwards. Oldham lies close to the Pennine Hills on the road from Manchester to Wakefield. The River Calder runs past Halifax, Brighouse and Wakefield and is fed by the Colne flowing in below Huddersfield. Together they flow into the Trent which takes them northwards to the sea at the Humber River with its ports of Hull and Grimsby."

*4 and 5. 1834/1835 Myers survey Map of Halifax Parish
held in Halifax Library.*

Green shows parkland: hatchings show slopes: blue rivers: railway marked but not completed until late 1840: wooded areas shown by trees: houses and tracks and roads marked

Historical and Geographical Information on West Yorkshire in 1800

Halifax—In 1832 a town of 12,000 lying above Hebble Brook, a River Calder tributary: overcrowded, dirty and full of the cloth industry. The centre of England's largest parish which stretched 11 miles by 17 and where 80,000 more people lived scattered over its moors and hillsides. Bad harvests contributed to widespread poverty and famine. The Piece Hall, Europe's biggest cloth hall, opened over fifty years previously in 1779. During the sixteenth and seventeenth centuries its woollen industry was driven by an army of independent crafts people and traders. The industrial revolution of late eighteenth and early nineteenth century saw a shift away from independent hilltop clothiers, weavers, spinners, dyers and fullers to larger mills in the valleys employing more women and children at cheaper rates. The factory system was being established. During the nineteenth century Halifax battled and lost its pre-eminence to Huddersfield, six miles to the south, on the banks of the River Colne.

Huddersfield—A smaller centre than Halifax, from 1800-1840, it was a centre of political unrest. Financially it prospered but many small businesses faced decline and disruption due to the concentration of wealth in the hands of increasingly powerful mill-owners. Large gatherings, such as 7000 at Steep Hill in 1814, and in 1839, increased fear— as did militia forces imported from other English areas, brought in by the government to quell political discontent. Militias were raised from volunteers; the men were not regular soldiers but were led by army officers and were paid when required to serve. The British had held a deep aversion to a standing army since the turmoil of the Civil War in the seventeenth century.

Elland—Part of Halifax parish but with its own ancient chapelry of St. Mary. Since medieval times, Elland bridge over the Calder enabled passage between Halifax and Huddersfield. Above the town to the south east lay Upper Elland and to the west rose the hillsides on which was perched the small hamlet of Greetland. The churchyard of St. Mary's has gravestones recording long-past woollen merchants and clothiers. People farmed sufficient land in their closes to keep themselves in food. They used the profit from wool worked in the winter to raise their annual income above subsistence level.

Upper Elland—**A** small hamlet on hillside above Elland on the way to hill-top Rastrick with a collection of houses today named as Banks.

Rishworth—In 1822 this was a small settlement lying six miles west of Halifax, beyond the nearby township of Ripponden, on the road to Oldham. The road then climbed on up to the moors before descending to the Lancashire cotton towns on the west of the Pennines. This small collection of houses included a Baptist chapel and manse, a school and a mill, and housed a population of 1588.

Grimescar—Steep wooded slope behind Fixby Hall lying behind Upper Elland and leading very sharply downhill to Longroyd Bridge over the river Colne and thence to Huddersfield.

Lockwood and Dungeon Bottom—Small settlements lying beyond the Colne in the next valley of the River Holme which flows into the Colne just before it reaches Huddersfield. Further downriver the Colne flows into the Calder and together they then flow into the Trent and finally come to the sea on the Humber.

Brandyholes and Sunnybank—2 farm-steads on the steep hillside of **Greetland** looking south over Blackburn stream which flows into the Calder above Elland Bridge.

Rastrick—A village above Calder River, a mile or so beyond Upper Elland, whose business later moved to Brighouse in the valley below.

Brighouse—A quiet trading centre, lying on the river Calder and its canal, keeping its small town feel despite overtaking Rastrick in size and importance during this period.

Wakefield—An older market town downstream on the Calder River where Magistrates held Quarter Sessions dispensing justice over debts and small criminals.

Elland Canal—An early canal from Manchester on the western side of England, through the Pennine hills and past Elland onwards to the Trent River and from there to the eastern port of Hull on the Humber estuary with its long-established trading connections to the Baltic Sea.

Colne Canal—With the opening of Stanedge Tunnel in late eighteenth century, Liverpool and Huddersfield were connected by water—easier for freight traffic.

Copley Bridge—A toll bridge over River Calder for traffic going from Skircoat up to Greetland carrying long established pack horse trails.

Liverpool—A sea-port to west of Halifax reached via canals, taking trade to America and the Far East.

Hull—An ancient port on the east coast, at the mouth of the Trent and other Yorkshire rivers, trading with the Baltic. The Calder and Colne both fed into the Trent so sea port access was secured for central Pennines area by improved canalisation of the rivers both to the east and the west.

London—200 miles to the South and several days distant for all goods but nevertheless well connected by stage coaches and a network of inns for business people and traders. Political administration was run by local magistrates and landlords. Parliament was the means by which rules were set for ordering disputes. By 1832 the whole country was in an uproar over the lack of representation in Parliament for newly important regions and towns such as Manchester which was without representation while Dunwich, formerly a busy Suffolk port but now a tiny hamlet, sent two MPs to Westminster. The House of Lords was forced by the King and the Commons into passing the Great Reform Act in 1832 improving voter representation and interests across the country. Nonetheless, it was nowhere near one man, one vote and women were totally unrepresented.

Harvests were bad in closing years of eighteenth century and again after the eruption of Mount Tamboura in 1815. In the mid-1830s many Europeans faced more disastrous harvests. This economic distress encouraged the development of unrest and ever louder calls for greater voter representation. The Chartist movement grew to its climax after three years of harvest failures across Europe including the terrible famine in Ireland 1845-8 in which there was major de-population across the island. In the 1850s harvests improved and Chartist pressure decreased.

Canals eased transport with locks, wharves and jetties. One man and one horse moved heavy goods previously carried more slowly and expensively by packhorses over the Pennine Hills.

Turnpikes and improved and tolled new roads were built to improve freight traffic in the late eighteenth and early nineteenth centuries. Previously deeply rutted and impassable in winter mud, and baked hard in summer, these ancient roads had made trade slow and difficult. Roads were straightened and directions changed, their funding paid by local tolls authorised by individual Act of Parliament for local companies and landowners.

Fields and moors were 'enclosed' giving better pasturage and more control to bigger landowners; the poor lost grazing for their animals and hunting for small game. The fairness or otherwise of enclosing land formerly held in common was deeply contested at local meetings but frequently passed by individual Acts of Parliament.

Fixby Hall—A house and park on the hilltop between Huddersfield and Elland. Inhabited at this time by the Thornhill family, their steward Richard Oastler, was a vocal supporter of the Factory Act (1833) which limited the hours worked by women and children under 18 to 10 hours a day. He rode into Elland for the regular Sunday service at St. Mary's while his wife followed on a donkey. (see *Olde Elland; Lucy Hammerton*)

Maisters—In seventeenth and eighteenth century Yorkshire small crafts-men and independent maisters flourished: weavers, fullers, spinners, combers, tenters and a host of other related skills co-operated with each other, often co-ordinated by clothiers—middle men travelling across the hills, taking wool to craftsmen in their homes, and the resultant pieces of cloth weekly to the cloth halls in towns like Halifax, Huddersfield, Bradford and Leeds. Clothiers were maisters in their fields and employed small teams of workers in workshops across the hills. They ranged from one man operations to bigger merchants trading with others across the country. In the late eighteenth century mills grew in size and importance and their masters, mostly mill owners with some capital to invest, grew richer and more powerful. Maisters retained their independence but by 1850 they were largely replaced by factory and mill masters employing hundreds of waged workers. The piece working of earlier days vanished. These Mellors were clothiers who lost their battle to remain independent—hence their emigration to a land where they built and retained their own businesses.

England's response to poverty and criminal behaviour was incoherent; political electioneering was corrupt. The banks were not yet a source of reliable credit—debts were not systematically resolved. Dickens wrote extensively about these problems in *The Pickwick Papers*, *David Copperfield*, *Great Expectations* and *Nicholas Nickleby*.

Lock up in Elland town outside the Savile Arms had written above the door, "Whoso obey the law is wise."

Halifax Prison in Gaol Street with wall drawings uncovered in 1909 from late eighteenth century; on its demolition in 1975 the drawings were again reported in local newspapers.

Wakefield Prison—Prisoners held there were brought before Quarter Sessions Magistrates.

Prison in York Castle—Prisoners were held here before trials; it was the site of Luddite executions in January 1813 carried out 48 hours after the trial was concluded so fearful were the authorities of riots and disturbances.

Prisons in Southwark, London—King's Bench next door to Marshalsea both now demolished. Dickens' father was imprisoned in 1824 in Marshalsea for debt. Both these prisons held debtors in poor conditions against which Quakers like John Howard, Elizabeth Fry and others campaigned for many years before system was fully overhauled in 1869.

South Australia—Declared a province on December 28th 1836 by Act of the British Parliament. The British Government, worried about national unrest, viewed settlement in the colonies as a way of providing the poor with a new life. To fund this, land in South Australia was sold to rich Englishmen, enabling the South Australia Company to offer free passage to 11,518 migrants between 1836 and 1841, workers who would develop the Province. People emigrating were mostly skilled craftsmen and professional classes hoping to ease their financial difficulties—and who had some financial reserves with which to cushion their start in the new land, not really the working craftsmen the government had desired. The UK government published advertisements and held popular public meetings in Scotland, Ireland, East Anglia, the West Country including Gloucestershire, Kent, Sussex and in the West Riding of Yorkshire—all areas of unrest and poverty. The one type specifically excluded from this new state were convicts—many of whom had been transported to New South Wales, Victoria and Tasmania (then known as Van Diemen's Land).

Adelaide—The capital of the new state of South Australia was laid out on a grid system by Colonel Light and in 1841 had 2900 households, approximately 9200 people in the town and perhaps some 6200 beyond it. As distances were great and roads mostly absent, the population was probably bigger than recorded by, among others, Daniel George Brock, later Delia's husband. Riding in the territory to the north of Adelaide with his dog Sergeant he recorded what he saw in his first journal for the South Australian Register, the newspaper of record for those early days. Port Adelaide served the capital as its lifeline to England. In 1838 George Gawler, a military officer of distinction from the Peninsula Wars, was appointed Governor and sailed for Adelaide on the Peston Bomanjee along with Hannah and Joshua Fisher, Delia Mellor's eldest sister and her husband. The South Australia Company wanted to increase the number of women travelling out as the early ships had been full of young men. Certainly the speed with which both Delia and Mary married after their arrival in July 1840 suggests it was straightforward to make marriages to secure their futures in Adelaide, while possibly more difficult in Halifax, given their father's chequered history as a failed clothier and manufacturer.

Thomas and Peggy Mellor's Family in 1840

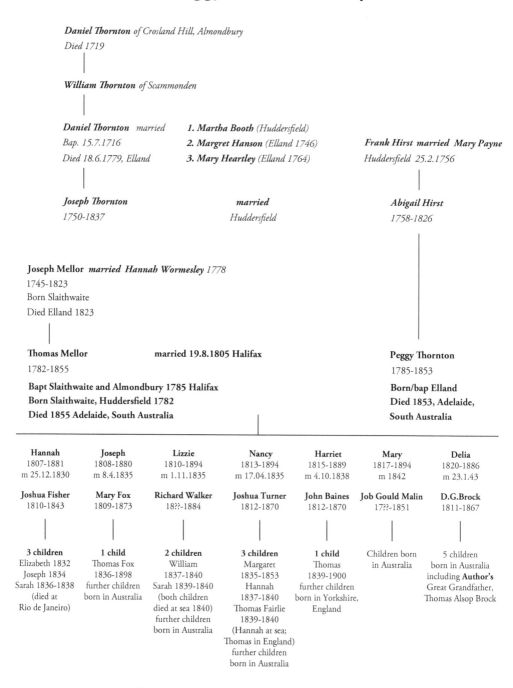

Daniel Thornton *of Crosland Hill, Almondbury*
Died 1719

William Thornton *of Scammonden*

Daniel Thornton *married*   **1. Martha Booth** *(Huddersfield)*
Bap. 15.7.1716   **2. Margret Hanson** *(Elland 1746)*   **Frank Hirst married Mary Payne**
Died 18.6.1779, Elland   **3. Mary Heartley** *(Elland 1764)*   *Huddersfield 25.2.1756*

Joseph Thornton   *married*   **Abigail Hirst**
1750-1837   *Huddersfield*   *1758-1826*

Joseph Mellor *married Hannah Wormesley 1778*
1745-1823
Born Slaithwaite
Died Elland 1823

Thomas Mellor   **married 19.8.1805 Halifax**   **Peggy Thornton**
1782-1855   1785-1853

Bapt Slaithwaite and Almondbury 1785 Halifax   **Born/bap Elland**
Born Slaithwaite, Huddersfield 1782   **Died 1853, Adelaide,**
Died 1855 Adelaide, South Australia   **South Australia**

Hannah	Joseph	Lizzie	Nancy	Harriet	Mary	Delia
1807-1881	1808-1880	1810-1894	1813-1894	1815-1889	1817-1894	1820-1886
m 25.12.1830	m 8.4.1835	m 1.11.1835	m 17.04.1835	m 4.10.1838	m 1842	m 23.1.43
Joshua Fisher	**Mary Fox**	**Richard Walker**	**Joshua Turner**	**John Baines**	**Job Gould Malin**	**D.G.Brock**
1810-1843	1809-1873	18??-1884	1812-1870	1812-1870	17??-1851	1811-1867
3 children	**1 child**	**2 children**	**3 children**	**1 child**	Children born	**5 children**
Elizabeth 1832	Thomas Fox	William	Margaret	Thomas	in Australia	born in Australia
Joseph 1834	1836-1898	1837-1840	1835-1853	1839-1900		including **Author's**
Sarah 1836-1838	further children	Sarah 1839-1840	Hannah	further children		Great Grandfather,
(died at	born in Australia	(both children	1837-1840	born in Yorkshire,		Thomas Alsop Brock
Rio de Janeiro)		died at sea 1840)	Thomas Fairlie	England		
		further children	1839-1840			
		born in Australia	(Hannah at sea;			
			Thomas in England)			
			further children			
			born in Australia			

People's names which are in italics lack further corroborating information.

One child died in England before departure; one died at Rio in 1838; three died among twenty-four deaths from measles in 1840.

More grandchildren were born in Australia after 1840 and three more Baines children in England and more child deaths— families expected to lose children. Thomas and Peggy Mellor were lucky to raise all their seven children.

Information derived from Joseph Mellor's ancestors booklet published in Australia which claimed Daniel Thornton, an ancestor from Halifax was of more substance than the Mellors and that they had a well-respected descendant engaged in early photography.

I used searches on Ancestry records of births deaths and marriages; Australian born family not recorded as all after 1840.

Preface

A Family Embarks at Blackwall
April 1840

6. River Thames from London Bridge 1841, unknown artist, (wikimedia) Tower of London on left in middle background.

It caught my eye. The glint of the spring sun sparkled on the turning crank as the men ran out the freshly caulked rope. I dropped my endless cleaning and went out to the shipyard through our own little gate. I loved hearing the noise of men working; the gulls crying as they swooped overhead to catch scraps of food. It was April and the grey endless winter was passing. I watched the birds settling on the masts as they stood proud over the half-finished hulks. A wag tail was bobbing in a puddle when a little boy ran up to it with his arms flapping wildly. It flew off and a boy cried out, "Mama, Mama, it's frightened of me. See how strong I am."

His mother stood a little way off holding her skirts in one hand to protect them from the mud. She must be a traveller, I thought, shoes quite unsuited to muddy shipyards. On her hip she carried a babe, about six months old I reckoned.

"William, William. Come here. Come. You mustn't run off like that, come back. We don't know where Pa has gone. We must wait."

"Shan't" said the little boy running on ahead skipping through puddles.

His mother cried out sharply, "William, Pa will be so angry."

"He won't Ma—he won't know."

"I'll tell him, William. Come back now."

"You won't, Ma." And the naughty boy ran off through more puddles, making himself dirty and damp.

I could see the poor young woman had no control of the child. He was heading towards the Steaming shop—the men wouldn't like to see him there. They didn't like small children endangering themselves in their workshops. His mother needed help. I ran after the boy and caught up with him as he was contemplating a deeper, wider puddle.

"Come here, William. Come back with me. Come to your Ma like a good boy," I said.

The child looked blankly up at me. He shrank as I held his hand but he stood still and so did I until his mother came up to us both.

"Oh William, you're such a naughty boy. Thank you, thank you so much. His father is looking for the Embarkation office and William ran off to explore. I couldn't keep up with carrying the babe here. I don't know what would have happened if you hadn't chanced by."

"It's nothing," I said as I thought—if he's looking for the Embarkation office they must be emigrating and should not be in the ship building yard. "I think you're in the wrong place. Would you like to me to show you where you should be?"

"Well that's so kind of you but I mustn't take you from your work."

"No trouble at all. I wanted a little break—now the sun's shining after such dull weather as we've had these past weeks. It's not far. Which ship are you sailing on?"

"We're boarding the Fairlie, bound for South Australia. Me and my husband and all my family. We're a big party but we stick together as a family. We're going to a better life."

"You're not from these parts. You don't speak like a Londoner." I was curious to know how far they had already travelled.

"No, I've never been to London before. We come from up north, from Halifax in Yorkshire." She smiled as she spoke of her home. "It's so different at home. We know everyone, we know where to go, and people talk slower. It's easier to catch what they say. And it's so flat round here. Nor do you have woods like ours on steep valley sides—they look lovely in the spring, with their mist of green hovering overhead."

She spoke so well of her home I wondered what had driven her to emigrate across the world.

"Come then, dearie," I said. "I'll show you the Embarkation yard for your ship. It's beside the River, beyond the taverns of Blackwall Lane. They'll point your husband to the same yard. It's busy there though so better hold the boy tight."

I led her across the shipyard beyond the 200 foot long workshop where they cast nails by the ton for the ships. They were moving the new masts into the mast pond this morning so we had to watch for men swinging huge long timbers.

As we came up behind the yards of the two taverns nearest the river a crowd poured out of them moving in a bewildered manner following like sheep the first man through the gates.

"Your husband will be ahead of this crowd so we had better squeeze through. Shall I take the boy so he's safe?"

"Please do, please. It would be terrifying to lose him. I never imagined crowds like this."

"These crowds are nothing. There are bigger ships than the Fairlie, which carry upwards of 300. Then we really see crowds—every emigration ship welcomes its passengers and hundreds of hangers on— families saying goodbye, hawkers selling all that people might have forgot, and then mongers selling pies, eels and whelks—we love them down here among the docks of London. But today it's not so busy— we'll soon find your husband—and the rest of your family."

I took her and the boy through a gate into the cobbled emigration yard. The counting house and offices surrounding it had their doors open, billboards propped against the walls and queues of anxious passengers. There was a cacophony of sound as the hawkers called out their wares, officials yelled embarkation numbers, and agents shouted names of passengers boarding under their auspices. The boy stopped suddenly. He pointed to a coop of chickens and pulled me over to see them.

"Not now. William. First we've got to find your Pa—then we can look at the little chicks. They are tweeting happily in their baskets." As I turned back to his mother I saw her give a relieved wave. The boy started calling, "Auntie, Auntie."

"That's my Sister Turner with her little Hannah," his mother said to me. "Now we'll be safe. Her husband Joshua will have found my husband and they will have our papers. William, can you see your cousin, Margaret? Look, she's over there trying to ease her way through the crowd." I saw a youngster about six squeezing between two women with big skirts. A slender young woman moved over to us, weaving past the porters pushing their barrows perilously close to unwary passengers. She gave a gasp of relief as she spoke to her sister.

"Lizzie, I'm so glad to have found you. My Joshua was worried you'd missed the way. He and your Richard have gone to the office for their papers. I believe Mother and Papa Thomas are already here with Joe and the girls. I'm going mad keeping an eye on my two girls, let alone your wandering imp. Come here William and say thank you to that nice lady for helping you."

William looked as if he would make a dash for it so I held on and moved closer to the woman who was holding another infant by the hand. I reckoned the child wouldn't run so quick with his cousin nearby. I handed the boy over to his aunt and turned to say goodbye to his mother.

"Are you comfortable? All your party with you? Over there to the south is the wharf-side where you'll embark on the boats that'll take you to the Fairlie—there she is, bobbing at anchor out in the river, a fine three-masted ship built a while ago now. We've had her in the yard to mend many a time. She's a sturdy ship, and a good master and crew. You'll have a good voyage aboard her."

"You're so kind, so kind. It's good to hear she's a stout ship. It's rather terrifying to be here at last—ready to leave England forever to find a new home."

Her sister interrupted. "Hurry. Look there's my Margaret coming back to us. She must have seen Mother and Papa, or at least Delia and Momo. You mind the children and I'll help Margaret out of that crowd."

"Nance, I don't know that Hannah will mind me."

"Of course she will but get your friend to help if you're worried."

I could see that Nance was frustrated by her sister's anxiety and stayed by Lizzie's side to check the two children were standing safely together.

"You sound a big family," I said, curious as to how many were going together on the Fairlie. Mostly the emigrants were young men, occasionally accompanied by their new wives but rarely by their parents. This family here seemed to be three generations—the old and the young. I would like to have spoken to the old people for being so brave and adventurous at a time when they might have expected to sit back. You wouldn't catch me emigrating at their time of life.

At the same moment that Sister Nancy reached her child Margaret, three healthy young men emerged from the crowd and hailed William's mother.

"Heigh ho, Sister Lizzie. We thought you had mislaid yourself—getting cold feet perhaps?" the tallest one laughed. "Your Richard found me and Joshua as I was getting Papa's papers examined. The girls had to get their own done but wives go on ours—easier to manage that way. I've got to get back to Mother—she's trying to keep us all together in a tight group—crowds are swirling round her and she looks black as thunder at them. Unless young Delia keeps fluttering her eyelashes at everyone we'll have a fight on our hands. Papa is strutting around saying that people push so much down here in London town, muttering that he, Thomas Mellor, shouldn't be pushed about like a commoner. Once he gets his ticket in his hand though he'll queue for embarkation—and stop fretting I hope."

"It's his way of coping, Brother Joe—and Mother's. She always gets cross in crowds, she never likes them, and this is surely a big, heaving crowd. This lovely lady here saw me lost outside her cottage and has walked me and the babies through to here. So kind bringing us to the right place."

I was listening keenly but was overwhelmed by the numbers of relatives they mentioned.

"I see emigrants most months but I've never talked to any before." I looked appraisingly at Joe, a robust young man.

"So what do you think of us?" he raised his eyebrows at me.

"Brave," I replied. "Brave to be going you know not where, brave to say goodbye to family though I can see you have many of yours with you, brave to sail across the sea to an unknown land. I respect you. We see some odd people in this yard—rude, unkempt and full of swearing—but your family seem very respectable. And yet you are going, leaving this land of plenty."

"We've had our share of troubles in this so-called land of plenty. One of my sisters has indeed stayed in Yorkshire with her husband and baby son. We parted with many tears about two weeks ago. And yes we had trouble with our father who refused for many months to join us. But our youngest sister, Delia, persuaded him by finding all the books and newspapers she could about Australia, and our eldest sister encouraged us to come in her letters from Adelaide since she arrived there two years ago. So you see us—my parents, my five sisters, three brothers-in-law, my own wife and five little grandchildren—all ready to be Australian Mellors and leaving behind the old Yorkshire Mellors. We're leaving troubles here to find independence and our freedom to be God-fearing citizens."

Joe looked full of pride and hope. I wondered whether he would find all he wanted.

At that moment a shout went up. "Boarding! Boarding now!" The crowd surged forward and Joe dived quickly back to find his parents and two younger sisters standing with his own little family.

"Good luck," I called to his departing back.

I turned to the boy's mother. "You'll be fine now. You have your husband and sister with you. Hope you find all you want at the end of the journey. Good luck with the voyage—the Fairlie's a good ship with a good master—I hope your boy William grows up a good strong Australian boy. William, will you look after your mother on this voyage?"

"I always look after Mama." The little boy answered with dignity but not entirely accurately.

Lizzie held the baby and her sister held both the little children's hands while the eldest child, Margaret, walked close. Their husbands strode ahead and were lost to me in the surging crowd.

I wondered what troubles had driven them out of Yorkshire, what ideals inspired them to go—and how they would fare in that fearful long journey to the bottom of the world. What follows is the story I would love to have known in the moment I helped them leave England in April 1840.

PART I
POLITICS FAIL
1797–1813

7. April 28ᵗʰ 1812, William Horsfall, millowner of Marsden, is felled by four gunshot wounds, on the road home after attending Tuesday market at Huddersfield, West Riding, Yorkshire, a political assassination by Luddites, discontented at losing their means of earning a good living. This picture, though full of artistic licence, was published in newspapers at the time.

PART I—Chapter 1

Ambitious Thomas Mellor
1797-1805

8. Looking down the Calder valley, from the hillside of Banks,
Upper Elland, West Riding, Yorkshire. (Author 2019)

Back in 1797, eight years before his wedding in 1805, Thomas Mellor strode down to Elland town, away from his childhood home at Banks in Upper Elland. He passed sullen miners' families who stared at him with blank, unsmiling faces. Over his shoulder he carried a stout stick with a bundle tied to its end. In the bundle he carried a Holy Bible, and his favourite story of Robinson Crusoe, written by Daniel Defoe a century earlier during his stay in Halifax Town, three miles up the hill. Between his precious books, Thomas had folded a nightshirt, a good over-shirt and a strong pair of working breeches. Fifteen years old, he was leaving home to start as an apprentice at his Uncle James' woollen workshops at Brandyholes, a farmstead lying high on the opposite hillside.

As he tried to leave his parents' yard that morning his mother kept him waiting as she thought of yet another 'last word' to remind him of all that he should be doing now he was venturing beyond her sight.

"Thine Uncle James'll keep thee busy, Tommie boy. Thine aunt, his good wife, keeps a clean home and a full stock pot—but there are no books, my son. Father and I have taught thee to read and write. We believe an educated man will not be made a fool by conniving strangers. To get anywhere in this world a man needs to be educated. But Uncle James lives by a different creed. He thought all in family should work early, learn early and live by the wool that brought in the money. No school for his children. He's a good wool man and tha' mun listen to all he tells thee—it'll be good—but thou munna' forget what thy father and I have taught thee. And Tommie, dinna' forget to take time on the Sabbath, on God's holy day to come to chapel, and to come back here. Thy father shalt be missing thee boy, and I shall too but….." and Hannah Mellor lifted a corner of her apron to wipe her eye of a small smut—or tear perhaps, thought her son. Shaking herself, she looked her son straight over.

"Tha'll do my boy, tha'll do. Keep smiling, keep polite and keep thy views hidden."

She reached up to the son now taller than her, gave him a kiss on his ruddy cheek and tapped him on the shoulder.

*9. Looking down from the Stainland Road, Greetland onto Brandyholes
(Author 2019)*

"Run along boy, run along 'afore I get maudlin."

"Quieten your mind, Mam. I'll be fine. I'll remember all you and Dadda have taught me. I'll smile, I'll be obedient, I'll mind my tongue. And Mam, I'll not miss a Sunday dinner. 'Twould be a crime to deprive me of that—so I'll be back. And reet soon I'll be bound."

With another quick peck on his mother's lined and weather-beaten face Thomas picked up his stick, jauntily swinging it over his shoulder. He strode out of the yard and loped off down the hill, whistling as he went. Without turning his head, he raised his hand, waving it over his shoulder at his anxious mother. He was carefree and full of ambition—a young man, he thought to himself, at the start of his journey to wealth and prosperity.

Thomas' father, Joseph had signed a contract with his brother James of Brandyholes, across the Blackburn valley, in Greetland. For seven years this contract bound James to provide dwelling and a learning of the woollen trade to his nephew, Thomas. Joseph handed over a payment and in return Thomas swore to abide by Uncle James' rules, to be diligent in pursuit of his business, to keep himself living decently and soberly, to avoid the young ladies and to maintain himself without a wife until the apprenticeship should end. He also swore to keep his master's business secrets so that none could take advantage of James' clothmaking expertise.

10. Sunnybanks House—next to Brandyholes—as drawn for a book of local places of interest in 1840s— from Archives, Calderdale Library, Halifax

Joseph Mellor had considered sending his son Thomas over the moor at Ainley Top, down to the Colne River at Lockwood, near Huddersfield; some of his family still lived there. Cousin Joseph Mellor, younger than he, lived at Dungeon Bottom on the River Holme, doing well with a team of strong youths serving as apprentices in his shearing workshop. A mile up and over the hill, at Longroyd Bridge over the Colne, was another workshop run by Cousin Joseph's sister-in-law Martha, and her second husband, John Wood. The Elland Mellors knew that these Lockwood cousins, living so close to Huddersfield with its prospering Tuesday markets, were well informed about business opportunities in the area. They had good business contacts with the gentry and with clothiers, traders and merchants. Young Thomas would certainly learn about business there. And yet, Elland Joseph hesitated. In those workshops there was too much talk, too many opinions expressed about people's rights. Dungeon Bottom Joseph seemed too quick with his tongue, told too many people what he thought of politics. Elland Joseph thought that unsafe.

Elland Joseph kept his own counsel. He did not get involved in long discussions about the politics of the day. He found his brother James to be of the same mind. James kept quiet, looked around him, and worked out the best way to buy and sell his cloth. Joseph put Thomas into the less adventurous family because there he saw his son learning more reliably and more honestly. Besides, he chided himself, Thomas' mother would not be best

pleased if her son was too far from his childhood home. So, articles signed in January 1797, Thomas Mellor, aged fifteen, set off to start his apprenticeship in James Mellor's workshops at Brandyholes, on the other side of the Black Burn valley from his Elland home.

11. The view towards Upper Elland over the Blackburn valley from above Sunnybanks, Greetland (Author 2019)

In the farms and hamlets on the hillsides of this, the biggest parish in England, James Mellor was known to be cautious. He could never be persuaded that the threat of French invasion was as drastic as some of the wilder pundits declared it to be. He thought his King unwise to pursue the long war against the French, but he thought it fanciful that working men and women of England would follow French workers in slaughtering their gentry and aristocracy. Uncle James reckoned the country was governed— mostly well, and according to historic laws. He was fierce in his belief that children should learn by working with wool. Wool between a boy's fingers, wool being twisted and spun and dyed, being fulled and woven, wool bought in from the backs of the sheep and sold as cloth in the Cloth Halls of Yorkshire—this wool would teach the youngsters how to live and prosper—not some fancy minister teaching ancient languages spoken by ancient peoples, cooped up in a dark school room. Girls too learnt best how to keep house and feed the family by working alongside their mothers, watching her spin, clean, tend the sick, blend herbs to beat back sickness, and stitch the tiny stitches that kept fine clothes on all their backs. James was a strict but fair master to his apprentices.

The new apprentice, Nephew Thomas, with the assurance of youth, found the world a gladsome place. Uncle James thought him hopeful and full of energy. James would make him a clothier, like his forebears, proudly independent, a sturdy maister, making England the workshop of the world.

Both brothers, James and Joseph took their families to hear god-ly sermons preached in the chapels built by Dissenters on moorland hilltops. As young men, ten years before, they had gone out to the moor to hear the righteous brothers Charles and John Wesley, preach to thousands. Singing, now welcomed in chapels and parish churches, attracted congregations, among them Mellors, both men and women. They sang till their chests burst; they sang 'Amazing Grace' by John Newton, the sea captain rescued by God from his sin of trading in slaves across to America. They sang 'Just as I am, without one plea' written a hundred years earlier by Isaac Walton, and John Bunyan's ever popular,

'To be a pilgrim'. Their religion was heartfelt and Biblical, favouring Non-Conformist views. Chapel was the place where, week after week, friends and relatives gathered for a Sabbath day of listening to the Bible, to hear prayers laid before God, to follow instructions thundered from the pulpits, to worship the Lord in the beauty of holiness. Families brought picnic lunches, the girls taught in Sunday school and the children played around the tombstones while the adults, dressed in their 'Sunday best', bowed and nodded at each other. The Mellors in Elland, the Mellors in Greetland, the Mellors in Marsden and the Mellors in Lockwood were all respectable, chapel-going members of society. They made the wheels turn in their mills and workshops, they kept their families fed from their closes. The Mellors and their ilk were changing England in very dramatic ways, not all of them easy to understand or welcome.

As he strode above the river Calder, with its banks freshly straightened allowing trading barges to connect to the eastern sea at Hull and

to the west at Liverpool, Thomas was not thinking of difficulties nor of dangers. He vaulted over heavy tombstones of long dead Yorkshire wool traders, who had so prospered that large, solid slabs of stone recorded their piety and success. With delight, he leapt down the long flight of steps through the Elland churchyard and out onto the road to Greetland.

12. Gate and Steps down from St. Mary's Church, Elland (Author 2019)

The new apprentice was wondering whether he and his cousin Robert, Uncle James's youngest son, could still escape to the moors. As boys they had run on Greetland Moor trapping small animals and gathering birds' eggs from their nests. They had knocked on housewives' front doors and then run to hide, laughing in their secret place as the irate women shouted at the miscreants disturbing their day's work. They never knew how, but most of these peccadilloes were reported back to Robert's mother and grim was the welcome they felt as they arrived back for their tea!

Turning up the road to Greetland Thomas passed a few cottages, stone-roofed and one storied running at right angles to the road he walked. Half-way up he paused outside the Rose and Crown, a small coaching inn where stage-coaches unloaded their passengers for refreshment with ale and their horses with water. A lad, a friend of Robert's, came out of the yard leading a high-spirited chestnut horse. He looked across at Thomas, saw his bundle and smiled.

"Off to work, Thomas, is it? You've your stick and bundle— travelling far?" he called over as Thomas sat on the low wall opposite the yard.

"Aye indeed," Thomas called back. "I'm off to Uncle James' at Brandyholes. I'm to be his new apprentice."

"That's a good place to work. He's a fair man and he's allus got the wool coming in—and going out for that matter. His missus keeps a good table, or so I've heard."

Thomas replied with a laugh and shrug. "It's good enough but there are many mouths to feed and if one don't mind one's manners, the place is lost." He wasn't sure that this boy knew quite how fierce his aunt could be.

The stable boy grinned back. "We've heard of your jokes and japes with Robert, that's for sure. It's no wonder you've had the back end of your aunt's tongue. You'd better be keeping yourself out of trouble now that you're a working lad."

"Aye, that I will and all—as long as it's not too boring being good." Thomas was eyeing the beautiful horse with obvious awe. The glossy chestnut was standing patiently holding his head still and watching the two boys carefully.

"I have to be minding me' business myself. This beauty here is William Horsfall's mount and he's a testy man, wanting everything yesterday. If I haven't given him water and brushed him down by the time Master Horsfall comes out ready for his ride over to your own relative, Benjamin Mellor, I'll get no tip and that means no cheese for my dinner tonight."

The stable-boy led the horse across the yard to the mounting steps with its iron ring for hitching the horse's bridle and went for the pail of water.

Young Thomas had heard of William Horsfall, the ambitious mill owner who wore impressive over-coats and rode magnificent horses. The gossip went that he was a harsh master at his mills in Marsden, in the upper Colne Valley. He drove hard bargains and was wont to undersell his rivals. Ready with his whip, he had no time for most of

his neighbours. His aim was to rise high so he could mix with the 'better sort of man'. He chose his horse to impress—and Thomas was impressed. He knew he wanted to ride in the same style, to be as well turned out as this rising man. Thomas watched the horse being hitched to the ring, then picked up his bundle and set off up the hill.

13. Mill and weaver's cottage in Greetland (Author 2019)

He climbed on, past Sunnybank with its row of cottages behind the big farmhouse. He heard the spring water bubbling from the rocks and turned down the track to the barns and house of Brandyholes. Three-storey weavers' cottages stood tall against the lane with barns and sheds crowding closely around. At the farmhouse door he raised his hand to the knocker but realising it was half-open he pushed, and stepped inside. Blinded by the dazzle of the low sun, the darkness inside obliterated his sight. Hesitantly, he stood on the threshold, suddenly over awed by the newness of his role in this familiar room.

14. Farmhouse and cottages at Brandyholes (Author 2019)

"Oh it's you, young Thomas. Come inside. Don't stand there gawping. This ain't no lion's den, and you be no Daniel neither lad. Just come on in and gather yourself. You'll be sleeping in the barn with the other two apprentices. Across the yard. Go, set things down and come back over. I take it you'll be joining us in some mid-morning porridge? Them men'll be in soon—and hungry. They've been out on the hillsides working since sun-up so no lingering if you want a bowl."

His aunt stood at the table with a big pot in front of her. She didn't look up and, seemingly, did not expect an answer. Thomas turned and moved swiftly across the yard to the barn with the ladder propped against the wall. He climbed easily to the loft door.

The morning's newness had whetted his appetite so he moved quickly. In the loft he saw three bed pallets laid on the floor under the rafters. He set his stuff down beside one and went back to the house-body, or the kitchen. The men had come in from their work in the woods and on the closes. Thomas had to stand at the back of the queue for his portion. He kept his mouth closed, carefully watching what the men did. Weavers piled into the crowded room, combers and small children following behind. Thomas slotted himself in their wake. He was part of James Mellor's establishment at Brandyholes. An apprentice clothier, he was on his way.

PART I—Chapter 2

A Narrow Escape
January 1805

15. Older man at weaving looms; Golcar, a village high above Longroyd Bridge in Colne Valley Huddersfield
(Colne Valley Museum, Golcar, West Riding, Yorkshire by permission author 2019)

The seven years of his apprenticeship to maister, James Mellor were kind to his nephew, Thomas. The household was well run, he was well fed, the workshops were well-organised and people co-operated productively. Thomas learnt to speak wisely to his fellow workers. He minded his tongue in front of both customers and suppliers—and he asked for guidance from those who knew how to do things. He poked his nose in quiet corners to uncover unexpected reasons for why things were as they were. He watched men and machines at work and he learnt what to expect from a good craftsman. He developed a love of fine woollen cloth and of the smoky colours this wool could be dyed. Men began to ask him his opinions and he learnt to persuade uncommunicative weavers to accept his price for their woollen pieces of cloth, their kerseys and worsteds. Customers enjoyed doing business with him and he learnt to chat easily over a slow pint of ale and then to close a good sale in the shop-lined arcades of the cloth hall. Thomas at twenty three was ready to become a maister. He was enjoying himself.

In January 1805, as on most wintry Saturday mornings, Uncle James sent Thomas two miles up the hill to Halifax's Piece Hall with bundles of cloth gathered in over the week from hill-top weavers. Once there Thomas opened the shutters on the small room next to his friend Humphrey Holroyd's business. Together they brought down the bars and shutters of their stalls as the sound of unlocking padlocks and un-packing bundles resounded around the great square. Carriers and carters shouted at their animals to hey up and move over while merchant voices were subdued and infrequent. The familiar ritual and routine of setting out their tables with the week's goods took everyone's intense concen-tration. By the time the bell rang at ten o'clock the windows were open, the tables in the shops behind spread with cloth, the shelves arranged with neat folds of cloth pieces. Men stood ready, pouches hanging from their belts. The doors opened and the shuffle of many feet, the clatter of clogs, the buzzing of voices spread around the quiet arcades. Within five minutes the bustle and noise of 315 stalls doing business drowned every other. For the next four hours trading was intense—until the bell

sounded ringing out from its roof top. Business done; the public left. The huge doors to the lanes and alleys of Halifax town were bolted shut and the clothiers turned into their stalls, packing away and tidying up.

Thomas, nearly finished with his tidying, called over to his friend in the neighbouring stall. "Humph, what about a drink when we've finished. I sorely need to whet my whistle—so much chat for so long my throat's quite dry."

16. A Corner of the Halifax Piece Hall (Author 2019)

"Give me some moments and I'll be with you Thomas. These pieces here are all a'jumble."

"You be slow, my friend. What are you doing? Dreaming life away, I guess."

"My last customer shillied and shallied, first this piece, then that. He had me take them all out one after the other—and then didn't buy an inch. I was screaming at him…in my head only of course."

"I'll warrant you were, Humph. Was he tricking you, looking at all your cloth and stringing talk out so that outside he can offer a cheaper deal?"

"No, I don't think he was one of them chancers. But I do reckon he was sussing out how good was the market. With business so slow the agents from London and Manchester are always trying to find cheaper suppliers for dealing outside the Cloth Halls."

"It's the war, Humph, the trade embargoes with Europe that

Napoleon set up, that aggrandising devil. The Frogs follow him and now he controls so much of Europe he's freezing out our business—and we suffer. Wish we could end it and get back to normal."

Thomas was exasperated by the barriers to trading suffered all over Europe. It was true that embargoes were sometimes broken, that goods could travel between England and the Continent, but conditions were difficult and despite his contacts with the army and navy, smaller clothiers like him were losing out to the bigger ones. The universal fear that Napoleon Bonaparte would try to invade Britain had everyone alarmed. Thomas, tending to the optimistic view, rather discounted that panic but nevertheless it dimmed his hopes for a bright future.

Humphrey called back to him, "Never mind all that, Thomas. We'll get by. People need warm clothes whatever happens. C'mon now, it's drinking time. I've a strong thirst."

The two young men lifted the bars, slotted them across their shutters and clicked the padlocks into their hasps on the window frames. They  pulled their heavy overcoats close around themselves, hiding the weighty pouches hanging off their belts. Pickpockets in the crowded alleys and lanes outside were only too eager to take their money and their keys. Half an hour later they were sitting in their favourite inn across the town in Bull Cross with two tankards of ale standing on the table in front of them. They'd eaten a good pie and felt ready for the walk back down the hill to the Calder River and over the little bridge at Copley.

17. Belfry over the Piece Hall (Author 2019)

Suddenly, there was a commotion. Outside they heard swearing and sickening thuds landing on yielding bodies. Cudgels were raised and blows rained down. Startled they looked sharply at each other and rose as one.

"It's the Press. Quick, Thomas, quick."

"I'd heard they were in town but didn't think it true. Out by the back, don't want them to see us. They'll ask no questions, just grab us. Then we'll have to pay good money to be free—if they let us go. Don't want to go sailing on the open seas—scary stuff."

They shot down the back passage of the inn, out into the yard behind. Cautiously they looked up towards the front and saw a burly man standing across the entrance with his back towards them.

"It'll have to be the back gate and up and over that wall there. They won't be guarding that—they won't know about it." Humphrey mouthed at his friend as he turned to run down the narrow passage.

Thomas, as the taller youth, jumped up to the top of the wall and turned to lend a hand to his shorter friend. Once over the wall they raced

along the alleys, always turning down hill. Up one little street they saw a crowd of women surrounding a struggle. The women were beating against thugs who were handcuffing a boy, yelling at them to leave him alone. Someone saw them and shouted. They ducked into a doorway and ran. The Press Gang gave up. It was enough to deal with the women without running after two sturdy-looking lads. They could come back for them another day.

18. Piece Hall, first floor balcony (Author 2019)

The King needed sailors for his navy, the navy that enabled merchants to trade their cloth despite the French blockade. The Press Gang, formerly working in seaside ports where sailors lived when not serving at sea, had to move to inland towns to press more young men into His Majesty's ships. Landlubbers with no knowledge of the sea or of ships were now caught and consigned to the narrow confines of sailing ships armed with rows of cannon. No landlubber wanted to serve. The money was never as good as it was claimed to be; the food was lousy and gave men rickets and scurvy; the portion of rum was never enough to dull the dreariness of months at sea. Men were away for months and sometimes years. Thomas and Humphrey ran fast downhill, away from the Press.

19. Merchants in one of the 315 rooms (Author 2019)

Thomas was panting and tugging to loosen his neckerchief. "Reckon we're safe now, Humph. We're here at Skircoat Green. Look back—we can see the road clearly, no trees hiding anyone. Let's slow down, my legs are turning to jelly."

Humphrey too was sweating and loosening his coat as he ran. He panted as he talked.

"Thank the good Lord they didn't see our pouches. Wouldn't trust any of that lot to keep their hands off 'em. Indeed the pouches would have given them reason to chase us harder. They're a low bunch of men, even if they are serving His Good Majesty, God save him."

"It's wrong, plain wrong to take men off the streets like that. We've got lives to lead. We can't just leave everything and go. What would the women do? What would happen to business?" Thomas was indignant and gesticulating wildly as he fulminated against the Press Gang.

Humphrey shook his head more thoughtfully.

"If only they'd treat with Boney and stop this endless war—then there'd be an end to all this." One of his cousins had been seized a few months before and he knew all too well how hard it had been for his aunt to cope with her lad's unexpected departure.

Thomas, with his ambitious plans for success as a clothier, was desperate to secure a remedy against this disaster.

"They say they don't take married men. Perhaps I'll do something about that. Perhaps I can find me a good girl to take to wife." He was horrified at losing his valley as well as his ambitions within those valleys. He needed to protect this home, his vision.

20. Ancient packhorse track up through Kings Dean woods from Copley Bridge to Greetland Moor (Author 2019)

"Hey boyo," yelped out Humphrey in considerable surprise. "You won't catch me marrying to escape the Press Gang. I'd sooner run all day and run all night for a month than do that. That's a mug's game, Thomas. Are you soft in the head? No! No babies, and no trouble. My legs'll do the running, thanks." Turning to look at his friend to see if he were joking or not, he saw a serious expression on Thomas' face. "Oh no, Thomas. You be not serious—have you an eye on a pretty girl? You'll rue that, Thomas. Keep away from women. They're nothing but trouble." Humphrey gave his friend a shove on the shoulder and they walked along companionably.

While Humphrey took the road across the Calder at North Bridge up to Elland, Thomas turned the other way, down past Lower Skircoat, to the narrow stone bridge at Copley. As he reached the little toll house, he called the toll keeper and handed over his penny. The woods of North Dean beckoned. The copper forest floor rose steeply ahead, its silver beech trunks thrusting upwards towards the light. Thomas stopped to gaze: his favourite wood, his favourite hillside. Even with fear in his belly Thomas paused in wonder, listening to the calls of the birds as they sang from the tree tops asserting their territorial rights.

21. Stile stones, Greetland Moor (Author 2019)

As he climbed the snaking packhorse trail he thought about pretty Peggy Thornton. She was the daughter of Uncle James' friend, Joseph Thornton of Lockwood, over Huddersfield way, the younger sister of Mrs. Hannah Fox of Rastrick. When Joseph Thornton came to see Uncle James he often called on daughter Hannah living on a farm in Rastrick, and brought with him his younger daughter, Peggy. This daughter, formerly a little shadow of her lively elder sister, was growing in her back chat with her father's friends. Thomas had caught her looking at him under her lashes as he joked with the other apprentices.

Peggy was fun. She came of good family and would help any business thrive. What is more she did not purse her lips with displeasure when she heard of jokes and tricks played among the young. She did not furrow her forehead with a deep frown when she heard of wild behaviour. As Thomas crested the steep hill, squeezing through the stone gap in the newly laid drystone walls, he paused for breath on the edge of Greetland Moor. He took in the wide view across to Upper Elland, and stood, as always, in wonderment at the beauty of his home hills. Fields and woods framing stone cottages and snaking walls, spread out and led his eye

over to Ainley Top and Elland Upper Bank, the haunts of his childhood. Peggy, he thought, would be a good companion— and understand his feeling for the land. Thomas strode on to Brandyholes, pleased with his escape, pleased with his morning's work and pleased with the thoughts of Peggy. Married men were exempt from the Press. Marriage would keep him safe; it was time to speak to her father.

22. Looking towards Upper Elland (Author 2019)

PART I—Chapter 3

House Moves
April 1805

23. House at Banks (Author 2019)

Thomas' thoughts of marriage remained unvoiced. After Easter, he went home to Banks, his father's big square house at Upper Elland, on the road to Rastrick and Fixby. It lay under Ainley Top from where water flowed northwards down towards the Calder and southwards towards the River Colne and Huddersfield—a prospering centre for fancy woollen goods. From Ainley Top his mother gazed northwards to her son at Brandyholes. She glanced south to Grimescar woods and saw the road to Younger Joseph Mellor's busy workshop in Lockwood.

As he walked into his childhood home, his mother Hannah called from the back kitchen, telling him sharply that she had missed him at chapel the previous week. He entered, giving her a quick peck on her cheek. She gave him no time to get his breath back before lecturing him about the Sabbath day.

"Tommie, just because there be fairs over Eastertide, tha' munna neglect the Lord's calling. Money is wasted at Fairs and there's trouble with drinking—and young lasses crowding around without their fathers and brethren nearby."

"Mam, I'm grown now. I take care of myself—and I make my peace with the good Lord in my own time, in my own way, not when the minister calls me to."

"Thomas, my son, the good Lord must be heeded at all times. No times are thine: all times are His."

"Amen to that, Mam. And amen again." Thomas was adept at sidestepping his mother's admonitions. "How be ye keeping? As well as ever, I trust. And Dadda, is he well too?"

His mother, with a floury hand, pushed her hair back from her eyes. She was kneading dough for a pudding, her greying hair straggling out of its bun. Eyes creased up in a frown, she punched the dough a bit harder.

"Tommie, I dinna know. I'm worried. Thy father hasna' the strength he once had. He avoids riding up to Halifax and over to Huddersfield, and he spends more time on his papers than he used. He isna' young, he's slowing down. He hates it and fights in himself every time he aches in his knee, which is often especially when it rains. I reckon he's turning things over in his mind all the time. He never talks. But thou knowest thy father, keeps things close to himself and lets it eat away at him."

Thomas nodded and tried to sneak a bit of dough from his mother's bowl. She rapped his knuckles and he was forced to drop it. He knew well how little his father talked: about business, about the family, about anything. Even when they met up in the Piece Hall on Saturday mornings, they never exchanged more than general comments about trading, and those they did were often monosyllabic.

His father, Joseph Mellor, had done well. Carving his way to a comfortable subsistence, he kept his family fed from a farm augmented by a good wool business. For the last twenty-one years he had lived in this big square house with its fertile closes. The local Pitchforth family, who sold stone to London for paving its streets and mined local coal and ran their own mill, was his landlord. Joseph Mellor, well respected in the district as a wool man, kept his word. Well known and well liked in Elland Town, despite being a man of few words, Joseph Mellor was proud of his standing.

24. And 25. Spinning wheel and baskets of wool in a typical clothier's home, Golcar Museum (Colne Valley museum, Golcar 2019)

Thomas was pleased this father had placed him with Uncle James, and not at Dungeon Bottom with Cousin Joseph. Uncle James was approachable, and more trustworthy than Cousin Joseph—who seemed unpredictable in his politics and his friends. Rarely did anyone see Joseph the younger with his relatives; his mother, who spoke her mind freely, dismissed 'them over at Dungeon Bottom' with a quick pursing of her lips and a shake of her head.

After seven years with Uncle James, Thomas traded on his own account as well as his uncle's. He often chatted with the more adventurous, younger clothiers and exchanged views about manufacturing wool. His father, more of a merchant, a middle-man, kept his own counsel, learnt where were the best bargains, then bought and sold quickly. That involved much riding over the moors, much listening, and a good reputation so that men trusted him for a good price and for quality cloth. Despite his father's reputation being so fair throughout Calderdale, Thomas knew William Horsfall, was riding a better horse, with more workers in more workshops, more mills, and was making more noise in the neighbourhood. Watchful Thomas was beginning to realise that men like William Horsfall drove workers harder, ruling with an iron rod and keeping workers close in narrow terraces of cottages. Thomas still dreamed of a stylish horse but was less sure that Horsfall's way was best. He wanted to be well respected by his neighbours, to live in good health on good land. Wool came from the land—and so did food. But working the land meant a man needed physical strength. If his mother was worried about her husband's waning strength, then her worry mattered. Thomas gave her his full attention.

Being married to a taciturn husband made his mother garrulous. She spoke in a jumble of breathless, half-finished sentences. Thomas found it hard to follow her, to determine what was important and what could be put to one side.

"This dreadful war with Boney—dragging on and on. They ne'er listen down in London—the war's good for them but it isna' good for trade here—wool prices down—people buy cotton not wool—though much good it'll do them when the weather gets nippy—and he has to travel further to find customers—and suppliers up on the moors are getting fewer—the canals take lads and lasses away—the moor pony tracks are neglected—life isna' right—people dinna' respect the old ways—wool bundled into warehouses along the canal—no chance for a respectable trader to make good contacts and find a good sale—I dinna' know what Dadda has to do to trade."

Thomas found it hard listening; her worries poured out in an endless stream. Many times he had heard her anxieties about change. Many older people in Elland moaned about what they saw happening around them, about the changes to their trading, but this time Thomas thought she was more rambling than usual and was avoiding her main concern: his father and his aching bones.

He was just about to bring her back to the problem of his father's tiredness when Joseph himself walked into the kitchen. "Good to see thee, young man. Good for thy mother. She has enough to worry about without missing thee, son. I want a word. Come with me to the workshop."

Turning on his heel, he abruptly left the kitchen. Exasperated, his wife threw her dough onto the floured board. "See he canna' take time to welcome thee—let alone explain anything to me."

"Mam, I'm sorry. I'd better go—it never does any good to keep the old man waiting. I'll tell thee how I find him."

Sighing, he went after his father to the workshop in the yard outside, the shop where he had first learnt to spin and sort the wool on which all their comfort depended. Thomas caught up with his father and they went into the shop together. It was empty and, unusually, very tidy. The tools were in neat piles along the walls, and not a wisp of wool escaped onto the floor. In fact, the great baskets that held bales of wool awaiting spinning and fulling were empty and stacked one into the other. Surprised, Thomas looked round,

"Dadda, what's happening? Why no wool?"

"Thomas, I'm selling up. 'Tis time. I canna' get around like I used. My knees crack and ache. I canna' keep going all day and everyday like before. I know Mam is anxious. With thee up in Brandyholes with thy Uncle James there is none to take up the slack. For ten years I've held that small house in Elland as a freeholder, keeping it against this day when I stop renting here at Banks. Mam and I will go down. We can manage a place that size and still be comfortable. Thou canst carve thy own way, settle down as thou shouldst with a good lass, and build thy family and fortune. I'm sixty one this year, not the man I was. I want to keep Mam happy while I can. She dinna' know I'm selling up— none do. Next month rent falls due, on quarter day in June. I'll not pay another quarter's rent. Then the world will know."

Thomas took a step back. Such a long speech from his taciturn father. His head reeled.

"Dadda, I'm shocked. How canst thou do this? 'Tis so sudden. I canna' believe it's the only way. There must be another. Thee and Mam canna' leave this place—'tis in thy bones. It'll break thee to leave thy work, the land, the moor. Thou mun' think again."

"Thomas, cease. It's hard eno' without thee kicking up. 'Tis life. We are but a sparrow flying through our time. We work, we pray, and we go. It's my time to go—shortly but not yet. I want to go with all in order, with Mam safe and secure as anyone can be. I want to enjoy life more, do less worrying, less travelling. It's good to go down to Elland now. I've told Pitchforth's agent we're going and he's content. Come and tell Mam. I've been waiting for thy help."

With a short glance round his beloved workshop, Joseph Mellor stepped out firmly, pushed his shoulders back and, without checking to see if his son was following, walked back to his wife. She had finished her dough making and was sweeping up the table from its powdery, floury whiteness. She put her hands on her hips and said,

"Well I know thee, Maister Joseph Mellor. Thee be planning something—out with it. 'Tis no' good eno' to tell young Thomas. Thou mun talk to me."

"My Dearie, we're selling up. I've given notice on Banks and we will be leaving to go down to the cottage and land in Elland for the next quarter. I'm shutting up workshop. We'll be better that way. Less travelling, less trouble. Young Thomas knows. He's bothered but it's for the best. Thou seest that surely? Now, can we have some dinner and leave off talking?"

The blood drained from his wife's face. She felt winded as though he had punched her. She had known trouble was brewing. But not this. Not this eviction from her home of the last 20 years. Not this cessation of life as she knew it. How could this dour man think it was in order for him to decide her life in an instant, no hint of what he was thinking, no thought for how she felt.

She shouted at him, "How dare thee! How dare thee! Change my life in an instant—and take no thought to me. How dare thee change all, and ne'er talk on't! I'm not doing dinner today—not anymore— manage thyself. Decide alone— no more from me. Thee be a traitor, a rat. I'm gone."

This was shouted back at Joseph from the back door as she ran across the yard. Thomas and his father stood together, stunned into shaken silence. She ran on, past her patch of vegetables, out through the gate and up the moor steps as fast as her heels would carry her.

"I must go to her, Father. I must."

"Aye. Do that Son. Make her see sense, lad."

26. Moor Steps above Banks (Author 2019)

Utterly exasperated by his father's calmness in the face of his mother's distress, Thomas left and followed her up the steps. He knew where she was headed: to the rocky step above the house, looking from Ainley Top down into the valley. It was the place he imagined when he looked out from his new home in Greetland, imagined her sitting laughing in the warmth of the sun as she took a break from the noise of the men and machinery in the workshops around their home. It was the place he had run to as a boy when he was troubled and fearful. It was a place sheltered from the cold northerly winds, a place where he could hear the moor birds calling, the larks and peewits, a place where he could watch the insects busy about their collecting, a place where both he, and his mother felt at peace and full of wonder at the Good Lord's work. He ran and, as expected, saw his mother rounding the bend ahead and turning towards their flat stone. He caught up with her and together, without saying a word, they moved towards their seat. Panting, they sat down. Thomas listened to his mother's harsh breathing. Gradually it eased, and tears began to run silently down her cheeks.

"How could he? How could he decide—and expect me to meekly agree? How could he—after all these years—think I would just go along, as always make myself obliging to his commands? How could he be so high handed, so overbearing? He's worked hard. He's been a good man—never raised a finger to me—but this. This makes me a possession, something with no likes of my own, no wishes. This makes me invisible. I'll never forgive him—never."

Thomas could see how wounded was his mother, but he knew this was what his father always did. Why would his mother be so upset now, when she had had so much experience with his inability to talk decisions? What was it about this decision that was any different from any of the others? His father was a man of few words and of decisive actions, made without consultation. Then, as he looked across to his new home, he remembered what it had felt like those seven years ago when he had first lived at Brandyholes with his Uncle and Aunt. Nothing was in its right place, nothing felt familiar or comfortable. No one noticed if he did anything unusual, no one noticed if he felt unsure of himself. Even the cats in the yard seemed foreign and uncaring. He had nowhere to call his own, nowhere he recognised the animals, the birds or the sun on its leafy journey through the woods around him. So often he had gone outside, looked back over to Banks, and reminded himself of the sun shining on that part of the valley whilst there, in the gloom, on the shady side, he had felt sick with longing to be on his own hillside. His mother knew what it was to be homesick. She feared life in the bustle of Elland town. It was harder to escape the neighbours, to hear the spring birds come back, harder to run up on the moor. He put his arm round her shaking shoulders; they sat in the quiet, secret shade of rock and tree.

Moments later, his mother shook herself and said, "We'd best be going back. I'll not be cooking for thy Dadda this night—but tomorrow I'll face what he's done. I'll do what has to be done—not tonight. I'll lick my wounds alone. I'll have to move down to Elland like he says. Maybe it's for the best—for him anyroads—and maybe that's best for me. Maybe."

Thomas, by now very hungry, was anxious for food but loyal enough to his mother to know that he faced his walk back down to Elland Town and up to Greetland with nothing in his belly, unless he could take a hunk of bread from her kitchen.

As they walked back, his mother said, "I don't see that man ever seeing how unkind he is in his refusal to talk about stuff—but that's as is, and I have to be used to it by now. I'm not going into him—he can worry about me for once in his life—I'll go up to my bedroom—alone."

"I'll come in with thee, Mam. I'll see Dadda and tell him I'll help with the move—when he tells me to come, I'll come—but thou, go to thy bed. He'll come round in a bit. He'll realise he should have talked to you before." Thomas gave his mother a hug as they came to the gate, and then walked into his father's office room in the front of the house.

Shutting the door behind him, quickly and curtly, Thomas said to his father,

"Mam's back. She's upset and doesn't want to eat. I understand how she feels about leaving this place. And about having such short notice.

I'll come back next week, and we can talk about the move and how I can help. I'll not have thee muttering about doing it all thyself. It's tough moving out and it'll be doubly tough on Mam. I'll be there to help, and you must accept that help. Good night now. And think on Mam. She's not like thee, a person of few words, she needs to talk things over. That's not bad, just not thy way. Night Dadda."

"Night, son. I'll be glad of thy help. Night." Joseph grunted at his son, shaken by his wife's fury and his son's agreement with her.

Without waiting for his father's reply Thomas backed out of the room, shut the door and left. As he walked back to Brandyholes his mind ricocheted with questions; about his mother, his father, and his own future now his parents were leaving his childhood home.

PART I—Chapter 4

Decisions
Summer 1805

27. Clothiers on the road -
(book published in 1860 held in Halifax Library)

His father's decision to shut up at Banks, so soon after his own scare by the Press Gang, jolted Thomas into urgent attention towards his future. Thomas had heard stories of travel. People were sailing round the world. Captain James Cook had discovered lands in the Southern seas where it was said, "there be dragons and wild monsters." Some were making fortunes by travelling to India, the West Indies, and to China. Some however were fleeing. Friends and a few relatives had fled to America for freedom for their religious beliefs; others had been transported to Australia for misdeeds: poaching, damaging property or arguing against the gentry and magistrates. That travelling was different; it was neither free nor self-chosen. Transportation, fleeing religious oppression, the Press, all were random, and violent, and forced on English subjects. Their force, the King's force, was irresistible. To move by choice was, for Thomas, incomprehensible; to move by force was disaster writ large.

He feared the sea; he was a landsman who had only once glimpsed the sea. He had journeyed to Hull with Uncle James to see what business was there. What he saw, he didn't like. The Humber estuary was an unending expanse of grey water with low horizons and mewling gulls wheeling in vast, empty skies. The sea spread in front of him as he stood on the wharves, a flat, monotonous grey reflecting grey acres of cloud; gulls screamed as they dived around the ships at the jetties, sailors swore, and dockers yelled roughly. Thomas loved his hills, his valleys, the fresh green of the spring and the golden colours of the autumn. He knew the birds that sang at dawn and dusk, their names and their differing cries. His heart gladdened when he found the first snowdrops and the daffodils bobbing their yellow trumpets among the hedgerows. He feared the sea, its loneliness, the lack of landmarks and his inability to navigate a course through such course-less water. He had to preserve himself.

Married men were exempt from being 'pressed'; Peggy was pretty, he fancied her, so he was serious in suggesting marriage. But first he had to settle his affairs and establish himself as a credible husband to Miss Thornton. Her father would expect no less from her suitor.

A month later, Thomas walked over to visit his cousin Joseph the younger at Dungeon Bottom on the edge of Huddersfield. He took a hunk of bread and cheese and excused himself from his aunt's place for the night. Loping down the hill he passed the Rose and Crown where Robert's friend had become chief ostler with no time to chat with passers-by. William Horsfall and his prize chestnut now frequented the road between Huddersfield and Marsden. Weekly he rode to Huddersfield cloth market, over Longroyd Bridge past John Wood's cropping workshop. His business at Ottiwells Mills was thriving, threatening John Wood's and Cousin Joseph's trade. The maisters and apprentices at both workshops were full of invective against the new mill masters.

28. Clothworkers in Workshop like Joseph Mellor's -
(Book of prints of occupations held in Halifax Library.)

Commonly it was said that Horsfall drove his workers hard; men, women and children. No school, no learning, just scavenging around the deadly machines to collect fluff for re-use amidst the danger of accident if they fell asleep among the machines. Starting at sun up, working until sun down, it was a fourteen-hour day ruled by the factory bell. Too poor for care at their empty homes the children came to the factories where they had no sunlight, no play and little food. Many grew with shortened stature and deformed limbs. Horsfall was a mill owner who believed any improvements in his workers' lives lessened his own rewards. He used his whip to make his factory workers produce more, and ever more. When trade faltered, he had no hesitation in turning off as many hands as he could. He gave no thought to how they could find food without wages.

Horsfall was not well regarded. He and Cartwright, a Methodist chapel man and mill owner at Rawfolds near Hartshead, were often heard vowing to revenge themselves on any who flouted their way of doing business. It was whispered Mr. Cartwright defended his mill with guns and beat his workers as and when he wanted. The tough, rowdy minded young men from the cropping workshops at Dungeon Bottom and Longroyd Bridge saw their prized craft vanishing into the maws of machines; they bad-mouthed the mill owners whenever the talk turned to hardship. Even amiable Thomas took against Cartwright the Saturday he gave his father, Joseph of Elland, a short price for cloth that had not sold in the Piece Hall.

While aiming to become a successful clothier, Thomas was not prepared to use foul means to get there. He knew the value of keeping friends in the wider community. If he wanted to trade, find good wool to sell to the Manchester men, he had to keep on good terms with the Dalesmen who sheared the sheep, with the mills in the valley who spun it into yarn, with the fullers, dyers and tenters working the wool for the weavers on the moors, and with the merchants in Halifax and Huddersfield where the final pieces were sold. Thomas understood all the processes essential for quality cloth—like his father and his uncle and his Mellor kin, Benjamin, John and David. He saw himself following his father and his grandfather's footsteps to improvement.

Unsettled as he was by his father's decision to move down to Elland, Thomas was thinking of his future. A workshop and land in Crosland

Half near Cousin Joseph came up for rent but he felt it was too soon to set up on his own. He owed his uncle James two or three more years of work but was unsure of what should come after that.

He needed advice though, and for that he searched out his worldly, well-connected cousin Joseph. Hence his walk down through the woods of Grimescar and over the next hill into Cousin Joseph's workshop at Dungeon Bottom, a mile beyond John Wood's cropping workshop at Longroyd Bridge.

Striding down the old road through the woods, Thomas heard a woodpecker racketing away in his search for insects. He saw the shiver of branches as a squirrel flew from one tree to the next. At the pool's edge, down in the valley bottom, a wagtail bobbed up and down searching for food while the sun came dappled through the bright wet green leaves onto the valley floor. It was good to be walking. It gave him space

to think. Cousin Joseph Mellor was a few years older and Thomas wondered how he would find him now he had his own workshop full of young men. Joseph rarely came to Banks to see his relatives. And in the past, when he had visited, cheeky young Thomas had been silenced by this lofty man who told the world how it should go on.

29. Former Mill in Dungeon Mill Bottom (Author 2019)

Cousin Joseph was canny and in touch with the wider world. He had opinions on the general climate of politics during this unending war with France and the new one with the United States. He had views about trade and about working practices and where trade was going with the endless embargo on European business. Thomas told himself he would hear the best way forward. He stepped on down the hillside, full of ideas for his future.

In the shearing workshop, Thomas was unnerved. Joseph talked in riddles and it was never clear what he really thought. At one point he was praising the French revolution saying that, like the French workers, good Yorkshire working men needed to be heard by the government down south in London Town. Then an apprentice came in and he asserted loudly that new Parliament Acts were improving working men's lives. He said he had a friend, Francis Vickerman, a rough diamond to be sure, who was ploughing money into mills, expanding the work he was putting out to weavers, and building bigger and better spinning and fulling works. People would see great benefit in this explosion of trade. Cousin Joseph told Thomas that orders were coming in both for him and for his brother-in-law, John Wood at Longroyd Bridge. He added that Joseph of Elland was giving up business at the wrong time, that soon he could subsist on wool alone, that he had no need to keep on farming the closes. Cousin Joseph had never thought much of Thomas' father's business sense and he took no trouble to hide this from his son. He imagined that was why young Thomas had come to talk to him. Though affronted that Joseph was dismissive of his father's skill, there was sufficient truth in his remarks for Thomas to feel uncomfortable. He turned the subject and left the workshop, wishing his cousin well and thanking him for his time.

Half an hour after leaving Cousin Joseph's shearing workshop at Dungeon Bottom, he had walked through Dungeon Wood, and trod up the hillside to Lockwood to see Uncle James' friend, Joseph Thornton, father of bright-eyed Peggy. There he knew, there would be no political talk. The Thorntons kept their views—if indeed they had any—very much to themselves. They knew folk in Huddersfield and

Halifax. They sold well their fancy woollen cloth pieces; when they had sufficient money they improved their machinery and their business prospered. Joseph, a strong chapel man, dressed modestly and soberly; he knew his Scriptures; he served as an elder in his congregation. He walked quietly, worked steadily and kept his family close and loving. His wife's kitchen was warm and laughing where all the talk was of family and family doings. Thomas felt safe with this family; no fireworks nor wild tempestuous calls for action, no shifty evasions when new people dropped in.

After a convivial afternoon with the Thorntons, Thomas called in on John Woods at his cropping workshop. There he saw another cousin George Mellor, a lad ten years younger than himself, and John Wood's stepson. His father had died, leaving a widow and three young children. Fortunately, the widow Martha Mellor had been able to marry her first husband's foreman, John Wood; he kept the business going, and the family comfortably off. Young George, however, as his father's elder son, always treated his stepfather with sullen anger and never forgot his own father's usurpation. Thomas found him a tough, unapproachable lad but feeling sorry for him, gave him a friendly shove on the shoulders and told him to look out for him at the next Huddersfield market. George grunted back at him and sent him off on his walk with a wave. Thomas left with the feeling that George regarded him as a friend rather than a foe in a world filled with enemies.

Cursing as he fell into a deep puddle along the road, Thomas swore at Cousin Joseph. He was wealthy enough to be instructed by the magistrates to keep up his stretch of road. Clearly Joseph was insufficiently in awe of the magistrates to do any such thing. It impeded the travel of his customers, and of himself in going to Huddersfield Cloth Hall, but Joseph saw no reason why he should ease anyone else's way. This cavalier approach to neighbourliness angered Thomas. Joseph might be respectable at chapel but it was clear he kept chapel teaching at chapel and did not let it sway his business dealings. Without further thought, Thomas decided that setting up business in close vicinity to Joseph was a bad idea. He would let the place on Crosland Half go to another

Mellor. He was better off in Greetland, or even Skircoat, nearer Halifax. He would stay alongside Uncle James and the people he knew and trusted.

As he moved through the woods along Grimescar Edge his mind wandered to Peggy. She was a fierce wench—giving as good as she got from any cheeky lad. Her father was an educated man despite not giving Peggy much of an education herself. Thomas enjoyed watching his uncle and her father nattering together. They both laughed from the pit of their stomachs and could be heard exchanging jokes from several yards outside the inn. As a longstanding elder, Joseph knew much about the weaker members of his congregation but, he kept his own counsel. He was never the first to throw stones at his neighbours in difficulties, saying instead, "There, but for the grace of God, go I. Let him without sin, throw the first stone."

The gossiping neighbours ceased their chatter, in Joseph's presence at least. He never raised his voice against anyone and kept his own council about town affairs. His wife kept a neat and tidy house—and welcomed all to her table. Thomas thought Peggy must make an excellent wife—and she was pretty. He made his resolution. He would take Peggy and her family to the singing at High Hoyland on Ascension Day, six weeks hence. A Mellor cousin with a fine voice was singing in Handel's Messiah, and Bach and Haydn were being played at the same concert. It would be a long day with a ten-mile carriage ride in the morning, and the same again homewards after the concert. But it was May, the days were lengthening and warmer. It would be good to show Peggy that talent ran in his family—and the religious music would appeal to her chapel-going parents.

He knew Peggy loved singing as he had heard her complaining about the choir at chapel being led by older members whose voices were wobbly and cracked. She would love to hear strong, bright, young voices at Hoyland. His mother would enjoy taking a picnic to entertain the sober Thorntons. This would be a grand outing; he must talk to his mother.

Then he had to talk to his father, to mull over his marriage plans, his business moves, and to let him know how Cousin Joseph seemed 'not quite straight' in his views. In his heart he hoped to ask Peggy for her hand at the concert but he had to get clearance for his proposal from her father. Indeed, he needed his own father's approval before he built any solid plans. Thomas walked home deep in thought.

PART I—Chapter 5

Musical Picnic
May 1805

30. Tombstones in High Hoyland churchyard (Colin Park - Wikimedia)

Three weeks later, Thomas' mother, Hannah Mellor, threw her window open to a vast dome of sharp sky, limpid and magnificent. The sun's light was rising behind the hills. The trees outside her window, scarcely clothed in their delicate tracery of fresh, unfurling green, shivered overhead; underfoot, the damp, dark ground, lay quiet while the birds clamoured in bursts of thrilling song, interspersed with the drumming hammer of the woodpecker and the repeating call of the cuckoo. Today, Ascension Day Thursday 24th May 1805, she was riding over to High Hoyland to have her soul lifted by music— and, she hoped, her life enriched by the betrothal of her son. She ran downstairs to the kitchen and busied herself in preparation for their picnic.

Hannah pressed and starched her best dress. She hung her husband Joseph's one dark, dress coat behind their door to shake out its dank mustiness. She persuaded him to wear his stock of snowy white cloth around his neck for this, his son's, important day. Neighbours were lending them their carriage so that the ladies could join the men travelling across the moors beyond Huddersfield, ten miles southwards on the road to Sheffield. Hannah wanted to impress the Thorntons so her son Thomas could live as he wished. She also wanted to sing—she loved singing—as did the Thorntons. Hannah felt that singing and company were as good a reason for a church service as listening to God's holy word—a view that might have shocked the straight-laced Dissenter Joseph Thornton. This Ascension Day, her husband's kin, Mr. Mellor, was leading an imposing rendering of sacred music by the greats: Bach, Handel and Haydn. Today the rafters would be ringing with the rousing Hallelujah chorus from Handel's Messiah. Hannah loved the intense longing in 'I know that my Redeemer liveth' and the fury and venom of 'Crucify Him'. She saw herself in for a day of treats and, because it was religious music, she was satisfied that she was loving her Lord as well as her own enjoyment. She hummed John Bunyan's 'To be a pilgrim', her favourite hymn tune, as she packed the lunch which they would share among the tombstones of High Hoyland parish church before the two o'clock concert. She felt herself to be a pilgrim entering the sunny uplands—and about time too, she thought, after all her years of struggle.

The hooves of a horse clattered in the cobbled yard outside the house. Hannah heard her son's voice talk soothingly as he dismounted and tethered his horse to the ring beside the mounting steps.

"I'll bring thee some oats, my beauty, and some water. A brief stop and then up and over and on to Lockwood."

Two minutes later Thomas pushed open the back door and stood on the threshold, staring open mouthed at the pile of bread, ham, eggs and cheese crowding the kitchen table. His mother was busy pushing it all into a hamper, and it was not going smoothly.

Going over to give her a kiss, Thomas spoke to her sternly. "Mam, Thou are not feeding the British army, nor are we starving harvest workers. Mr and Mrs. Thornton will want to refresh us when we pick them up at Lockwood. Dinna' put in too much food, please." He stood behind her, tasting the cheese as she cut it into portions.

"Son, dost thou want me to do the right deed? 'Tis important to welcome the Thorntons. Short of food and I would be shamed, and so would thee. I know what I'm doing and thou, Son, bear that in mind, with those instructions to thy old mother! How can anyone listen to such music without a full belly inside them?"

"True, Mam. I will heed my ways." A chastened Thomas waited to take the hamper out to the carriage but still tried to hasten his mother as she packed the final tasty little biscuits.

"Mr. Thornton is a meticulous man and does not like to be kept waiting," he urged her.

"I know, I know," muttered his mother at her impatient son. "Just go now and take the hamper outside. I'm going upstairs to put on my best riding dress. And, thou, call thy father from his accounts—which he should not be doing this Holy day—but I needed him out of the way and doing his accounts achieved that. He was fidgeting me in getting all this ready, just like thee, son."

Half an hour later, the Mellors were on their way. Thomas, mounted on his sturdy grey horse trotted beside the coach where his father was sitting on the riding box, handling the reins of the sluggish pair of horses lent by the neighbours. His wife sat inside the four-seater carriage with its narrow doors and small windows; the food basket strapped on the rack on top. They took the old road, down the hill through Grimescar to Longroyd Bridge, across the Colne, and up and over to Lockwood. The weather was good. A dry spring meant the road was free of mud with a firm footing for the horses to manage the steep climb down. Hannah could see her favourite woods and the party saved money by-passing the toll gate on the new road but condemned themselves to a slow and lurching ride over the rutted track.

Thomas was anxious. Joseph Thornton had agreed that he could address his daughter but, he had stipulated, Peggy herself must be in agreement. He would never force his daughter's hand. By turn and turn-about, Thomas veered wildly from thinking the saucy Peggy would accept him as she enjoyed his company to despairingly accepting that she found him wanting and would never be his wife. Joseph Mellor, as usual, kept his thoughts to himself; he offered no comfort to his son as he silently handled the reins, keeping his eyes focused on the ears of the leading horse as they twitched forwards and sideways in response to the sights and sounds of the woods around him.

An hour later, after crossing the Colne at Longroyd Bridge, the horses' hooves clattered into the yard of the farm near Lockwood. Joseph Thornton had moved his family back to where he had been born, away from Greetland, back to a closer proximity to Huddersfield Cloth Hall where he did most of his business. His wife, Abigail, was glad to move back to her side of the hills—both of them had been brought up there. Now as well as good wool, the Thorntons had better land. They were content and pleased to be welcoming visitors from Elland.

All was bustle in the Thornton yard. The horses were watered and flagons of ale handed up to Joseph Mellor as he sat on the box, keeping the horses still and calm. Hannah Mellor was offered a cup of tea in Mrs. Thornton's charming new teapot bought recently in Huddersfield. As was expected, Hannah Mellor duly exclaimed about how pretty it was, and then told her hostess what a good cup of tea it made.

Mrs. Thornton thanked her but said a little sadly, "But it does not pour too well. I make such a mess when it comes to pouring out the tea."

Hannah replied that pouring was always a test for every teapot, and they both agreed that the oldest ones were best for pouring, but never looked as pretty. With these exchanges completed, the Thorntons were ready to go, and Hannah Mellor quietly determined to look out in Halifax for a new pot for herself from Josiah Wedgwood who was creating such elegant fine china in his Midlands potteries, near Stoke on Trent.

32. Teapot made by Josiah Wedgwood's firm in early nineteenth century

Once inside the carriage, with Mr. Thornton travelling backwards with his daughter, eighteen-year old Peggy beside him, and the two married ladies facing them, they had a comfortable chat. Mr. Thornton looked out over the fields and woods as they trundled through Huddersfield and up the valley to High Hoyland. Peggy stole glances at the handsome young man riding beside the carriage. Her father considered the state of the land and farms that they passed but she only considered the state of Thomas' boots, his neat trousers and his untidy hair. Peggy was flattered to be asked to be married but, as her father told her, at eighteen she was very young to take up household, and she had to think seriously about young Thomas' offer.

"It's up to you, young lady," her father had told her. "I like young Mellor. He's open and honest. He's been well brought up and is attending to friend James' business in an attentive and alert manner. The Mellors are a good family and their business is good, steady if a little unexciting. He will no doubt make a good husband and you would have my blessing in the matter. But you know your own heart and, if it is not for you at this time, your mother and I will quite understand."

Joseph Thornton spoke truly of Thomas but in himself he was vexed by this proposal. He found young Thomas too confident, too sure of himself. He chided himself for being an old greybeard who was reluctant to give up his pretty daughter but he knew how tough life could be and he didn't want his girl to be shackled in an unwanted marriage. He did not want her weighed down with children, with running a house; he did not want the lively girl whose laughter filled his home to become down-trodden with daily cares. Perhaps, he acknowledged to himself as he watched Peggy walk out of the room after this conversation, he did not want this beloved daughter out of his own life.

As she listened to her father, Peggy's head reeled. She knew Thomas had been flirting with her when she met him at James Mellor's house in Brandyholes—but that he was serious about settling down had never crossed her mind. He was always joking around. He loved being with his friends in whatever hostelry they happened to be near. He spent hours with his beloved sheep when he was not in the wool shop. He rode out questing for new business and, it was said, had a roving eye for a pretty girl. Peggy had kept her eyes down when he was about, but had slid him a watchful look as he went about his business. He was good looking, broad across the shoulders, open faced and strong in arm. He rode well and spoke softly to his horse. He coaxed him with oats kept ready in the capacious pocket of his riding coat. Peggy liked that trust between a man and his horse. If a horse trusted its rider then Peggy felt, a girl could trust him too. But marriage—that was a big question. Of course, she would marry one day, but she had not thought to do so yet, despite filling her bottom drawer with her stitchery like any good girl should. Some of her friends were marrying, and she loved looking after the children of her sister Fox over Rastrick way—but her own? The question turned over and over in her mind throughout the fortnight leading up to the Ascension Day outing. She was not averse to being wooed by a handsome man. She gazed out of the window, glimpsing the man who wanted to marry her, cantering along beside them. She too was looking forward to the music at High Hoyland church—but less so to the question she must answer once there.

Slowly the carriage was pulled towards the church at the top of the hill. Coaches and carts of every shape and size unloaded passengers at the church gate and then caused a clutter as they tried to turn away to let others in their place. People dressed in their Sunday best sauntered along the lanes, milling around, hailing old friends and bowing to new acquaintances. Young men hoisted hampers onto their shoulders and carried them into the churchyard. Families were gathering round the larger tombstones and spreading their rugs for ladies to sit down. Hannah Mellor was pleased with her own spread of food; none put her to shame with a bigger spread or better baked pies. Her party climbed down gladly from the carriage stretching their stiff legs. Space inside was cramped. As a group they followed Thomas and settled around a large white table tomb, carved with the name and dates of a young woman and her infant son. Her grieving husband had been eloquent of her virtues and generous to the stone mason who had carved her name, and many perfections, with utmost care. Stonemasons charged by each letter carved. Her epitaph said she was blessed as a peacemaker—and Peggy wondered what arguments she'd had to settle.

Peggy and Thomas helped unpack the hamper. Both felt constrained and awkward, and Hannah soon shooed them away as she felt she could do it more easily herself. They wandered off down the churchyard to gaze unseeingly over the fields spread out in the valley below. Their mothers watched them go.

"Dost thou know what her answer will be?" Hannah pressed Abigail Thornton anxiously.

"No, I'm afraid I don't, Mrs. Mellor." Abigail was as anxious about this decision as her daughter. She knew what it was to struggle with an unknown new partner in the early days of marriage; she and Joseph had settled to a good relationship but not all did, and she wanted her daughter to have a better time of marriage than many she saw.

"I'm not sure I would have given the decision to her myself—young girls never really know what is good for them—but her father was adamant that it was up to her and nothing would shift him. He's always been besotted with Peggy; nothing has ever been too good for her."

"My Tommie is very anxious about her decision. He can't keep still—like a cat on a hot bake stone. He was very short with me when he arrived this morning. Since his father told him of our move down into Elland Town he's been unsettled, not sure what he wants to do, nor where he wants to be. I wonder he settled on Peggy as they are both so young. But she is so pretty and so well mannered that it would turn any man's head. Thou hast done a good job with thy family, Mrs. Thornton."

Abigail Thornton acknowledged this compliment with a nod of her head and held out her hand for another pie.

"Thank you, Mrs. Mellor. Not only have you done a good job with your own children, you have done us proud with these delicious pies. I am eating too much but it is so good I cannot resist. I hope those two children don't take too long. The concert will start and we need to secure good places in front of the church, so we can see as well as hear—and avoid those huge pillars that block one's view. I am looking forward to it, especially to your cousin, Mr. Mellor—such a wonderful ringing voice, it sends shivers down my spine."

At that moment, Thomas bounced out from behind a tombstone pulling Peggy along with him. He had a great beam on his face and he made a bow to his mother.

"Mother, meet the future Mrs. Mellor. Peggy has said she will marry me and I am the happiest man alive."

Both mothers scrambled to their feet and embraced their children. There was much exclaiming and smiling and commotion of kisses. The fathers were rather drier in their approval but smile they did, and shook the young man's hand with energy and enthusiasm.

"So now we are set for this sacred music. I for one will hear the Hallelujah Chorus with a full heart. We stand for that, I believe—it's becoming quite a custom to stand for it—and to all join in too." Abigail Thornton spoke for them all. Such a celebration for children happily betrothed.

Hannah Mellor swept her party into the church with decorous speed to find those precious seats with a view. Neither she nor her son could stop the smiles splitting their faces. It was a good afternoon. But, normally scrupulously tidy, she had forgotten to tidy away their picnic. The emotion of the announcement had quite knocked her off her usual composure.

Leeds Intelligencer

Feast of Ascension

Thursday 24th May 1805

High Hoyland Parish Church

Grand Choral Concert

Singers in Sacred Music

by

Bach, Handel and Haydn

Mr. Mellor leading

Concert begins at 2.00pm
Doors open at 1.00 pm

33.Notice in Leeds Intelligencer, May 1805

PART I—Chapter 6

Halifax Wedding Bells
19ᵗʰ August 1805

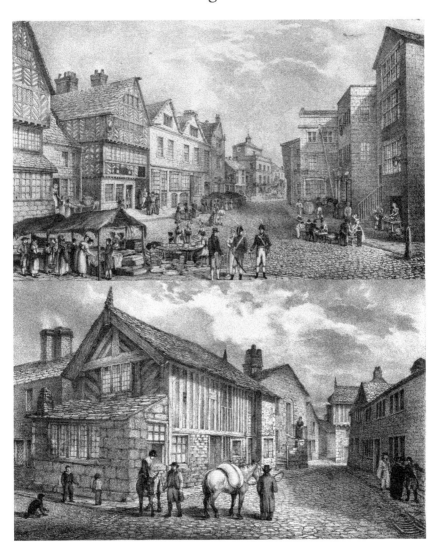

34 and 35. *Two views of ancient Halifax, held in Calderdale Archives, Halifax Library*

Two months later on August 19th 1805, the wedding banns had thrice been called in Halifax's big, stone church. Perched on the side of the hill above the Hebblebrook beneath the higher slope straddled by the Piece Hall, the parish church stood surrounded by graves, large slabs of stone hewn out of the Yorkshire landscape. The churchyard filled with substantial graves of prosperous wool merchants and clothiers as the demand for English cloth increased. Halifax, the small town at the heart of this extensive parish, had grown noisy, a centre for hamlets and homes dotted on the moors, and for the towns beginning to grow along the narrow river valleys. With its Assembly rooms, its grand Square Chapel, its sturdy yeoman houses built in stone, its new theatre, and its baths, Halifax attracted to itself an air of refinement and elegance. It embodied town living as opposed to the roughness of the hillside cloth-workers.

Joseph Thornton, a good chapel man, avoided parish churches; he disagreed with their ceremony and hierarchy of vicars, deans and bishops. For himself, he found the stirring outdoor preaching of the Wesley brothers closer to God. In them he heard clear instructions as to how a religious man should be watchful of his own behaviour and should be awake to the clarion call of the Lord to Holy action. But, the law said, the parish church was the place to make and record a marriage, and so the Thorntons, law-abiding citizens that they were, married in the parish church. The Reverend Christopher Atkinson, minister of the Church of England in the parish of Halifax in the West Riding, Yorkshire, would marry his daughter to Thomas Mellor, clothier of Elland.

Thomas, not the most attentive of listeners to Sabbath services, distanced himself from the elders of the Square Chapel in Halifax, the large chapel sitting between the parish church and the Piece Hall. There, he felt, people put on their best black frock coats, their smartest little bonnets, their dainty shoes and rolled up to morning service in their shiny carriages. As a lad, impatient with long sermons, he had watched his elders preening themselves in their Sunday finery. With much nodding and bowing between those who thought themselves important enough to notice and be noticed, Thomas observed the social pretensions of many of his neighbours. Their hands were as dirty in the week as any labourer toiling in the fields and mills but, come the Sabbath, with be-gloved hands, showed their 'inborn gentility'. He knew he was too rough with his words, too short in his temper, too anxious to be moving outside rather than studying at home. His preferred form of prayer was the soldier's prayer, "Lord, I will be busy this day; I may forget Thee, but do not Thou forget me." In his marriage, however, he wanted his Peggy to have the best, to be married in the best place. Agreeing with the ladies, he had visited the church people to have the Banns called in Halifax's Anglican parish church.

During the discussion with the minister Thomas learnt that he would have to sign the register to make a record of his vow to love his Peggy "Till death do us part." It was not enough to swear in public that he would love her and keep her—it had to be written down and signed by both of them. He could sign his name, and would do so proudly, as a clothier, but Peggy could not. She would make her mark, a cross. For

Peggy herself this was commonplace; the Thorntons were a prosperous family but they saw no need to spend money teaching their girls to write. Thomas however was troubled that his wife, an independent-minded girl with firm views about how to run her life, could not sign her name. She had to make a mark like any labourer's daughter. Quietly, he determined that his family should be able to read and to write. As a clothier he would see to that. First though he had to marry her.

36. South Door, St. John, Halifax

In the heat of the August sun, Thomas stood against the stone buttress nearest the church porch. Anxiously, he looked out for his best man, Humphrey Holroyd, who lurched around the corner of the square with a few minutes to spare before the church clock struck the hour. Humphrey, the joker, the talker who kept a public room at the inn alive after Saturday trading with his chatter and tall stories, had for this day to be serious. He was to be Thomas' witness at the ceremony.

"I thought you'd forgotten, Humph," Thomas said as Humphrey put his arm round his shoulder.

"Me forget your shackles day, my mate Tommie. Ha ha. I won't forget it in a long time. 'Tis the day I lose my companion, my friend in trouble—and out of it."

"Don't Humph, not today. I'm not going to be lost as your friend. Peggy herself won't want that. She's the best girl in the world and she'll make me very comfortable and you too when you come over to see us—as you must. Find a good girl yourself, Humph. It would make

life better. I know it would." Thomas brushed some crumbs off his friend's jacket and straightened the neckerchief tied loosely round his neck.

Humphrey shrugged off Thomas' hands and said, "Aye, aye, aye, but what happens when the good times break, when the bairns are crying through the night, and the butcher wants paying for the meat he's sold?"

Thomas replied that he was sure that Peggy would keep his life in good order through all the difficulties of children and housekeeping.

37. Gargoyles, St. John Halifax

"I'm sure she will my friend. She's a good girl. But what happens when the harvest fails, when wool stops selling? What happens if the French invade this land?"

"Humph, your head needs head testing. When will wool ever stop selling? We need to keep warm whatever happens to Bonaparte and his army. Besides, Nelson'll keep those Frenchie ships away from our shore and as for wool, it's sold for centuries—why should it stop now? Harvests can go wrong, I'll give you that, but with wool behind us we'll not starve. We're in a good corner of this land. We'll do well. So Humph, a good wife makes a good life better. Try it."

Thomas was keen to change his friend's mind, to keep close to him as they had been during the last seven years of apprenticeship. Humphrey however, like so many young men before and after him, chose to see more benefits in a bachelor state than in the burdens of the married man, the householder and maister.

"Nay, my friend. I'm not the marrying sort. I leave you your pretty Peggy and the worry about paying your bills. She'll turn your mind to more cheerful thoughts, and then we can stay good friends. Come on, Thomas, into church with us. I've got the ring in my pouch. Let's get the two of you married."

Whistling a cheery tune, Humphrey took his friend by the arm and led him through the porch into the dark of the quiet church, out of the sun-light of the churchyard, into cool solemnity and away from his levity. The minister, already in his black cassock with his white bands around his neck was at the front of the church holding his Prayer Book, its fine pages edged with gold.

"Morning, Thomas. Morning, Humphrey!"

The minister who had served Halifax for 20 years and would serve another 20 more knew both these young men as good wool men: they found wool, they shipped it to spinners, fullers and dyers, they stretched it on tenters, and took it to weavers to be woven into pieces of kersey. They knew the quality of a cloth by its feel, by its weight and by the density of the warp and weft. He knew they came from chapel families—those ministers were good to their people. Despite his respect for their work with the poor, Rev. Christopher Atkinson despised men who preached of adult baptism, who urged elders to govern congregational behaviour, who thundered from the pulpit to browbeat God into His people. He was different, a part of the Established Church, the Anglican church.

His God, he felt, was a more loving God who looked with bemusement on the antics of His people. The minister knew that, with his soft and stumbling speech, he could never attract the crowds that swelled the chapels. His God believed in the established governance of the land. His God supported the magistrates and the gentry who kept order and had done so for many centuries past. Their God encouraged challenges to the rules of peace and justice, especially over religious and political freedoms, and appalled many of those who kept the King's justice. Being a sensible man, he saw the chapels supporting those in difficulties and urging people to better themselves, to educate their congregations, all for the advancement of God's glory. These two young men, he found likeable, and admirable in the way they set about running their lives. The Reverend Christopher Atkinson might have strong views about what Dissenters preached, but he treated his many parishioners much as he treated his own flock—and accepted Thomas slipping between church and chapel attendance with equanimity.

"Now young man, I want to give you a word about what you are about to do. You need to think of Peggy as you make your vows. Remember the good things in her. Carry those good memories forward as you go into trouble as well as into joy. Call on them when bad things happen—as they surely will—bad times come to us all and more times than we would desire. Then, heed the Lord, keep to his ways; you will survive in good heart. Turn from His ways, turn into unkindness, slothfulness, hard heartedness, then Thomas, the harsh times will eat into your spirit, and into the good spirit of all in your household. That's what today's promises mean. You are promising to remember God's call in times of fear and misery, as well as in the easier times of plenty and of health. Look after your Peggy. She is bright and full of laughter. Keep her that way—do not lose her gaiety." The minister sighed, unsure whether or not his serious words had fallen on deaf ears. He hoped not; he believed God worked in mysterious ways guiding his wayward children towards a loving life.

"All's well now Thomas. Sermon over. Let's go and do it." The minister stood up and ushered them towards the altar.

Thomas thought the minister was carrying on rather seriously. He was fully confident that his bad times would not be as bad as most other's bad times; he was strong and made a good living. Mellors were survivors. Mellors stuck to the lore of their forefathers. He knew the British bulldog would snarl at the French and that they would run away. But still, today, he would do as the Minister said and pay attention to Peggy—that was, he thought to himself, the easy part. She was lively and beautiful—what more could a young man need?

As the three men were standing, huddled together looking over the Prayer Book service, they heard the latch on the south door lift. They turned as one to see Peggy and her mother move into the cross aisle. Behind them came Joseph, a thin, tall man with a slight stoop brought on by the hours spent beside the machines of his mill. Joseph Thornton, unhappy in this place of ceremony and ritual, walked diffidently, as one unfamiliar with the space. He led his daughter up the wide aisle to those waiting at the altar. This quiet minister with his fine cloth and educated words seemed too remote, too absent to convey the intensity of his Lord's presence. Joseph heard no stirring calls on the hillsides from this preacher, no ringing verdicts on the fallen, and, worst of all, he mumbled. The family had pleaded with him to put aside his long running feud with the Established Church so that Peggy might marry with an easy mind. That pleading had won him over and he entered the church, with a smile to cover his reservations, to walk his daughter up the aisle to her chosen husband.

Joseph Thornton never spent money he did not possess. Aware of the dangers of trusting unreliable family members, his fancy cloth business carried few debts. He knew from neighbours that poor harvests and new machines were making hands idle in the West Riding countryside. He felt the dread of 'playing' at home for workers. It was the fear of all working people: those times when none were taken on in the new mills, when clothiers could not supply weavers with any orders, when shopkeepers could not sell their goods in the market place, the time when men stopped at home, when women swept and tidied the house all day, when children felt their bellies rumble with hunger. The time of 'playing' not working. Joseph estimated that Thomas, a confident young man well versed in the ways of woollen cloth would, like him, survive the ups and downs of the market. He hoped his girl would be safe from hardship with her Thomas; that trade in the West Riding would recover once the war was over. There was a lift in his step as he walked up the aisle, a thrill of pride at having such a beautiful daughter and a bounce of satisfaction that his child would prosper.

Vows exchanged, ring given, Thomas planted a big kiss full on his bride's lips. She blushed and then grinned back at him as they turned to face their excited families. Not many could leave their work that summer's day but those who had left the harvest in the fields, laughed and slapped Thomas on the back and persuaded him and his wife to stop by at the Inn across the church square to have luncheon and a drop to drink. Peggy in her best dress stepped across the cobbles and into the noisy public room. Thomas ushered her towards an empty table and everyone sat around her. Humphrey, forgetting his anxiety about losing a friend, toasted Peggy's bright eyes and drank a yard of beer in excellent spirits. Later Thomas, mindful of his new duties as a husband, suggested they step home down, over Copley bridge and up to Greetland, to the cottage he was now renting as a family man. Peggy agreed with alacrity and together they left Halifax and walked home. Their married life had begun.

PART I—Chapter 7

A Winning Pen
Michaelmas 1806

38. Sheep being rounded up for their penning (Author 2019)

The following year, nine months after their August wedding, Peggy persuaded her husband that it was good to go to chapel, on Ascension Day, to give thanks for their union and for the prospering of their workshop. He put up a brief argument but soon realised that giving way was the more sensible option. He had hoped to head off up to the moors to see if he could catch a rabbit, or a bird for the pot. His wife was becoming a good housekeeper although, in the first weeks of their married life, he had expressed dislike of a boiler chicken only given the briefest of cooking time, a spring chicken's time, not a battered old bird's long gentle stewing time.

"Too tough, inedible," he'd said as he pushed his plate away. Peggy was mortified. Next day she went down to Elland to her mother-in-law to find out exactly how Thomas liked his chicken. Hannah had checked over the novice cook's timings and Peggy came back reassured that, despite her short treatment of the stringy old bird, she was learning and would soon be satisfying her husband at every meal.

Thomas, still proud of his new standing as a family man, wanted to keep his wife happy. Despite his desire to go hunting on the moors, the Ascension Day outing to Rishworth, a mile along the Oldham road from Ripponden was a happy choice; its new roadside chapel members had been sent forth from Salendine Nook, tucked beneath the Grimescar Woods, and it seemed a fitting celebration of their happy day the previous year at the concert at High Hoyland. It seemed especially good to Thomas as Luke Roebuck, the current pastor at Rishworth, was likely to give way to his cousin, Tom Mellor, a learned member of the Salendine Nook Steep Chapel congregation. It was always wise to keep in contact with steady members of the family.

At the Rose and Crown, early in the morning, the young couple stood on the forecourt awaiting the stage coach from Halifax to Oldham to take them up the Calder valley to Rishworth. As they bumped along the rutted track upwards out of Greetland Thomas, sitting on the top of the coach, found himself talking to Jonathan Vickerman, a friend of Uncle James. Jonathan had his own wool work shop at Skircoat, on the other side of the Calder River on the way up to Halifax. His family was not helping him expand his business, and he had too little capital to buy the new machinery constantly being invented. Jonathan was a pleasant man and made good company in the Rose and Crown although, after seeing poor quality cloth being sold from his stall in the Piece Hall, Thomas privately thought that Jonathan was less exacting of his workers than was Uncle James. Ever the cautious man, Thomas kept these opinions of Jonathan's workmanship closely to himself.

"I'm worried I am," Jonathan confided to Thomas. "Despite Nelson's great victory last October—God rest the poor gent's soul—nothing's getting better. True the Frogs won't invade us now, our wall, His Majesty's navy'll see to that, We're still fighting him on land in the Peninsula but for what? High food prices, terrible rents and none get good prices for the their wool. The papers, the Leeds Intelligencer and the London Times for that matter, both write that Parliament favours the landed gentry—the radicals are not getting a look-in. The likes of us get no attention, none at all."

39. Stage coach from book of prints held in Calderdale Archives,
Halifax Library

Jonathan loved talking politics to whomsoever he could; it never bothered him if his audience was uninterested. He had spun this line before so Thomas was skilled at nodding sufficiently to make him think he was listening attentively without raising any expectation that he himself wanted to contribute. As a tenant of the Pitchforth family, well to do if not exactly gentry, it was unwise for Thomas to assert that Parliament was not attending to the interests of the Dalesmen of Yorkshire. Landlords could become very difficult if they felt tenants were agitating against them. Thomas did not want to find himself out of a home, so he nodded harmlessly. Then Jonathan turned to his favourite subject: the bitter feud between himself and his brother Francis.

"It's not just the gentry either. It's our own. They think they're above us. Once they employ more men, use more machines, build bigger mills, they think they're masters, no longer maisters like us working alongside everyone to make cloth together. Brother Francis with his new machines and his 20 workers reckons he can't pass the time of day with his own kin."

Personal diatribes were more difficult. Thomas had known the Vickermans all his life; Francis and Jonathan had scrapped throughout. Then Francis had worsened that battle by telling his father that Jonathan was courting a girl from a low, loud family. Their father was enraged; yelled at Jonathan to leave her alone, and all the while Francis stood in the back of the workshop where he thought none could see him, gloating and smirking at his brother's discomfort. Greetland and Elland men steered clear of taking sides in this dispute; the Vickermans were known for being touchy and aggressive. Thomas turned away to ask after his neighbour's health.

To his surprise, the neighbour engaged with Jonathan. "I be in good health, thank 'ee, young Thomas. But I couldn't help hearing Jonathan—and I agree. Those Parliament men must listen to us. With this War costing so much, there'll be bound to be an Election soon, then we must get those who come bribing us with flagons of ale to change what they say up in London."

Thomas was uncomfortable. He didn't like getting involved in these long and heated discussions; that's what had made him so awkward at his Cousin Joseph's shop. He remembered that Jonathan had placed his son, also named Francis, as an apprentice with Joseph at Longroyd Bridge. How much, he wondered, had passed between Jonathan and Joseph. Knowing how gossip could distort reputations Thomas was beginning to regret his ride over to Longroyd Bridge the previous winter. He looked out over the moors. Land was being taken from the commons on the moor, "inclosed," people said. Roads were being straightened and built between long stone walls, replacing ancient packhorse paths that criss-crossed the moors. Down in the valley, he glimpsed another mill going up alongside the river, another wharf being constructed to line the canal basin so more trade could pass onwards to the ports. Changes were crowding fast on his valley; Thomas was not sure they were all for the best.

Thomas liked the old ways. He loved his sheep and for months he had been grooming his pen of three ewes for the Wharfedale Agricultural Show at Michaelmastide. He raised ewes brought in by Mr. John Rastrick and they regularly produced sturdy lambs, but this year they had produced of the best. He had his eye on half a dozen which he kept close to the house after the main flock had gone up onto the moors for their summer grazing. With Peggy inside the coach and him on the roof, he could not talk to her of his hopes for the judging at the end of September. Instead he dreamt of receiving the cup with their owner Mr. John Rastrick while inside, his wife enlivened herself by humming some of the hymns she was hoping to sing at chapel.

After a day of gossip about family and friends, much singing and prayer, and for some, deep thought, Peggy found herself tired and irritable. Thomas asked for a place inside the coach to support her and she rested her head on his shoulder. He had to ask the coachman to stop for her to be sick on the side of the track and then to endure what he saw as impertinent questions from the two older women sitting opposite him and Peggy. They had been married nearly a year and the gossips were already asking why a baby was not on the way. Thomas hated the intrusion of their long meddling noses.

"Mind your own business," he told them roughly as they crowded over Peggy as she was climbing back into the coach.

"Never mind them," said his weary wife as she climbed back in and sheltered herself beside her husband's broad back. "It's that pie I ate last night. It had a queer sort of taste about it."

It wasn't the pie. The town gossips were right. A baby was on the way. Thomas swelled with pride as the bump started to appear. He loved the rounded swelling of his wife's stomach. As the year closed in he would put his hand on her belly and feel, with delight, the sudden kicks that the baby, his baby, spilled out into their world. By Christmas, he thought, Peggy would be big with child, a time of good omen for babies everywhere. He planned to make their home warm and toasty. All summer he found wood, piling it high in the woodshed alongside the back door. He cut peat on the boggy moor and carted that home so he could bank down a fire and keep it in all night. His baby was going to be safe and cosy. From his shearings Peggy made a warm wool rug for the cradle which he was crafting for their child. He gathered in sweet smelling hay to keep the cattle well fed through the winter so Peggy and her child would have rich milk, butter and cheese. God willing, Thomas and Peggy were going to nurture a strong and healthy family.

But first, Thomas was going to show his pen of three ewes. In late September with the leaves beginning to turn burnt orange with golden edges he herded his best shorn ewes to Mr. John Rastrick's yard. He loaded them into a cart and drove them to Otley, near Bradford. As their owner, it was Mr. Rastrick's name entered on the lists, with Thomas' besides his. All summer long, Thomas had brushed those ewes, checked their hooves for pests, kept their eyes clean, anxiously peering at their teeth every morning. He kept them close so they could do themselves no damage. Lately he had been hand feeding them the best of the summer's hay. He built them a shelter in the lee of the close wall to protect them from sudden summer downpours. Peggy felt he was treating those sheep as children while she was growing theirs inside her belly. By the 29th September, 1806 he was in a lather of anxiety.

His sheep were in peak condition, but would they catch the judges' eye? Would they outshine the others?

Peggy loved the agricultural shows. They were times of merriment, of greeting of old friends, of watching the new and of praising the skill of the old. This year though she would stay at home. She imagined the tents sprinkled with flags, the competition to swing the hammer, the arm wrestling at the tables along the avenues of stalls. She knew there would be dancing late into the night, and the women would sell their best pies, cheeses and loaves. Onions, leeks, carrots, cabbages, all piled on trestle tables, and judged, the bigger the better. The tables would be lined with glistening white cloth, the entries neatly labelled with the grower's name. Visitors' voices would be hushed as they inched their way around the exhibits, comments mumbled to their neighbours, giving nothing away. None said too loudly that one vegetable was better than any other, though of course they made their own assessments. Prize-winners of the past would be pointed out to newcomers, but no exhibitor volunteered information about his own entry or about any of his fellow competitors, unless to bemoan the poor weather. This growing business was serious, and it was a very serious matter who won. Peggy loved watching people desperate to win, pretending that it was of little or no importance to them. This year though she had to leave Thomas to attend without her, while she kept herself safe at home.

At the Show, the crowd surged over to the ring of rope besides the animal pens. It was time for Thomas to attend his own pen where his sheep were held close by fences of woven hurdles. A grandmaster, with a trumpet voice, announced each class, each animal, each hand and each owner as the bigger animals were led into the ring. Farmers from all over the West Riding watched attentively, saying little. John Rastrick walked his prize shorthorn cow around the ring. She won the rosette with her shaggy coat, her bright eyes, and her horns dressed with a ribbon. Applause rippled through the crowd. Mr. Rastrick was well liked in the area, and it was not feared that he would take all the prizes—unlike the overbearing Sir Henry Ibbotson, who expected his hands to carry everything as victors.

Thomas became gloomy about their chance of winning. This first win might have been considered enough for Mr. Rastrick's animals for one show. The judges might prefer to award the prize to men from their own areas: Killerby, Driffield and Otley. They moved as a body down to the pens. Instead of walking the sheep in a ring, the judges peered in each pen. They leant on the hurdles; they prodded the animals to see how they moved; they opened their mouths and lifted their hooves; they rubbed at their backs to see how their fleeces were shaping up for the winter and next May's shearing. Thomas's neat shearing of the May just passed was clear in the orderly way this year's wool was lying on the ewes' backs and flanks. With sternly unexpressive faces the judges moved around Thomas' pen and on to the others. Thomas was left standing beside his pen, carefully watching every judge and seeing how the other ewes responded to them. His sheep were certainly the best, in his mind. Nonetheless, he was anxious. He wanted the glory of winning, his relationship with the animals acknowledged and rewarded. But this year, with his own family about to expand, he wanted the prize money.

The huddle of men stood apart from the crowds. It seemed an agonisingly long huddle but, in time, the oldest man walked over to Thomas' pen and pinned the red rosette onto his hurdle. Three guineas was given to Mr. Rastrick—who like the gentleman that he was— gave half to Thomas. No time to celebrate in the beer tent though. It was a long ride back to Greetland and the ewes needed to be back in their close by nightfall. Once Mr. Rastrick had helped Thomas load the sheep on to the cart, he mounted his horse and rode off home at a gleeful canter. Thomas followed more slowly. Mr. Rastrick, Thomas thought, had good right to be pleased. It was his eye that had brought the ewes at market and without good stock, no shepherd could raise a prize winner. It was right that they shared the prize money. They could be proud. Now to tell Peggy, Thomas thought to himself with delight.

She was asleep when he came into their bedroom later that night, but she stirred and woke herself.

"Well?" she asked.

"We won."

"I knew thou wouldst." Peggy turned over and went back to sleep. Thomas jingled his thirty-one shillings and sixpence in his pocket before setting it out on the mantel where he hoped she would find it in the morning.

"So thou knew, my lass, thou knew, didst thou?" he grumbled as he changed into his nightgown. "It's more than I did, I'm sure. But never mind who knew, it's just good to win."

And with that he climbed in beside her, a contented man.

The following Saturday Thomas rode up to Halifax and went to the Reading Room where the newspapers were kept for all to read, once they'd paid their subscription. Usually he read while he sipped a coffee after his day's business. Today he asked to buy a copy of the Leeds Intelligencer. There in the bottom righthand corner was four column inches on the Wharfedale Agricultural Show, and there, third from last, was written, "For the best pen of Three Shear Ewes, Three guineas to John Rastrick, Esq. Mr. Thomas Mellor." He folded the precious paper carefully and slipped it into his great coat. It would be pleasing, he thought, to show Peggy, and to leave it out in the front parlour, so that anyone who happened by would see it. It was not exactly bragging, Thomas told himself, just letting people know how his skill had been judged.

Thomas did not enjoy his moment of glory for long. The towns and countryside became awash in a sea of electioneering. Bribes given and taken, ale consumed in large barrels, pamphlets published and scattered in the towns. Politics gripped everyone, whether they had a vote or not. Time and again Jonathan Vickerman and others with a grudge to bear, repeated their political monologues in hostelries all over the West Riding. With the New Year the results came in from London. The leading Whig gentleman, Henry Lascelles lost his seat, and the two radicals, William Wilberforce from Hull and his friend, Mr. Fawkes, were elected to Parliament in his stead. They promised reform but Jonathan held to his gloomy prediction that no one would be better off for the change—except those pesky slaves about whom Mr. Wilberforce cared so much.

A week later the reason for Jonathan's gloom became apparent. A notice was posted in the Leeds Intelligencer that all his creditors must send in an account of their demands. Jonathan was having difficulty paying his bills and his creditors, led by his own brother Francis, were calling in their monies. Thomas and Uncle James were shocked that his own brother was siding with the creditors. Family were there to help in times of trouble—not make things worse. The Mellor creed within the family was all for one and one for all. No wonder Jonathan had sent his son, a younger Francis Vickerman, out of the family to Joseph Mellor at Longroyd Bridge as apprentice cloth shearer. Young Francis was a firebrand and known not to keep too careful a stop on his tongue. He needed to be kept out of the way of his hard-bitten Uncle Francis and of his mill-owning friends, Mr. Cartwright and William Horsfall.

Uncle James worried now that his friend Jonathan was in trouble. These things had a habit of creeping through whole communities. Times were hard and money difficult. His business was good with his sons and his nephew but was it safe, would it last? Thomas saw his uncle

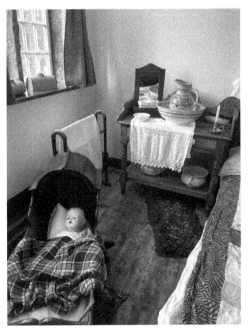

age, saw worry lines being etched into his face but, as a young man full of his own life, not for long did he consider it. With youthful ebullience he became absorbed in the coming birth of his first child in late January 1807. As the old year rang out he made an account of his own year, and on the whole, reckoned it to have been good. The next would bring more joy, more pleasure and more business. Thomas Mellor, clothier, was on the march.

40. Early nineteenth century weaver cottage bedroom with crib at Colne Valley Museum, Golcar.

And so was his family.

Four months later, in January 1807, Peggy sat beside the window stitching her tiniest stitches across fine white woollen cloth. She embroidered twisting stems of golden leaves across the yoke of this tiny gown, the last she would be making for her baby. Next, she slip stitched the binding for the seams, setting the tiny puffed sleeves into the yoke and back of the gown. The long skirt lay heaped on the chest beside her, waiting for her to gather it and set it into the yoke, so that, when finished, the cloth would fall in soft folds over the baby's tiny legs, keeping it warm whatever the outside weather. She had already made five of these little gowns and they lay, neatly folded in the chest in her bedroom, waiting for the day when she would pull them out. This was the last she would make. Then she would line the cradle. During the long winter evenings, Thomas worked on the arch of the hood. Now it was her turn to create soft pillows and warm drapes for the babe. Its time in the rocking crib would be gentle, soothing and safe.

This stitchery brought back the stitchery she had done two years earlier. Towels, bed linen, mattress covers, pillow cases and table linen, all neatly folded and placed in her chest. Her mother, Abigail, was proud of the stitching she had taught her daughter. As a small girl Peggy had started on hand towels and face cloths; she had practised her darning on family clothes and her father, Joseph Thornton, had brought home fancy cloth from his mill. Now Husband Thomas was making Kersey cloth—strong and useful—but not soft enough for their babe. Peggy stitched soft woollen cloth beside the window until the sun went down.

As the light dimmed Peggy looked over the parlour with affection and pride. This room was pleasing with its fireplace, its mantel shelf above, and the big window onto the garden, with its sashes and panes neatly dividing the glass. She could see it becoming a warm place for family gatherings. Her Thomas was a clever clothier, thought his proud wife. As a partnership they worked together—she soothing weavers who wanted their cash earlier than Thomas could pay it, and charming fullers when they wanted work done in a hurry, while Thomas sought woollen cloth over hill and dale. He trusted his wife to keep tight control of the work that came in and out of their household. Over the coming months she would be busy with the babe but she could still attend to customers while her hand rocked the crib. Peggy felt full of warm anticipation—this was a time not to be hurried, a time of preparation, a time that seemed long now, but so short, so precious when seen from the other side of the birth.

Thomas' whistle pierced the twilight of the parlour. The kitchen door banged behind him.

"Thomas, I'm here in the front parlour. We've been waiting on tea 'till thou camest home."

"Thank thee, thank thee, my darlin'. I'm famished. I've been in the saddle all day—my legs feel like jelly now I've finished. I'll take off my riding clothes and be with thee in moments."

Peggy rose and went through to the back room to check that all was set right for their meal. Martha, their new young servant girl who cooked with Peggy, had prepared a satisfying meal of scones and bread and eggs and pies. Over tea Peggy told Thomas how ready she was for the baby, all was done and in good order, but she was a little afraid, she admitted.

"My sweet life, it lies in the hands of the Lord," said Thomas.

"Amen to that," said Peggy. "But still..." And her voice trailed off into silence.

She looked over at him as he lay sprawled in the Windsor armchair set by the fireside.

"When this child comes, I want to name it as it comes out to us. I don't want it to be nameless, to feel as though it doesn't belong, it was not expected, not welcomed. If it's a boy, it must be Joseph, after both thy father and mine. No question there but a girl, that's different. I'm not so sure."

"Not thy name my darling—that is special to thee. I only have one little Peggy and 'tis thee, my darling, no one else. What about my mother's name, Hannah? Mother is an inspiration and an example to us all. Hannah who gave her first son to the Lord—though we're not going to do that to our baby. Hannah trusted the Lord and was virtuous.

My mother would be pleased too—her granddaughter will need her virtues and her strength. Would that please thee, my dearest one?"

"Indeed, it would. My mother, I know, does not want her name, Abigail, to be passed on. She doesn't like it, never has and so would be upset if a grandchild were to take it forward. We'll never call a babe of ours by that name. Hannah it shall be. I'm glad to agree that. But," she looked at Thomas tentatively, "Thou hopest for a boy?"

"Whatever comes I will be glad, Pegs, as long as you both are safe and strong."

Two weeks later, on January 24th 1807, Hannah Mellor was born. She was sturdy and bonny and like all their children, suckled well from the beginning. Safe in their cottage at Brandyholes, high on the hillside overlooking the Blackburn stream, with fifteen acres of close nearby the baby flourished; she grew healthy and strong. Eighteen months after her arrival, brother Joseph was born. At six months, he would sit in his highchair in the kitchen and giggle at his older sister as she twirled her spoon round her wooden bowl. They became such good friends that when little Lizzie arrived, two years later, Joe turned to Hansie, as he called her, rather than to his mother, who he considered had deserted him by introducing an intruder into his life. Joe tempted his sister to adventures in the yards around their home. Often she was dubious but, never wanting to miss out, where Joe was, there was Hansie, keeping him safe and laughing at his giggles when he teased out snails from under their stones or carried wriggling worms on sticks into his mother's kitchen.

Four more sisters followed Hannah and Lizzie: Nancy, Harriet, Mary, and then, at the end, baby Delia—but never a brother for Joe. Hannah loved all her little sisters, but Joe remained the light of her life. If he wanted for anything, she ran and attended. Together they ruled the family. And Peggy relied on them to keep the others out of trouble. Alongside the wool in the barns, the weaving in the lofts of the cottages, the animals in the closes around their home, the children grew, lustily and noisily. The Mellors were a well-run family.

PART I—Chapter 8

Uncle James' Bombshell
November 1811

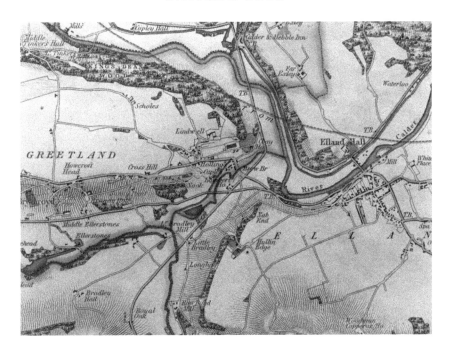

41. Myers Map showing Brandyholes farm south of Howcroft Head on Greetland Moor—Halifax lies 2 miles to the North. The river Calder runs beyond Kings Dean Wood and south of Copley Hall. Ellerstones is a mill operating on River Blackbrook

On a cold Sunday afternoon in late November 1811 Thomas, now turned thirty with three children, climbed up from Brandyholes to the Huntsman pub on the road to Rishworth. That morning he had been with Peggy and the children at the Methodist chapel in Greetland. Now he needed time alone to think out all their futures.

As he had promised back in 1805, he'd helped his father and mother move down to Elland, to his father's small parcel of freehold cottage and closes set amongst the rows of terraces climbing up the valley behind the mills along the River Calder. There Joseph had his own vegetables and grazing to keep him and his wife. Those living nearby in the small terraced houses kept 'factory' time—no sun moving through the heavens to measure their day, merely the big clock face high on the factory wall to call them to work; a bell ringing out when it was time to come, and time to go. Around his old family home at Banks, coal was being worked by ever younger children, more cottages carpeting the hillside. Coal scrap littered the land and quarried stone scarred the closes. Grime and dust covered doorsteps and windowsills. Children no longer seemed to run free.

While he was climbing and shielding his face from the biting autumn wind, Thomas looked across the Black Burn valley to his old home. The young man was feeling nostalgic. Terraced houses clung to the valley with gardens too small to grow the food that children needed for their good health. People shook their heads over the dirt, the noise of the mills, the children unable to roam and glean the berries and nuts growing on the moors and in the woods. Miners, a fierce people, and their families laboured all of God's days in the dark underground, with no chatter between themselves and other Elland dwellers. The world seemed less friendly, less forgiving, as Thomas walked along the ridge above the Black Burn mourning the times he had spent foraging and running free above Banks. His world now was a sadder place, he felt, with nowhere to stand and breathe the freshness of the moors. His mother felt constrained in the town, far beneath her beloved moorside but, like his father, he did not have the words to mourn alongside her or to show her he cared.

Every day his father busied himself on his land. As he had throughout his life, every Saturday, early in the morning, Joseph rode over Elland Bridge and up, past Skircoat Green, up to Halifax to see the old Piece hall at work, and to drink with his old friends. Thomas still thought of his father as the strong man of his childhood but the signs of old age were more obvious than either the son, or the father, could acknowledge. No one likes to think of ageing towards the inevitable end. On Joseph's last visit to his brother James, it was the younger men who shifted the bales of wool blocking the entrance to the shop in Brandyholes. Thomas noted that the two brothers came to feel the wool, as they always had, to see the weaving being overseen by young. The old men waited while the young cleared the way. As they shifted the baskets, Thomas recalled shortness of breath halting Joseph on his way up the hill. He no longer bent to touch the earth, to feel it the way he had trained young Thomas to do as a boy.

Thomas reflected as he stretched his legs out in the Sportsman at the top of the hill on Greetland Moor. He was now the stronger man; he was the maister. He was trading more cloth than his father ever had, and he was finding new machines to make cloth easier and faster. His Uncle James relied on him for contacts with weavers and clothiers around the valley but... Thomas hesitated. He knew that, despite his own success at Brandyholes, James had to consider his sons first. A cloth making business would fall to them when the time came and with the best will in the world, there would be no room for their cousin, Thomas. He needed to make his own way, to find his own workshop. Deciding this eased his mind. Indecision had blocked him for weeks. Gulping down the dregs of his tankard, he stood up with purpose. He needed to work out how to keep good friends with his uncle while he made his own way. With a cheery nod at the landlord he moved out into the windblown day.

As he walked, he thought: his wife was strong, their three babes enchanting, his work and family prospering. In the wider world, Nelson's victory, six years before at Trafalgar, had eased the nation's anxiety of invasion. However, the government now found itself in an unexpected war with the United States of America. A foolish war, thought Thomas, possibly damaging Great Britain more than it did the newly independent United States. As a wool man, he had lost a vital market and his trade suffered. The army did not buy sufficient coats and clothing to compensate for business lost to the farmers of America. Furthermore, those farmers were now trying to find cloth in their own country instead of dealing with English cloth. They were building their own mills. Despite this, Thomas' kin, Benjamin in Stainland and John Mellor in Halifax, were flourishing with growing trade. They were men of substance, good family men who led their lives with honesty and in awe of the Good Lord. This was the path he aimed to tread. His family would grow. Let the next child be a boy, wished Thomas devoutly. Although these were called 'perilous times' he—and his—would build and prosper.

42. Greetland Moor (Author 2019)

As he descended towards Brandyholes, past the water gushing from the rockside above the track, he felt the wind ease. Sheltered from its sharpness in his uncle's yard, he paused to shake the mud from his boots. Uncle James heard him and called out:

"C'mon on in lad. I've something to tell 'ee—and the all the rest of you."

Thomas pushed open the door into the dark, low ceilinged kitchen where he had eaten so many dinners over the last thirteen years. Around the table were sat his three cousins, and at the head, Uncle James with his hands spread out in front of him resting on a pile of papers.

"Lads," he began without waiting for a greeting from Thomas. "It's time for me to sell up. This place is too big, too much work. We're not getting in the orders we need to keep it going. I reckon we need to end it. I've had an offer but I'm seeing if I can get a better price. I'm putting it up for auction just before Christmas quarterday. We haven't got enough capital to put in new machines so we can't produce enough cloth. Ellistones Mill is putting in more and more machines so they make more cloth, and at cheaper prices. They keep people in work—and they pay. We can't do either. With this new war, prices are tumbling. I don't know what it is with this government that they keep fighting wars; they bring nothing but trouble, and I can't see what gain they bring. Last month I sold no cloth in neither Halifax nor Huddersfield. Not a single piece has gone to America. Even when the war ends, I can't see them coming back—they'll have found other suppliers and we'll be lost. If you lose goodwill, you lose trade; we need peace to trade, peace and friendliness."

Thomas was taken aback by this long speech from his Uncle James. More talkative than his brother Joseph, he was still a man for short, informative statements rather than reasoned arguments. Like his brother six years earlier, he had turned things over in his mind, and like his brother had decided without consulting anyone else. It was all so different at his cousin Joseph's workshop in Longroyd Bridge. There, in a busy workshop, the men found time to discuss all day long—and work at the same time. There they discussed what was happening in the wider world, in Nottingham, in Manchester, in London. A week ago, Thomas had called in there, despite his reservations about Joseph's secrecy; he liked to take a check on what was being discussed in the markets around. His brother-in-law John Wood's workshop at Longroyd Bridge was as busy and as argumentative—and the women had been as vociferous as the men. There it was openly discussed that shearsmen could not get a decent wage for their skill. His cousin George, now twenty two, was particularly aggrieved and demanded action. The anger he'd felt against his stepfather, John Wood, was being turned against the mill owners. Thomas was alarmed by his animosity. Here however, in Brandyholes, he had had no inkling that his Uncle had no sales in the last month. None of his Greetland cousins had seen this coming; Uncle James, like his own father, kept his own counsel—like a true Yorkshireman, thought his nephew Thomas admiringly.

Robert, the youngest son, spoke in a rush forestalling his fears for his own future. "Father how wilt thou live? What'll thou doest?"

"Not sure, son. This might come to naught. But they were talking to me in Halifax this last market day, about how they needed inspectors who knew their wool and their cloth. I could do that—and I would enjoy rooting out some of the sharpsters we come across far too often."

Robert grunted. The thought of his father without wool between his fingers, pieces of cloth bundled in bales at his door, was impossible to imagine. It was true though that people often asked for his advice on their wool; he was seen as good provenance for quality wool from the clothiers. Maybe it could work, thought his youngest son. Meanwhile he could join the mill at Ellistones—just down the hill after all—and needing foremen and machine masters. Their business was booming and Robert wanted to join the new way of doing things rather than keep on, like his father had, to the old ways.

Thomas, on the other hand, drew his breath in sharply. This news, coming on top of his decision to set up on his own account, was welcome. It released him from an obligation towards his uncle. Thomas could establish himself without fear of treading on his uncle's toes and could extend his range of contacts throughout the local woollen business.

"Uncle, 'tis sad news, sad indeed. But I can see how it is." Thomas smiled across at his uncle, for whom he felt great respect and now, after so many years of guidance, great affection. "As you know I had no luck in Halifax last week—and cousin Joseph over at Longroyd bridge is saying that shearsmen cannot get work. There's much talk—and pretty openly too—of mutiny and riot. The magistrates are worried but they don't understand. How can men follow the law when their bairns are hungry and begging for food? Then when a man is caught poaching, a man who speaks up for the hungry and workless, a man like cousin Abe Mellor, they transport him to New South Wales and brand him a criminal. Too many owners think only of their own pockets, and when work is thin they lay off all the men, keep the cheaper women and children—and then wonder why those men turn ugly."

Thomas stopped, wondering what had brought on this declaration. At Longroyd Bridge, he had argued the opposite. He hated the idea of riots and violence. He supported the old ways, the ways that had kept the peace for centuries, or at least since the Civil War against King Charles 1st. Perhaps it was his pity for Abe, a boy with whom he'd grown up and gone scrumping from neighbours' apple trees. Perhaps it was the sight of the old man hiding up in the barn on Greetland Moor, an old man with no work, drowning his sorrows in ale. Whatever it was, he felt keenly that the world was awry—and unfair.

"Young Thomas, have a care. Men listen and men tattle views like those. I grant 'tis hard for the shearsmen—they thought they had a skill for life and it turns out they haven't. They're full of grumbles and trouble, but they are going agin' the law and agin' the natural order if they think they can overturn the gentry and the law of the land. Have a care, Thomas, have a care. That cousin Joseph has always run close to danger. He keeps his workshop going but he's friends with the shearsmen of John Wood's workshop, and friends with Francis Vickerman the elder. The junior he keeps as apprentice, the older as drinking companion. Whom does he trust, or who trusts him? He's slippery. Thou 'ud do best keeping thy counsel—like thy father. I've done with it though. I've got a way out of a bad business and I'm going to take it. The Lord gives, and the Lord takes away. Blessed be the Lord. That's as it always has been, and it's not our place to demand differently."

"Yes, Uncle," Thomas replied very meekly. Recently, in the Piece Hall, he had encountered Francis Vickerman Senior, and had found him to be bad tempered and uncouth. Thomas remembered the friendship between Vickerman, Cartwright and Horsfall, and feared what that triumvirate could plot, especially in alliance with Joseph Radcliffe the fearsome magistrate from nearby Milnsbridge House. Uncle James was wise to caution care and quietness in these 'perilous times'.

"So lads," Uncle James continued, "I want John and David to show people round the property. It'll be advertised as a good business for a manufacturer and it'll go up on December 12th in the Mercury paper. There's packing up to do before then and your mother will need help in the house as well. Let's hope we get a good price for our machines; they cost a pretty penny when I bought 'em. I'm for dinner now. Shall we set to? Mother? Dinner?"

His wife rattled her pans in the scullery to show she had heard. The men cleared their throats and stood to share a mug of beer to relieve the tension of the news. It was obvious that his aunt had known what Uncle James had been saying and that it was agreed between them to do it this way—so different from his father's way of breaking the news to his wife. Thomas thought his mother had never forgiven his father for his high-handed way in deciding where they should live, or in taking her away from her beloved moors. Despite her continuing protestations though, she was content to be closer to friends in town. She could more easily come to Brandyholes to help with the grandchildren—and she was truly glad for that blessing.

Life is so complicated, Thomas thought. At our wedding I thought it was going to be straightforward. Now it seems less like a straight line and more like a devious and unexpected track through the woods and valleys. Perhaps nothing is ever straight.

With this thought, Thomas, who was better at action than at

thinking, moved over to help his aunt with the pot she had cooked for everyone. When they had eaten their fill, Thomas took his leave and went down to Peggy at their own little cottage and reported the day's news to his wife.

While Thomas had been walking back from Greetland Moor, his wife had been chatting in the back-kitchen with Mrs. Walker. Friends since they'd both married five years ago they had had their first babies within months of each other. The Walkers lived up beyond the spring of water at the turning off the Oldham road and little Mary Walker was a frequent visitor to the Mellors. Martha Walker often used to ask her friend, Peggy Mellor, to mind the child while she ran errands for her husband's shoemaking business.

Unlike so many in the hills and valleys of the Calder River, Martha's husband, John Walker, had nothing to do with sheep, with wool, or cloth. He was a cordwainer, a leatherworker and kept the town's people well shod and covered. His customers always in a hurry, wanted their shoes the next day never giving him enough time, so his wife ran over to this house, or to that, to deliver his latest pair. Even the tradespeople that he served with well-tanned pieces of leather wanted those immediately; belts broke at a bad time, a horse's bridle snapped on the eve of a long journey, jerkins needed mending before the bad weather became bitter. John Walker was a busy man, and his wife, Martha, always running. Within her though, sheltered by a barrier of silence, she quietly carried a sadness hidden from her neighbours. No other little ones had arrived after five-year-old Mary.

Martha was unable to carry a baby to term. She suffered the loss of an unborn babe every year—and it ground her down. In front of others, she put on a bright face, and said, "Little Mary wants for nothing. There's none to take the food from her mouth—and I can keep her in beautiful clothes."

Only her friend, Peggy Mellor, and her husband, John Walker, knew how much it grieved her every time her unborn baby died within her.

With daylight failing, four children rushed in from the garden. Joe, chasing little Lizzie, was holding a beetle under her nose. She screamed, and Hannah tugged at his breeches, trying to pull him away from the frightened toddler. Mary Walker, as usual, hung back from these family squabbles.

"Mother, stop him, stop him. Joe is scaring Lizzie."

"I'm not scaring her. I'm not," said the recalcitrant little boy. "I'm showing her a beetle."

"She's scared of beetles," shouted the indignant older sister.

"She shouldn't be scared. She's bigger than the beetle. He's tiny. She's a scaredy cat, silly girl. I hate silly girls." And Joe stomped off back out into the garden.

Hannah stroked the hair of her little sister and Peggy found herself wondering whether Lizzie would ever stand her own corner, would ever grow out of running for help to her big sister. Still, she was only a wee one and had many years in which to grow stronger.

"Take her outside, Hanse. It'll soon be dark. Make good use of the light while you can."

"Can we take the towels outside? We're playing babies and we need a blanket to put baby to bed." Hannah put her head on one side as she tugged at her mother's skirts.

Her mother could never resist this querying, reasonable tone of her elder daughter. What Joe asked for was always an effort, always demanded input from her own scarce time. Hansie's requests chimed with her own desires and attitudes. They fitted the routines of life and seemed to demand little of her as a busy mother.

"Yes, yes, as long as it comes from the dirty pile. I canna abide clean linen getting dirty. There's no washing now till Monday—and with the year drawing in, the mists, and short days it's hard to dry."

Hannah took her towel and ran quickly outside in case her mother changed her mind. Mrs. Walker spoke softly to her friend.

"You be very tolerant of the children taking your wash stuff outside; I hate my work getting disorganised by the children. Just as well our Mary keeps everything neat and tidy and in its proper place. I'd have her outside in the backhouse store to learn her some tidiness if she wasn't proper." Martha voiced her disapproval of Peggy's leniency.

"Anything for a quiet life." Peggy replied, repressing a desire to argue the point.

"Let's take a break, my lass" said Martha as she sat herself down in the Windsor armchair set beside the range with the rag rug at its feet. "I can smell scones in the oven."

"I hoped you might want some," Peggy said as she drew out the golden scones on their baking tray. "Quick—before the children come back in."

Outside, Joe had found an old horseshoe which he had hidden in his secret store. As a hammer, he seized a piece of wood which he was thudding down onto the iron of the rusty old shoe.

"I'm the blacksmith," he yelled as he sang songs he'd heard the old men sing. "Hansie, puff up the fire. Stick in the irons. We're making pitchforks and scythes."

Hannah was only too willing to play along with Joe. As an inventor, Joe was a pleasure at play. He gave out ideas all the time, leading them around the garden, inventing people to meet. Butterflies, cats, birds: all would become part of his army of villagers. Battles would be won and lost, voyages of discovery ventured, savages fired on, ships sailed and wrecked on the edge of the world. Stones in the ground became jewels from India and once, when he had found a woman's girdle with its keys attached, he became the Constable of Nottingham Castle. Hansie made the attacking force, Lizzie became a scout by creeping through the grass (she was at the crawling stage) and he was the bravest of captains defending the countryside with his troops.

43. Iron kitchen range (Author 2019)

Today he was the town's blacksmith. He hammered, shouting at Lizzie to keep the fire stoked, and sending Hansie off to get food. Hannah, always practical, wanted to know exactly what food he wanted and brought back sticks, stones, and leaves in the precise quantities that he'd required. Once she had supplied him she tried to set a hammock in the lower branches of the tree hanging over the stone wall. Joe had plans to sail to the Indies—sailors, she knew, slept below decks in hammocks slung from the beams above them. Lizzie would be confined in the hammock while her older siblings played.

Lizzie however had other ideas. She played peek-a-boo with the towel which prevented Hannah from tying it safely and brought it down over both their heads. Lizzie laughed and Hannah stamped her foot in frustration. Joe went on with his hammering and Mary watched from the side. Joe paid no attention to any of the girls and sang his songs at the top of his voice. The two older girls joined in and their chants rang through the November gloom. No one heard their mother calling them in for tea except Lizzie, who pulled at Hannah and Mary to make them

go in. Joe hid his hammer and horseshoe and ran back into the kitchen just as his mother was asking where he was.

"I'm here, I'm hungry," he yelled across the room. "I'm a smith. I'm hungry. I need food."

"So you are son, so you are," said his mother soothingly. "Sit down then, and Lizzie, c'mon with you, up into the high chair. Let us give thanks to the Lord before we begin."

44. Armchair with rag cushion and basket of bobbins (Colne Valley Museum, Golcar—early nineteenth century weaver's cottage)

Everyone mumbled, "For all thy gifts, good Lord be praised," and sat themselves down with a clattering of chair legs on the stone flags that covered the kitchen floor.

Lizzie threw her food on the floor and kicked Hannah when she came near to pick it up. Lizzie scowled at anyone approaching 'her' chair, 'her' space. Hannah realised that her little sister was not going to relinquish any of her things to the next babe already on the way. She foresaw arguments.

"Will the baby use Lizzie's chair, Mother?" she asked.

"Indeed it will, Hansie. You have all used it in your turn and it will be baby's turn next. We'll have to clean it before it's handed on though. And Joe, this time, no beetles in baby's crib. You must care for new babies, young man."

"I do, Mother, I do. But babies are so boring. I hate babies. All they do is cry and make work." Joe sounded so worldly about babies and the work they created. Both mothers laughed.

"It's fine, Joe. I'll make sure the next baby doesn't make you work too hard. But still you must take care, 'tis all I ask of thee."

Martha stood up to go. The men would be in for tea. Indeed, as she was saying farewell, the front door opened with its customary squeak. Thomas came in, squeezing past the two women. He went through to the back-kitchen where he took off his boots and put them out in the scullery. He sat himself down at the table with the children. Martha and Mary Walker left quickly and Peggy scurried around to set up her husband with his usual bowl, knife, spoon and mug. Then, with everyone looking longingly at the piles of scones and bread and pies, Papa told them to begin. And for a while all anyone could hear was the cleaning and scraping of knives on the plates.

As he scraped his last crumbs, Thomas looked around at his children and asked, "Was it a good day, my children?" He was hoping they would not launch into a loud and detailed account of what they had done. He had other things on his mind.

"Yes, Papa, it was," the children chorused back at him.

"Good," said their father. "Then it's time for bed. Off you all go while I help your mother." Pushing away his chair he stood up and went over to their mother, dropping a fond kiss on her head. "Off you go then—and no noise, especially from thee, young Joe. I know how noisy thou canst be, especially if thee be making up stories."

"I don't make up stories, Papa. I tell them. Today I'm a blacksmith and I be reprimanding all the people who come to my shop and waste my time with chat."

"Yes, yes, young man," intervened his father, anxious to avoid a long tale of the days' doings; he was eager to talk to his wife about the happenings at Uncle James that afternoon. "It's bedtime, and if you don't go now and don't go quietly, I'll get the constable—and it'll be the lock up for all three of you. So go, scram, go."

Recognising the firmness in their father's voice, the two older children left the room and crept slowly upstairs to their bedroom at the back of the cottage. They threw off their outer clothing—Hannah piling it on a chair beside her bed—and they jumped under the covers just as their mother was bringing in a clean and washed little Lizzie.

"Hansie, dearest, I'm tired so no stories tonight—let's have songs and rhymes. First, my loves, though, your prayers."

Hannah led her brother in the words they repeated every night. Joe followed a little behind her while Lizzie made whispering sounds to join the other two.

"Dear Lord and Father, we pray for our Mother and Father. We pray that our home may be full of love and honour. We pray for those in trouble who have no food. Lastly, O Lord, we pray for ourselves. Make us dutiful and obedient children. For our Lord Jesus' sake. Amen."

With their heads bowed, the palms of their hands pressed together, kneeling beside the bed, they recited together the Lord's prayer, and once finished, they scrambled hastily out of the cold and into their brick-warmed bed. Their mother sang her good night songs in her soft sweet voice. They were lulled to slumber. Peggy Mellor crept out of the room, downstairs to her impatient husband, content that the children were sleeping peacefully. All was well in her house and God willing, it would stay that way if they continued in the path of obedience to His will.

Downstairs, Thomas told her of Uncle James decision to sell up. He told her of his own decision to set up business on his own account. Together they planned and dreamed—paying little attention to the poor harvests and threatening wars that surrounded them in these 'perilous times'.

"Whatever happens, Thomas, we'll manage. We're together, and the children are growing stronger every day with our good Yorkshire air. Thou be good with wool and will make a good wool manufacturer. We cannot worry about Cousin George at Longroyd or even Uncle James at Brandyholes. They'll have to work out for themselves how to manage—but manage George must—and without breaking the law. None should break the law, no matter what. Take heed of Uncle James' words and mind thy tongue next time thee be over in Longroyd."

Peggy leaned into her husband and stroked his cheek.

"Come on, man, off to bed now. Tomorrow will look after itself. I look forward to setting up on our own. Come on, my clever clogs husband. Bedtime." With her lantern in hand, Peggy led Thomas upstairs to their bedroom, tiptoeing past the children's room so as not to wake them. The Mellors, undaunted, were ready for the next stage of their lives.

PART I—Chapter 9

Crowds on Greetland Moor
March 1812

45. Cartoons of early nineteenth century political meetings

Quarter day in March 1812 saw Thomas and Peggy moving away from their cottage, along the hillside towards Sunnybank. They rented a house above the Rose and Crown. Newly built, it stood four-square at the top of the village. They rented a messuage: the house, closes of land, barns for storage and workshops for weaving the wool spun in the mills in the valley below. They paid £20 a year in rent to Mr. William Waterhouse, and £2 a year in tax to his Majesty King George III. Four rooms were set on the first floor around the stairwell leading up from the wide hall below. On the ground floor were another four rooms—the front parlour on the righthand side of the hall, Thomas' office room opposite it on the left, the back parlour where Peggy kept house management, and the back-kitchen behind the office room. Behind the back-kitchen were outhouses for the scullery, the coal-house, the wash room with its copper boiler and the sheds where Thomas kept his tools for the garden. The farm tools were housed in the barns across the cobbled courtyard behind the house; the woollen cloth in smaller barns on the near side of the yard. Men came to work with Thomas and, while he rode the countryside buying cloth from the weavers, Peggy kept work well organised in the workshops around their home.

During the cold, wet winters coal fires were lit downstairs in the day but, only when someone was ill, were they laid in the bedrooms upstairs. As evening fell, candles were set in the parlour, and the back-kitchen, but to go to bed was to step outside into a blast of cold darkness—except on those moonlit, cloudless nights when moonbeams struck through the glass in the windows of the front hall. At bedtime the children ran sharply up the stairs, outlawed from the cosy warmth besides the parlour fire. But in summer, with their windows open, the talk of the adults sitting on benches outside the front parlour would drift up to them, only half heard but, like bird song, part of summer evenings, balmy after the day's heat had passed.

The back-kitchen boasted a new iron-enclosed stove for cooking and heating water—and on it sat the flat irons used to press Thomas' neckerchiefs. In front of it was the clothes horse spread with the freshly washed girls' smocks and the household bed linen. Out in the garden stood their little outhouse, and under their beds at night, they kept the china chamberpots that would save them the dark trip down the garden path for a chilly, spidery visit to the little house. On the side, in their parent's bedroom was a stand with a large bowl and huge curvaceous jug set in the bowl. At night Peggy would bring up this jug full of warm water to pour into the bowl for her nightly wash which she felt cleansed her of the day's dirt. The children often skipped this part of their nightly ritual.

During the day people bustled around the house, in and out of the barns. The children darted from barn to barn, avoiding chores when they could. If it was discovered that they had failed to sweep in the kitchen, or later sweep around the looms, they were summoned with a loud reprimand from their father. Sometimes he sent them into Elland to collect things he needed. Always he told them that they would go to school, that they would learn their letters, that book learning was as necessary as wool learning.

46. and 47. Laundering implements Colne Museum, Golcar, near Huddersfield, West Riding, Yorkshire (Author 2019)

Peggy, without being able to write her name, echoed her husband faithfully although she rebelled at the thought that she was somehow less because she had no book learning. Book learning was important for advancement, she knew that. She wanted her children, whatever the harvests, to have better lives than the poor she saw around her.

48. Wash basin and Jug   49. Bobbin case or shuttle
Both from Colne Museum showing early Victorian household furnishings
(Author 2019)

As so often in Yorkshire, indeed throughout England, April was a time of uncertainty. It could blow as bitter as wintry January, or it could blossom with butterflies and warmth. In 1812 it blew warm early in the month. The bobbing 'daffydowndillies', as Peggy called the daffodils, stood proud in the thin sun, opening their golden trumpets for the bumbling bees drawn out by the sun's new warmth. This April day was sun drenched and full of promise.

Joe, out in the lane, played with his pig's bladder, trying to boot it through the narrow gate in the stone wall around their home. His new boots, collected from John Walker only yesterday, were stiff and hard, and chafed his ankles. He told his mother that they hurt, but she, barely looking up from stirring her pot of porridge for the men coming in later, told him to get along, that new boots always felt stiff, that it would be comfortable shortly. In his discontent, Joe kicked the bladder so hard it soared over the wall and fell in the midst of his father's rows of onions. As he went to open the gate to rescue it, he saw a crowd coming up the lane towards him. At the front, men were shouting and waving pitchforks. Joe scrambled behind the gate and peeked out from behind his mother's rosemary bush. Six-year-old Hansie rounded the corner from the courtyard and ran over to join Joe. They crouched down, out of sight of the stream of noisy people pouring past their house.

"What are they shouting?" Joe muttered to his big sister as they peeped over the wall.

"Bread, bread, bread before mills," Hansie muttered back.

"Look, there's the cousins going up, let's join them." Joe dashed out in front of his favourites and begged to be lifted up and taken with them.

The lads were uncertain at first but then Hannah ran out and joined them and she too begged for a lift. The two children were raised onto the shoulders of these cousins and joined the friendly throng of people striding up to Greetland Moor behind their home.

Once up high, they could see much further, and saw Mary Walker marching up ahead with her young uncle. They shouted and she turned, saw them riding high above the crowd, and waited. People were singing and laughing. They wore their normal working clothes but it felt like a holiday and the children joined in happily.

A tall young man, up at the front, stopped and shouted back at the crowds pushing up behind him,

"Machines be made by the Devil; if the Good Lord had wanted machines He'd have made them in the Beginning. Did he make them in the Beginning?"

"No, never," the crowd roared back.

"Then let's get rid of them," the tall man cried.

"Tell the Government in London. Tell 'em we don't want no machines, tell 'em George—or you be no King Ludd," a voice heckled from the crowd.

Hansie then recognised the fair, sturdy young man as her cousin George Mellor from Longroyd Bridge. She didn't see him very often. But when she did, he tossed her into the air and she squealed with delight.

George shouted back at the heckler, "That's right, Abe. We're Yorkshire men. We work hard and we work well. We don't need machines to take the food from the mouths of our women and children. We'll tell 'em and they'll change—see if they don't. On and on my brothers, on to the moor."

Turning forward he waved his scythe-sword high in the air so that everyone could see its glint as it caught the midday sun. George was a leader, desperate to restore pride to his craft of cropping cloth, and food to the bellies of children. He urged his followers to break the machines that were breaking their lives by calling for the hammers—made by Enoch Taylor's shop in Marsden—to break the cropping machines made by that same firm and accountable for the loss of work for cropping shearsmen across the Dales of the West Riding. For every new machine ten croppers lost their jobs.

The children recognised more and more faces, people who lived in the cottages down by the mills, men who worked in shearing shops all over the Dales, weavers who lived in the hamlets on the moors above them. Here in this crowd they saw everyone singing and chatting. The children were enjoying themselves.

Once on the moor, the cousins set the children down.

"Now you three, this is far enough. There's going to be talking, grand speaking. You children should be running along. There's no call for you to listen to grown ups shouting the odds about how difficult life is. Go over there and play among the rocks. And then go back home. It's downhill all the way. But before you go, have you any food?"

"No, Sam, we've none."

"Have some of mine," said Sam, handing them chunks of bread and of cheese. "Now off you go, take care and go back to your homes." He strode off, to catch up with his cousins, already spreading out cloths for sitting on the moor to hear the speakers.

Hannah held Joe's hand as she and Mary asked each other where they could find a stream for drinking. "Not down there," said Hansie, "Father always tells us to drink upstream of any farm or house. Then the water will be clean; below and it'll have cow manure and farmyard mess floating in it. Let's go up where it'll be clear and fresh."

The children climbed on together until they found water bubbling out of the springy turf into a small pool. They cupped their hands and drank before Hannah sat them down and handed out the chunks of bread and cheese. They ate contentedly behind the stones and rocks hiding them from the mass of people sitting and standing around their cousin George and his friends. From soapboxes at the head of the crowd they were shouting and gesticulating wildly. The crowd were enraptured. They roared their approval.

This was the place Peggy brought them when she had a spare moment. It was her favourite spot. Here she could look down on the world, she could breathe in the fresh air, feel the wind in her hair—and feel the presence of her Lord. When she took the children, she made an afternoon of it, showing them the lapwings nesting among the stones of the hillside, listening to the larks ascending as they sang their songs. She found beetles and insects scurrying about their daily business among the stalks of heather, and she pointed out the shapes of mills down in the valleys, the plumes of smoke rising from the trees. Her children loved this distant world.

50. Spring on Greetland Moor (Author 2019)

They peeked over the rocks surrounding their spring of water. Greetland Moor was covered with people chatting, arguing and listening. The shouting from the soapbox got louder. Mary, rather more timid than bold Hannah, said, "Hansie, I don't like that shouting. Let's go."

The children backed down from their vantage point but then heard a band of pipe and drums coming up the hill. They looked over again. The crowd started, and stared at the group of soldiers behind the band with muskets across their shoulders. They fell silent and uneasy. On his box, George kept shouting, brandishing his scythe and pointing to his friend's hammer,

"We will destroy the machines. Enoch made 'em; Enoch shall break 'em."

His voice rose, but others hushed as the soldiers marched on.

The crowd rose, stood their ground and roared at the soldiers, "Do your worst, you traitors, you government slaves." The crowd raised their arms, waving overhead the sticks and staff they'd used for walking.

The soldiers halted. Their commander shouted, "Halt—or we fire."

The crowd, enraged by this command from those they saw as traitors, roared their defiance.

A shout from the commander. The rifles cracked and sputtered. Men screamed and fell. The crowd turned, and in terror started running away, running in any direction as long as it was away from those sputtering rifles. George ran towards the men who had fallen, men he knew well. He bent to tend them while the soldiers, now as full of fear as the unarmed crowd, turned to harry them back down the hillside, to chase them away. The children shrank down behind their rock, terrified.

For an hour or so they quavered in their place of safety. The sun shone, they played with the water as it trickled through their fingers, and Joe sank back on the grass and slept. The girls were unable to do that but Hannah resorted to storytelling and Mary listened entranced. The sun went low and its warmth left the moorland. Hannah no longer felt safe behind their rock. It was time to get home. Being out on the moor in the April night was no fun. It would be icy cold and full of fearful noises.

"Haste ye, Joe. We must go now. We must go home. Come." And pulling at Joe's hand she urged him and Mary to leave their hiding place.

As they crept away, they looked back at the lonely soap box still standing on the moor. The young men had gone, the injured had been carried home, the women had packed up their hampers of food. The singing had ceased. People scurried back, in silence, shocked. The militia had fired on their own people. Things were terrifying when this land of justice and of peace lived with such horror. The children started back down the path they knew so well, not quite believing that they had heard such terror on their own moor.

51. Twilight on Greetland Moor (Author 2019)

They walked down, a close trio, Hannah held Joe by the hand. He held her tight. Mary kept her handkerchief in a tight knot twisting it as she walked. Hannah pointed out potholes and stumbling stones set in their path. If they heard voices, the children froze and tucked themselves behind bushes, terrified that the soldiers might find them and fire their guns again. As they scuttled down, one woman saw them, and cried out, "Haste ye on bairns, haste ye on. It's no place for childer, no place at all. Get home to your Mam. Get home quick."

Without giving any reply, all three children hastened their steps. Little Joe was tired and stumbling but Hannah held him up. As the twilight deepened into dark, they arrived at their garden gate. They pushed it squeaking on its rusty hinge; their anxious mothers rushed out. Mrs. Walker gathered up her weeping Mary while Peggy Mellor bent towards Hannah and demanded:

"Where have you been? What did you do? Why were you out so long? Look at Joe, he's shaking. His clothes are torn. What have you done?"

Mrs. Walker looked over at her friend and saw the terror in her eyes and realised her anger came from deep depths of fear. The children could not see that and were shrinking from her—in yet more fear.

"Peggy, the children are home, they're safe. Thank the Blessed Lord for keeping them in His hand. Let's find out what they've done, where they've been."

Her friend's voice broke into Peggy's anger. She caught herself in time to stop herself shaking her fist at the children and instead, bent down and caught the two of them to herself, in a frenzied hold.

"Thank the Lord indeed that you're safe, my darlings. Thank the Lord. But what happened?" Peggy brushed the hair from Hannah's face and looked at her elder daughter with troubled eyes. How had her sensible Hansie allowed them to get caught up in such terror?

"Mother, we were hiding. We heard shouting, we heard guns, we saw shooting. We didn't know what to do. We hid, we played. Then it was quiet, and we came home. I was scared. What's happening, Mother? Why are people shouting, why, why? I don't like it!" the stoic little girl, who had kept her fears hidden while walking home, collapsed into her mother with a torrent of crying.

"Hush my poppets, you are safe now. You're safe. Mother's here to keep you safe. Hush. Hush." As she spoke Peggy held her daughter tight stroking her hair back from her streaked and dirty face. Martha Walker, with an equally distressed child, told her friend that she would go home. She would tell the men that the children were safe. Peggy nodded and sat the children on the settle at the back of the kitchen. She turned to the hob and drawing the pot towards her, poured two mugs of warm milk with cinnamon ground into it. "Here children. Something to warm you, to calm those fearful butterflies in your bellies."

Even toddler Lizzie realised something was amiss and remained silent while her mother comforted herself and the two older children. As they sipped their hot milk Lizzie shouted for her bread and Peggy was recalled to a sense of normalcy. By the time Thomas came in she, at least, was more composed.

Thomas however was not composed at all;

"Children, what happened? Why were you on the moors? Why did you go there? You could have been killed. It was crazy."

"Husband, they were not killed. They are safe. We have our own children here with us. Let us thank the Lord for caring for them." Peggy glared at her husband, shooting him dark glances, warning him not to make the children more fearful.

"Thank the Lord indeed. But I still want to know what happened? Hansie tell us how it happened. We need to know. Tell us."

Hannah, standing in front of her father spoke slowly, finding her words, and the order in which to put them, carefully and with difficulty.

"The cousins took us up. Everyone was laughing and singing. It was fun. Mary was there with her uncle. It was a holiday, like a chapel outing. We rode on their shoulders. We got to the top. They set us down and told us to go home. We wanted water. We went to the spring and started playing in the sun. Then we heard Cousin George shouting. We looked over the stones and saw him on a box. Then everybody stopped laughing. We heard the pipes and drums—the soldiers came—they shot. It was a dreadful sound. People screamed and ran. We hid back behind our stone. We stayed for ages. When it was quiet, we left. We came home."

"Hansie, you are a brave girl. That was well told my child. But never go up on the moors with your cousins—they're hot for trouble just now. Keep at home."

Thomas was impressed by the orderly explanation Hannah had just given him but he was terrified that the young hotheads of his family, and of the whole area, were brewing for trouble. It would drag him, and worst of all, his children into riot and terror. He knew people were 'playing' and starving, out of work and wages, but if people killed each other, no food would be put on their tables. It had to be done properly—as it always had been. Revolution was for the French—not for solid Englishmen.

"Thomas, you need your food. Hansie, bring your father his pie." Peggy was anxious to make this terrifying day seem more normal—and she knew of no better way of making things ordinary but by eating food as usual. They sat down in the back-kitchen, eating and drinking and afterwards brought out cards to play, Beggar my Neighbour, which made Hannah laugh, and Joe try to hide his cards. Then Peggy stood telling the children she would take them to bed and sing their favourite songs and a psalm of thanksgiving that all the family were safe.

Thomas gave the children a good night kiss. He told Hannah again that she had done well. "You did what was right, my girl. You looked after your brother. We all look after each other in this family. That's the way to keep safe. No matter what happens to others we look after our own."

"Even Cousin George?" Hannah queried her father.

"Especially George," her father replied. "He is a lost soul and so angry. He takes others into his pain—we must help him to see that there is a better, quieter way. Now good night, children. Don't worry about grown ups—that's our job. Keep yourselves safe."

"Come along," said Peggy scooping little Lizzie up under her arm and bending towards the other two. "Let's go up the stairs to Bedfordshire." Counting each step as she climbed, their mother helped the children up to the safety of their bedroom. She tucked them in and sat on Hannah's bed to sing them their favourite night-time songs.

Finally, she sang them Psalm 23 about the Lord being their Shepherd. Hannah felt safe with a shepherd to look after those people, those lost sheep on the hillside. She fell asleep, thinking of the sheep looking balefully at the children. Joe, already fast asleep, was curled up against his mother clutching his special rag doll. Later that night, Peggy went up and looked at the two sleeping children. She dreaded a world so angry and at odds with itself. She feared being unable to keep her children safe. Images of dead men stalked her mind as she held her children in a tight grip and fell asleep herself, in a daze of fear relieved. Husband Thomas came up later, gently eased her out of the children's grasp and shepherded her across to their own room, to their own bed. Fear had come to him. He questioned whether all was as it should be in his Yorkshire Dales.

PART I—Chapter 10

Murder on the King's Highway
April 28ᵗʰ 1812

*53. Drawing of four men firing on two riders on Marsden road
near Dry Clough, April 28ᵗʰ 1812
Halifax Library, Archives.*

The next morning, Thomas was standing stock still at the centre of a group of men in the square by the parish church in Elland.

"I know he's a cousin of yours," said a young man hitching his horse to the ring beside the Savile Arms mounting steps, "but he has a loud mouth, that George, a very loud mouth. He gets up on his hind legs and shouts the odds. Now men are hurt on the moor and he was there, urging all to demand things be set to rights. Needs to look at his own mouth first. Great blathering bleater."

"He's only a distant cousin, you know, through my grandfather, you know. He won't go on now, not now. The trouble'll stop him, that's for sure." Despite his horror at the news of the shooting, men he knew killed by his King's own militia, Thomas was anxious to let people know he didn't ally himself with his hot-headed cousin. He knew George was angry, he knew George shouted out his feelings as and when he wanted. But surely even George would know when to shout and when to stop shouting. Now was the time to stop.

An older man, thin and bent, intervened.

"How can he stop? Not now surely, not when Horsfall, Cartwright and Vickerman, have all vowed to get even with him, vowed to crush any rebellion, any protest for work and decent wages. Horsfall has said he'll hand-whip any protester with his own hands. Down at Holdsworth Mill, you know, there's been talk about what happens at Ottiwells in Marsden. Horsfall parades through the Mill and whips anyone he reckons is slacking. He's hated. Kids are maimed, he turns his head away; women are put off, no matter how many bairns; men hounded to keep at it fast and ever faster—or be sent home. He carries his whip at all times. William Horsfall is a bad 'un. Won't do no good calling for violence agin' him—he'll get the soldiers in every time. And where'd working men be then? Lying dead on the stones in front of mills, be sure."

"And Holdsworth aint a lot better. They're not above putting people off when they don't have orders," said a younger man whose clothes were ragged and dirty. "I was turned off last week, and told not to come back because there were no orders coming in. None of these mill owners care about the working people. None think of the winter, nor of the bairns with empty stomachs."

"How did it go yesterday?" Thomas persisted with his questions as he wanted to know how George could have become involved in such a gathering. It was as though he was a dirty lout, a common criminal. Mellors had suffered, that was for sure, but most were god-fearing chapel men, and god-fearing chapel men did not incite violence against the Masters.

"I don't rightly know the full ins and outs," said the horseman who was giving his mount a bucket of water, handed to him by one of the ostlers. "I reckon George, and his friends from Huddersfield way— you know that workshop by Longroyd bridge with his stepfather, John Wood—well they get talking and winding themselves up, you know. They are losing work by the day. Now there's machines to do the job— and they do it better, you know—the shearsmen can't find work. That lot see themselves as King Ludd—like the men from Nottingham you know—even some from the West Country, Honiton way. They're fired up to lead a revolution so they bind each other in oaths of allegiance, of silence. I'm not sure Elland men are up for it but that won't stop them. I hear they're up for baiting Cartwright at Cowfold Mill—and him and Horsfall have vowed to kill all attackers. It's an ugly business and I don't see a straight way out of it, that's for sure." He turned away from the crowd and, unhitching his horse led her to the back yard for overnight stabling.

Thomas was troubled that the anger among his neighbours against cousin George's rabble- rousing would turn them against himself and his business. He closed his mouth firmly and drew back from the little crowd. He turned up the hill, back to his house where Peggy was waiting for news about yesterday's riot. Hansie and Joe, much chastened by the fear of the soldiers, were staying close to the house. Mary Walker was at home with her own mother. Peggy and Thomas were anxious about their children. With Cousin George being named as a leader, how could the Mellor children survive name calling around the town.

Many townsmen followed George but many of the more powerful citizens most certainly did not. Unpleasant connections could lead to unpleasant consequences for any family in these troubled times.

He strode up the hill, looking neither to the right nor the left. He did not want to talk to anyone about what he had heard in the town, not until he had thought it through, and talked it over with Peggy. In his business, confidence was all. His customers would melt away if they thought there was any trouble attached to him or his family. The weavers would stop supplying him if they thought they would lose other contracts as a consequence. He had to tread carefully to keep thriving. As he arrived home, he looked at his still new front door with pride. While he had his house and barns and closes, he was a maister, a man of substance. Despite George, he and his family remained respectable citizens. Peggy, as a housewife, would steer him in caring for the children.

Thomas went in and told Peggy how George was being blamed for the uprising on the moor yesterday. He was worried about the children—name calling could turn into something nastier. Peggy's family were less hot-headed than the Mellors. Joseph Thornton had steered his fortunes through tricky times and kept on the right side of all his customers. He had survived what was now twenty-five years of war with France and several terrible harvests. His son-in-law wanted the children to go to him—to be kept safe in Lockwood, beyond Longroyd bridge, away from Elland chatter. If only the war would end, then the country would calm itself. Prices would come down, business would flourish.

In Thomas' mind, Cousin George had a point. Some of those mill owners, even their own relatives at Stainland, took their profits squeezing decent working people. Clothiers like him could not make a profit, the new mills put out cheaper cloth. Peggy's parents would be a refuge away from Elland fury. No one engaged Joseph Thornton in revolutionary talk, much less in action bringing down the law of the land.

Thomas spoke his mind as he stood in front of his frightened wife.

"I have it, wife. The town's gossiping hard. Everyone's ranting about the militia on the moor yesterday. George's name is on all their lips—

and they're connecting us with him. Not good for any of us. We need your parents."

"What do you mean, we need my parents? They're not here, they're in Lockwood." Peggy had rushed into the hall as soon as she heard her husband push open the door, and the two stood, talking anxiously.

"Yes, I know. But… if we take Hansie and Joe over to them for a week or so then none will yell at them while they are playing in the town or going on an errand. Elland men agree with George and the Huddersfield men but they don't want to follow his violence, they don't want revolution. They won't rise to follow him and King Ludd. They'll take out their rage on our children for being connected. We can't put them through that. Your father is known for keeping his own counsel—and respected for that too. None will force him into riot and revolution. He can keep them safe for a week or two, while it's still the talk of the town. Pegs, you know it's sensible."

Peggy stood perplexed. "I hate letting the children go, especially at a time like this. It doesn't feel right but Father is calming—people do respect him. Perhaps you're right Thomas, but I don't like it." Shaking her head, reluctantly Peggy went up the stairs to put together the necessaries for her husband to carry over with the two children early the following morning.

The next morning, when she went into the children's room, Peggy found Hansie and Joe playing under the bed, pretending to be explorers. They had set a ship-chair upside down on the floor beside their beds and were using their covers as a sail. Lizzie was cooing at them from behind the bars of her cot.

> "We're off to sail the ocean blue,
> We're off to find a land so new,
> We're off with men so good and true,
> We're sailing far, a merry band."

Peggy stood still for a moment. Did she really need to send this pair of innocent children away from their own home. It troubled her that events outside were affecting how her family lived.

"Oh poppets, that's a good fine sail you have there, but today it's not a sail you be needing but walking shoes. Papa's taking you over to Grandma and Grandpa Thornton for a week or so." She spoke to them as she raided the cupboard for their clothes. "Lizzie's too young. She's staying here but you two will have fun. You love your grandma! She's full of delicious tarts and pies for all her grandchildren."

"Good. When? Let's go now. Grandma, here we come," shouted one very happy little boy. He loved trips and moving anywhere but particularly across Ainley Top, over the Colne and down into Lockwood, a more wooded valley than those round Greetland.

"Why are we going there, Mother? Why? Is it because of yesterday?" Hannah questioned her Mother, wondering why yesterday's event should make them leave home.

"No, no poppet. Your father and I thought it was time to see your grandparents, and today seemed as good a day for your father as any."

"I don't want to go. Supposing the soldiers come again? I'm scared. I want you, Mother." Hannah stamped her foot on the floor.

"Hush Hansie, hush. Your father thinks it's for the best. The soldiers won't come there. Your Grandpa Thornton is well thought of, no ruffians come near him," Peggy replied convincingly although in her heart she agreed with Hannah. "I'm putting together a nice food parcel, so come down when you're ready. I'll take Lizzie down. At Lockwood no one will shout at you about yesterday. None of them know about it over there, my poppets."

Slowly the children came downstairs into the kitchen for their morning porridge. As soon as they were sat at the table their mother sat with them and watched them, propping her head on her hands.

"Papa will take good care of you. He'll take you by the old path, through the woods. You'll see no one. Most people go by the toll road now—it's better—but you'll have more fun chasing each other through those woods and you can find flowers to pick for Grandma Thornton." With these words, Peggy reassured herself.

Recognising the finality in her mother's voice, Hannah and Joe knew it was time to do as she said. Mother was a dear, but wise children did not give her cheek, nor question her edicts for long. Father, with his strap, stood behind her, and they had both made it clear that Christian children must be obedient, as all God's children had to be obedient to His will.

An hour later, Thomas stood in the hall, booted and coated, with his two children beside him. Despite the promise of early April, the weather was bitingly cold with a north wind whipping across the moor and blasting around the house. Fortunately, they were walking south and so the wind would be buffeting behind them, much better than pushing them backwards as they walked.

"Fare thee well, husband. Mind the children with care," Peggy bent low to both children and gave each one a warm hug before stroking their cheeks and admonishing them to behave well with their grandparents. "It's well that the wind's from the north. It'll push you over there, children. But don't leave too late, Thomas, you'll have it against you all the way home."

"I'll be home by sundown, dearest. You look after Lizzie and treat the men well when they stop for food. Any merchants coming by just tell them I'll be home by-and-by and look forward to doing business with them." Thomas gave a hand to each child and walked them purposefully out of the house down to Elland and then upwards and over to Huddersfield and Lockwood.

On his own, Thomas took an hour and a half to cover the ground to Longroyd bridge and then a further half hour up the valley to Lockwood. With the two children he allowed himself three hours. On the walk through the woods of Grimescar, there was much stopping and looking at birds swooping into their nests with twigs and fat, juicy worms to feed their hungry young. Hansie found primroses hiding near a bank of moss-covered stones and picked them for her grandmother. Joe chased the crows that cawed in the fields beside the bridle path, and then pointed out starlings scratching at soil disturbed by newly released cattle.

Thomas was proud that his young son was so observant of the birds around him. A child who could observe and remember what he had seen, would fill his head with information. He would go far. As he walked though, he wondered to himself what either child thought of soldiers shooting their own people. Would they grow up, like George, challenging things that were wrong? Or would they opt for a quiet life, a life where they could prosper whatever was happening to others? Thomas himself did not know the best course; he found it hard to know what to do in these perilous times, even harder to advise his children. He spoke out loud, to himself and to his children. "Never mind the troubles children, your grandfather Joseph Thornton is a wise man. He'll keep you safe and advise you the best way to go on."

Three hours later, they arrived, tired and leg weary, at Lockwood on the hillside above the River Holme. They went through the gate into their grandparents' yard. As at Uncle James' back in Brandyholes, the yard was surrounded with barns, workshops and cottages. No brook babbled beyond the yard. Instead, the road plunged down through the trees

of Dungeon Wood. Less than a mile away, Joseph Mellor's Dungeon Bottom workshop, busy and full of loud discussions, was a magnet for curious children. The woods of Dry Clough stretched up behind the farmhouse to the Marsden Road from Huddersfield. From there the children had looked back down the valley to the bridge across the Colne, so busy with its barges full of cargo.

54. Ainley Top above Grimscar Woods on the way over to Huddersfield (Author 2017)

Their grandfather stopped in his tracks as he was walking across the yard in the thin spring sunshine.

"Well I'll be blowed. Where be ye young 'uns sprung from? What you doing here, Thomas? And here's young Joe, you got a smile for Old Joe, young man? Abigail, Abigail," he shouted back to his wife. 'We've got visitors. Best come and see for yourself." He looked up at young Joe, atop his father's shoulders. He had chattered most of the way over but now he was struck dumb as he confronted his grandfather, a tall man, stooped a little with age. He hid behind his father's curly hair.

"Well young Joe, in your own time, in your own time." Turning to Hannah, he bent to kiss her. She remembered her grandfather with affection and reached up to give him a hug.

Formalities over he turned to his son-in-law. "Thomas you'd better tell us what's amiss. Why you're here so bright and early. Everything well back at home?"

Thomas hastily reassured his father-in-law saying that Peggy and the baby Lizzie were both well.

Baffled, Joseph Thornton told them to come into the kitchen. Grandmother Abigail Thornton was pressing clothes in front of her open fire when the children came in, shyly clinging to their father's legs. She saw Thomas' grim expression and acknowledged her husband's bewildered eyes with a nod of the head.

55. Truckle bed in weaver's cottage, Colne Valley Museum, Golcar (Author 2019)

"My poppets," she cried, using their mother's term of endearment. "How lovely to see you. I see a little bundle with you and I expect that means you want to find your own little beds in the attic room. Why don't you come with Grandma to set your stuff in place? Shall we let Papa talk to Grandpa while we do that?"

Holding each child by the hand and counting them up the stairs, Grandma Thornton moved the children out of earshot with no fuss. The children remembered with sweet expectation the scent of summer hay which their grandmother spread on their truckle beds. Summer hay was long gone but the smell lingered in the crevices of the wood underneath their heads. Their grandmother wondered what had brought the children to her but knew she would shortly be told all. Her present job was to settle them and make them safe with her. She did not expect the children's next comments.

"Grandma, we saw people shouting and running. We saw soldiers with guns. We ran away. We hid. People won't shoot here, will they? People won't run here, will they?" Hannah was pulling at her grandmother's skirts to make her listen. "Joe saw them too, didn't you Joe?"

"My oh my," said their grandmother sitting herself on the bed. "You'd better tell me more. I don't understand." She pulled Hannah beside her and cuddled Joe on her lap. She listened while the children poured out their garbled story. She was horrified but knew the children would be best served if she kept quiet and calm.

"I'm so glad you've come to stay with us. Your mother was quite right. It is quiet and safe here. No one will talk of marches or riots or revolts. Such a treat for me too. We can go to Dungeon Wood to find bluebells later on; they're nearly out but not quite yet. You can make dens with the fallen branches and I can find some kindling wood as we've used all our winter stock."

Downstairs, Joseph Thornton had been listening carefully to Thomas' tale of events on the moor. He shook his head as he listened with a grave face, his eyes intent on his son-in-law. Then he had his own news to report. He'd heard talk that Cousin George was planning a King Ludd expedition to Cartwright's Mill at Cowfold away to the north east of their valley. The country was waiting, tensely, the result of any clash over the next two nights. Cartwright had recruited Horsfall, and more soldiers, and was barricading his mill and guarding it at night. Joseph feared what would happen if the working men who rallied to George met the rifle fire of trained soldiers. Cowfold fortunately was a safe distance from Lockwood, the other side of the Colne, and none came recruiting in his parts. He could keep the children safe, away from jeering neighbours. His main concern was Thomas' cousin, Joseph Mellor and John Wood at Longroyd bridge. There was a lot of wild talk from those workshops but he reckoned Joseph Mellor was wily and had hedged his bets with both sides. The younger men were rash. George was a wilful hothead convinced the world was against him at every turn. But Joseph Mellor, in his cropping workshop would make sure no rebellion came near him. Joseph Thornton told his son-in-law that he could rest assured his children were safe with him for the next fortnight and that he could return to Greetland to keep his business going while the gossip died down in Elland town.

The children clattered down the stairs into the parlour and their grandmother ushered everyone into the kitchen and sat them down for a bite to eat. The tea, cakes and biscuits came out and were quickly eaten. Thomas soon left as he wanted to walk back in daylight. No sane man walked abroad in the dark with so much discontent raging across the valleys. With no hesitation the children waved him goodbye and settled with a motherless lamb in front of the kitchen range. Grandma was raising it after its mother had died in lambing. For both of the children this was exciting and they took turns in feeding it with little sips of milk from a saucer.

They had happy days with their grandparents. They explored the new canal towpath, squeezing past the horses moving slowly along the path with their loads behind them gliding through the water. The bargees waved at them as they padded along the tops of their cabins with spring bulbs in pots along the edge. They chased each other in the mysteriously named Dungeon Wood—Joe trying to find the Dungeon he believed must be there and Hannah trying to steer him away. They climbed amongst the coppiced trees and hid among the roots of trees uprooted in the winter gales. Some days they strayed as far as their cousin Joseph's workshop—they knew they should not be there—and never told their grandparents. It drew them with its business, its noise and its young men, teasing each other as they lifted their long shears and clipped the cloth on the tables in front of them. As the weather warmed, the young men took off their shirts and Hannah loved watching their muscles work using their strength to hold the shears over the cloth. Joe was more interested in the machines and spent hours watching the spinning jennies in the back room.

A week later, on the 28th April, Joe and Hansie slipped over to the Mellor workshop again. This time it was unwelcoming. The talk was of dead young men. Hannah heard there had been a fight and George had come home chastened. The men were muttering and one of them, seeing the children, brusquely told them to clear off. They wanted no children messing up their work. Hannah shrank from these harsh words and, dragging Joe with her, she ran out of the workshop. Together they ran back to Dungeon Woods, their favourite playground. For hours they played happily in and out of the trees. They sat in a hollow and ate their lunch, unfolded from their bundle. Afterwards, Joe kept spurring Hannah on, urging her to tell ever more complicated stories of adventure and leading her up among the trees of the slope upwards. They climbed on until Hannah realised they were at the Marsden Road which climbed up from Longroyd Bridge and Huddersfield. She told Joe that they were too far from home and should be turning back but he was happy building a den among the fallen trees and she started picking bluebells for her grandmother.

Suddenly, four rough-coated men on horseback broke through from Dry Clough Lane, moving into dense wood where the children were fearful of going. There brambles nipped at heels and heavy trees darkened the sun above. The children froze, shrinking down into their improvised den. They were invisible, and being quite still, remained so. It was late and Hannah knew they should be getting back to their grandparents but she feared the look of these secretive men, so kept herself and Joe hidden and still. Her bluebells lay on the top of a trunk visible from their den. Too afraid to put out her hand, she let them lie. Joe had his stick beside him, but that too was still, and disturbed no betraying bird to rise up in squawking warning that something was amiss in the hollow below.

56. Hillside behind Dry Clough Lane below Marsden Road
near Huddersfield (Author 2019)

A carter passed by on the road beyond the wood, urging his horse homewards. Other passers-by were none. Still the four men stood, motionless, dark shades in the wood, close to the roadside's little stone wall. Men and children, both were silent.

The children heard it first. Horse and rider clip clopping up the road from Huddersfield. The men heard and lifted their sticks. Suddenly Hannah was filled with dread. Those sticks looked like the sticks carried by the soldiers on Greetland Moor. She held tight to Joe. The sticks barked and stuttered. The rider fell. The men wheeled round, and fled into the depths of the forest down in the direction of Dry Clough Lane. They could be seen no more. Another rider galloped up to the fallen man whose horse was bucking and rearing, plunging in terror beside the stone wall. The chestnut bolted homewards along the road towards Marsden, empty stirrups swinging wildly as he galloped. The new man dismounted and bent over the still figure lying on the road.

Hannah and Joe could contain their terror no longer. They leapt out of the coppiced wood and ran with the devil at their heels, crashing through the undergrowth in the opposite direction. The rider who had ridden up to help the fallen man neither saw nor heard the children. The men making their own getaway noticed no unusual noises in the wood and missed the sight of small bodies fighting their way over fallen logs, under low branches and across muddy paths till finally they ran into their grandparents' yard and stood panting and terrified in their grandmother's kitchen.

57. Weapon said to have been used in Murder on the king's highway on Tuesday 28th April 1812, printed in Leeds Mercury. William Horsfall was shot by 4 men hidden beside the Marsden road on his road home to Marsden from Huddersfield Market.

"Grandma," they yelled. "Bad men! Robbers! Shooting, horse hurt. Man dead." Their words tumbled out, incoherent and so loud that none could understand. Then, as suddenly as they had burst into the house, they stopped and rushed to their grandmother, hiding in her skirts and shaking, gasping for breath, with chattering teeth and eyes wide with fear. Their grandfather came in and led them upstairs to their bedroom, away from all prying eyes.

Long and disturbed was that evening in Lockwood. People came and went in small huddled groups. They spoke in hushed tones. No one knew exactly what had happened. They did not know who had fired at the fallen man. They did not know why William Horsfall, travelling home as he often did from Huddersfield market along the road to Marsden, should have been attacked near Dry Clough Lane. The rider who took him back to Warren Inn reported that he was in a bad way and a doctor was called. The doctor bled him but did not hold out much hope. Two days later, he died. William Horsfall had met his end and no one knew by whose hand. Plenty hated him, but few would have dared to assassinate a man on his way home from market. The country people became speechless and uncommunicative. No one shared any ideas or suspicions with the magistrates enquiring into the disaster.

The children took no part in all these comings and goings. Old Joseph Thornton saw immediately that they had seen more than they should have done so kept quiet about how he learnt of the tragedy. He sent them to bed and their grandmother told them long stories about the old days when she was a little girl and played up on the moor with her brothers and sisters. She told them of the carriage that had taken them to church in Huddersfield on Sundays. She talked of animals, of horses, of fires glowing in their hearths, of their mother when she was a little girl. She reassured young Joe that the chestnut horse he had seen plunging in the lane was unhurt, simply frightened into bolting home. Horses always reared when startled.

Hannah though, she could not reassure. Hannah knew a man had fallen, knew a man was hurt. Hannah who imagined so well the scenes she painted in her head from the books she read was now painting a terrible picture of a real story, a real happening. She knew the men up on the moor had been badly hurt and she feared the same for this man, thrown from his horse into the rutted road. She was frightened for herself, for Joe, for her mother and father and baby sister. She wept slow silent tears for the flowers she had left behind. Grandma held her and rocked her; she sang softly to her but it was well into the night when her terrified eyes finally closed to sleep. Grandma could not take away this fear.

PART I—Chapter 11

Fear at Christmas
December 1812

58. Joseph Radcliffe, the Magistrate pursuing Luddites from his home near Longroyd Bridge, used unjust detentions and coercive interrogations, even serving on the jury that returned guilty verdicts.

December 1812 was bitter. Ice stood in the bucket left in the pantry overnight. Day time temperatures stayed low; people were hurrying their Christmas preparations. Reverend Tom Mellor stepped over from Rishworth to his cousin Thomas' comfortable house in Greetland. Thomas rarely went to his cousin's chapel, preferring he said, the order in the parish church. In the summer Peggy occasionally persuaded him to take the family to Rishworth, for a good day of chapel and family gossip.

The minister brought bad news, bad news for all Mellors and bad news for the people of Longroyd Bridge who counted George Mellor as one of theirs.

"Anyone at home?" he called as he pushed on the big front door. "Peggy, you there? Thomas, you in?" As he stood uncertainly in the hall, Peggy came through from the back kitchen. She had been sorting the apples in the stores. Through the open door, Tom saw piles of dried fruit, nuts, beef suet and cooking apples, all waiting on the kitchen table beside the large copper preserving pan. Peggy was making her Christmas puddings.

"'Tis good to see thee, cousin Tom," she said as she moved to help him off with his heavy coat. "Thee be drained. What has happened? C'mon on through. I've got a pot on the boil and there'll be a cup of tea for thee in a twinkling."

Following her into the back kitchen, Tom said, "Peggy, 'tis bad, terrible bad! I can't believe it, can't believe that the Good Lord has let this happen to our George. But… not our will but His." He gave way, covering his face in his hands. Peggy led him to the table and, as he sat, his shoulders heaved, tears dampening his eyes.

"Cousin, what? What does this mean? What's happened?"

"'Tis dreadful, Peggy—utterly dreadful. Ben Walker has turned King's Evidence. He's spent hours holed up in Magistrate Joseph Radcliffe's house and he's sold George and his comrades to the authorities. All for the glint of silver—a traitor like Judas—2000 guineas I was told— how will he rest when he sees mothers and widows weeping for their betrayed menfolk? They've taken George and his friends to York and chained them up in the Castle. The trial is spoken of as early January. How could Ben betray his friends? How can he live with himself?"

Peggy replied sharply. "It'll be the money. That Ben is weak, always has been. He followed the biggest bully in town. Always bought any bauble swung before his eyes. George's mother Wood'll be distraught. How will she cope? She idolised that George, he was the best of her children. Please tell me it's not true, just market tittle-tattle!"

"I wish it were so but no. I'm on my way to Dungeon Mill to give them news of the arrest and charges. I'm told the militia are out hunting for others too. They'll want to bring them to trial—and hang them if they can. At least Cousin Joseph will give his sister help in a practical way," said Tom, shaking his head at the depths of the despair for the family.

"I wouldn't be so sure of that," said Peggy. "Despite being family, that Joseph is a dark one, keeps his thoughts to himself. And for all he has apprentices in his shop to shout for King Ludd, he has friends who plot against the workers. Don't know that George can count on him. But time will tell."

Thomas Mellor walked into the back-kitchen, looked at the teapot beside his cousin, at the sugar bowl standing at Tom's elbow and knew bad news was in the air.

"I suppose Cousin George has been named as chief suspect for King Ludd and murderer of William Horsfall. But Cousin Tom, you must have expected this. George has been shouting his head off about injustice, about reform, about breaking the mills—it's all over the Dales. Fighting and murder isn't the way forward; can't have people breaking the law. How can we find work if the countryside's in an uproar? Peaceful protest—that's fine—but riot and murder? No, we must draw the line."

Thomas spoke fiercely remembering the terror of his two children when he'd ridden over to Lockwood, the day after the murder. He had sent them away from home to protect them from bullies in Elland. Instead they had seen murder done by their own friends. Thomas could not forgive the Luddites for the terror they had inflicted on his family.

Cousin Tom, who in his own congregation saw too many men put off from work, families going hungry, women scraping by on nothing so their children could eat, children dying of starvation, stood up and stopped Thomas with a raised hand saying.

"Enough, cousin, enough. How can people in dire need behave as instructed by magistrates who speak from loaded tables and big houses full of treasure? Our people need food, their wives need shelter! And if we cannot call out this treatment how can we bring change?"

Thomas grunted and pulled out a chair. Awkwardly Cousin Tom sat back down—while Peggy settled the children putting Lizzie into her high chair and ushering Hansie and Joe to their bench.

"Can you give us the Lord's grace, cousin?" Peggy spoke softly, urging her husband to lessen his frown and loosen the arms crossed firmly over his chest. Minister Tom gave the Lord's blessings on the food of the household.

Together, in silence, they ate. Slowly the atmosphere thawed. The minister stood up and said, "I must away now. I thank thee both for this meal. Peggy's right, Cousin Thomas. We each see what's right for ourselves and we mustn't fall out over it. The Lord bore his pain in silence—and we must do so too. I must to Longroyd Bridge and give them what comfort I can."

"Haste ye on then, Cousin Tom. The evening draws in mighty quick at this time of year and the frost sets in early and hard. Pay heed to your safety; there be thieves all too ready to pounce on an innocent man. I look to hear that all at Longroyd and Dungeon Bottom are safe." Peggy spoke softly as Thomas was still too cross to be kind.

With a heavy heart, Cousin Tom put on his great coat; Thomas withdrew the bolts on his front door. They both stepped into the yard and Thomas held the horse's head while Cousin Tom mounted. "I'm sorry we don't agree on how to make this business better, Thomas, but the Lord will guide us. We must all pray to the Lord."

"Amen to that," said Thomas and raised his hand stiffly in a wave as Tom rode into the gloom of the winter afternoon.

It was a bitter Christmas for everyone in Caldervale and in the Colne Valley. George was chained inside York Castle. He was writing to men he thought were friends to give him a character reference. But Joseph Radcliffe's harrying of the neighbourhood for witnesses, the presence of the Militia whose orders were to flush out the rebels—all this terrified the people of the West Riding. Like Thomas, many were horrified at the thought of life turning to murder and riot. Many though became sullen and silent, too frightened to challenge the soldiers but sure that George was wrong only in being caught, not in what he did.

EXTRAORDINARY
EXECUTION
9th January 1813

The Execution of these unhappy men took place yesterday, at nine o'clock, at the usual place behind the Castle wall, every precaution had been taken to make a rescue impracticable. Two troops of Cavalry were drawn up at the front of the drop, and the entrances to the Castle were guarded by Infantry. At five minutes before nine o'clock, the prisoners were upon the fatal platform. After the ordinary had read the accustomed forms of prayer on these occasions, George Mellor prayed for about ten minutes; he spoke with great apparent fervency and devotion, confessing in general, the greatness of his sins, but without any admission to the crime for which he suffered. He prayed earnestly for mercy, and with a pathos that was affecting. The surrounding multitude were evidently affected. William Thorpe also prayed, but his voice was not so well heard. Smith said little, but seemed to join in the devotion with great seriousness. The prisoners were then moved to the front of the platform, and Mellor said: "Some of my enemies may be here, if there be, I freely forgive them, and all the world, and I hope the world will forgive me." William Thorpe said, "I hope none of those who are now before me, will ever come to this place." The executioner then proceeded to perform his fatal office, and the drop fell. Some alteration had been made to the drop, so that all the whole body was visible when they were suspended; in former executions only the feet and head could be seen by the spectators. They were executed in their irons. They appeared slightly convulsed for a few moments.

59. Copy of Leeds Mercury 1813 (Elland Library)

Joseph Mellor in Dungeon Bottom said it would all blow over and gave no help to George—as Peggy had predicted. It did blow over for some, but not for the thirteen men in the castle. On January 6th the trial was held. Newspapers bayed for justice. The verdict came swiftly that same day—guilty. And the sentence: death by hanging two days later in York Castle on Friday 8th January, 1813.

Fresh militia soldiers were brought in from outside Yorkshire; mass funerals were banned but each family took the bodies of their men home for a quiet burial in the churchyards of their forefathers. Most Anglican clergy—and many Non-conformist Methodist ministers—refused to give these men a decent burial but an ardent young Irish minister in Hartshead near to Rawfolds Mill just north of Huddersfield, was prepared, so it was whispered, to do the decent thing and bury these men who had been fighting for their families and kin. His name: Patrick Bronte, father of Charlotte Bronte (1816-1855), later to be the author of *Shirley* and *Jane Eyre*.

As the coffin went past in Elland, Thomas Mellor took his young son Joe to pay his respects to Cousin George, that bear of a young man, who had thrown Joe delightedly onto his shoulders. Although he condemned murder, Thomas was proud of a cousin who was prepared to stand up for himself and for others. He told Joe to pull off his cap as the coffin went past. Years later Joe remembered the heavy coats, the backs of men standing ramrod in the chapel above the town, the heavy silence as they followed the coffin out of the chapel. Six men lowered the long wooden box into the ground. Alongside his father, Joe threw earth down on to the coffin, but he never really believed that it was his big cousin George inside, nor that George would never again tell him stories when they sneaked into the cloth-shearing workshop at Longroyd, would never again lift with pride those heavy shears that clipped at the finished cloth and made the finest pieces of cloth in the West Riding.

Joe learnt early to keep silent about George. He never told anyone what he had seen in Dungeon Wood. He learnt that things were not as they seemed: a bright joyful young man could turn murderous; a family member could be silenced in the heart of his kin. Joe learnt it was good to carve your own way—but he learnt to do it alone, without involving neighbours. Joe learnt to be independent in thought as well as action, to look after himself and his family. He learnt to respect law and order and to value the King's Justice over the people's justice.

Like his father, Joe was no radical.

This scandalous tragedy left Thomas and Peggy focused on their family and their business. They distanced themselves from tumult and disorder, from the discontent of "these perilous times." A name shared with George Mellor reminded customers and suppliers alike that Thomas Mellor's family might be more than they seemed: trouble-makers, rebels, unruly and discontented. Thomas and Peggy kept political opinions to themselves but "perilous times" have a habit of discomfiting even the compliant and decorous. The next decade would not treat them kindly, despite the happiness of more babies, and the solidity of their Greetland home. Politics has a nasty way of infiltrating private lives—despite people's best efforts at evasion.

PART II
MONEY TROUBLES
1817-1828

60. *Kings Bench Prison—Marshalsea, Southwark, London.*
John Dickens was a debtor prisoner at Marshalsea, next door to Kings
Bench in 1824. His son, Charles, wrote powerful novels about lawyers,
debtors and bribery at elections. These added to widespread calls for social
change during the nineteenth century.

PART II—Chapter 12

Savile Arms Meeting
July 1817

61. Ancient buildings in Elland—drawing held by Elland Library

Four years after young Joe was held aloft by his father to see over the heads of grim-faced chapel men mourning the death of George Mellor, Thomas called again for his boy to support him in a public duty. He stepped out, with his son, to a public meeting at the Savile Arms in the centre of Elland. At nine, Joe was young to be attending a public meeting, but with 6 children, and only one a boy, Thomas wanted that son to learn the family business. On a Monday morning in late July 1817 he told Joe there would be no school. He must dress neatly to come to the Savile Arms.

Joe was delighted. He was good at reading and writing but he felt that the real stuff of living went on outside school, in the workshops and markets of Halifax. A day in his father's company meant he was growing up, becoming a man. He was so pleased that he made no objection to his mother combing his hair, nor to his father inspecting the polish on his boots.

Hansie was not allowed a day off school. She loved everything to do with school but was mortified that it was her younger brother called to attend this public duty. She knew certain things were done by men, and others by women, but she resented the fact that so much was closed to her simply because she was a girl. Attending public meetings, let alone speaking at them, was never meant for girls. Hansie thought this mightily unfair; Joe thought it was normal.

As they passed through the little iron–gate, hinged on its tall stone pillar set in the garden wall, Joe felt his father shut down. His skip turned into a solemn step to match his father's silent stride. He thought of talking about his latest experiment with the cogs and wheels he had found in the workshop. His father's heavy frown and pursed lips warned him that then was not the time. He wondered what was going to happen—but did not dare ask.

After a 20 minute walk down to Elland Joe saw a small crowd in the square. Men, huddled in ones or twos, were talking quietly with nodding heads and serious faces. When they saw Thomas and his son the conversation fell quiet and their faces contorted in tight smiles as they acknowledged their fellow townsman. Joe saw the Walker men, the Vickermans, and the Turners. Without a sideways glance, Thomas walked into the Inn, Joe close at his heels. Inside, the glare of the outside sun left them momentarily blinded. Joe stood blinking on the threshold of the large low-ceilinged public room. His father moved towards an oak table. Papers lay scattered; three chairs solemnly faced the room from behind the table. Uncle James stood beside the end chair and greeted Thomas with a gentle tap on the shoulder.

"Bad day, Nephew. Bad day. I'm sorry. Many here be unkind, many here want their pound of flesh. None considers how near this day could be for all."

"I expected nothing less, Uncle. My hope is in my family—not like poor Jonathan crushed by his own brother, that scoundrel Francis Vickerman."

"As long as I have breath Thomas, I'll be there for you—so will your father and father-in-law. Mellors and Thorntons stand firm together. All for one and one for all. 'Tis right that you've brought along young Joe. He needs to learn the family ways. You ready to be a man, young Joe?"

Joe bristled with pride, being spoken to as though he was a lynch pin to the family.

"That I am, Uncle. I'll work hard for Mother and the girls—Papa knows that."

Uncle James patted him on the shoulder with a smile. Then he turned to a new man who had just come in. The newcomer was dressed in a dark, sober coat with white bands set at his neck in the manner of a Dissenting Minister.

"Afternoon, Mr.Cadney. Pleasant weather today!" said Uncle James.

"'Tis indeed, James," replied the lawyer. "Thomas! Time to be doing now. You ready?"

"Aye, man. Get it done with quickly."

Joe was bewildered by this. Normally his father and Uncle James led the talk in town conversations. They were maisters. People worked for them. They bought and sold wool and turned it into cloth. They set up workshops to turn the wheels and weave the spun wool. They took the pieces to market and people came to them for a wage. Yet today, this dark-clothed man wearing his coat on a hot summer's day, was leading the talk, calling for order and quietening the room. The three men moved into the pre-arranged chairs and faced the audience. Joe stood behind them, looking cautiously out at the crowd feeling safe behind his father's ladder-backed oak chair.

"Folk, quiet. Order. We're here this afternoon to hear the list of debts carried by Mr. Thomas Mellor in his business as a clothier. Neighbours have brought this action as they cannot see their money coming back to them. It was, as we know all too well, a terrible winter, these months past. In the kindness of these creditors, they have allowed Mr. Mellor time to pay them back—but, enough is enough, we are here today to list all those moneys and to agree a share for each one of you."

At this an angry voice was raised demanding payment now and in full. "Money is precious. We want it now. No one can trade when 'skivers' wriggle out of their dues." The heckler spat out 'skivers' with venom.

"But the law, my friend, the law." Mr. Cadney coughed, interrupting the angry man. "We must be legal, my friend. The law says we must list and order all monies owed by Mr. Mellor here. So, tell me out loud, what money is owed to you, and it will be listed. I see Mr. Mortimer and Mr. Wheeler by the door. They will take your details, my friend—and then the dividend can be set which we can all agree on. Have you our friend's details, Mr.Mortimer?"

"Mr. Cadney—I have a short list in my hand but not including this gentleman. He has never submitted a claim—as he should, if he wants to be considered. Your Claim, sir?" He held out his hand to the loud and angry man.

Mr. Mortimer, dressed as soberly as his colleague the lawyer, waited with his hand extended, but the man had no list to give him. He stood in the centre of the room like a bull facing down his enemies, his eyes darting everywhere, his cheeks puffed out, and his breath coming in angry flurries. Joe blanched. He had seen that man at his home the previous week. The unexpected visitor shouted at his mother, marched over to the workshops and yanked open the door with a loud bang—the shouting increased. Joe wanted to hit him for yelling at his mother but Hansie had held him back. She held him tightly, restraining the taut fierceness of Joe's muscles. A nine-year-old boy was no match for a grown man.

As he retreated in the face of calm, slow legal manners the agitated man spat at Thomas and Joe. "Yous'e scum," he said. "I'll git 'ee, ne'er you mind. I'll git what's mine whate'er that clever lawyer says. I knows right from wrong—you cheated me. It's you that made me lose my work, you and your fancy ways. Just you see—I'll git 'ee, I will."

Uncle James moved himself tightly beside Thomas. Joe melted further behind his father, away from the glare and stale odour. Neither of the Mellor men yielded an inch.

"C'mon, John. That's enough now. The Mellors here may be bad maisters, or maybe not, but they be good neighbours, and have always had a kindness for men in trouble. Save your anger for the owners, for the big men, for those who work people ragged." Abe Hanson, a big man who often led the townspeople in speeches against the mill owners, stepped up to the sweating man. People watched, fascinated.

The organiser went on,

"'Tis the big men we need to rail agin. You came to the Union meeting back in January. You came to Steep Hill meeting. The thousands there are with you. But 'tis the owners, man. They be the enemy—not these maisters John, not 'em. If we hurt 'em, we hurt ourselves. We got to do it together, John—work with demands for better pay, better hours. We can't do it by hurting our own, John. Leave 'em be; keep your ire for the big stuff. Come with me. Come outside, John, Come."

And gently, still repeating his name, Abe led the bewildered and angry John out into the sunny square. Everyone watched, in awed silence. They knew how angry this large, sweating man had become when he lost his work. They knew how he had threatened the small clothiers when they could give him nothing to do. They knew how he hollered louder and longer after a night over his ale. They had seen the blows he could land. They were relieved that Abe Hanson had intervened and led him away. Abe had spun his silver tongue over 7000 souls on Steep Field outside Huddersfield last January demanding more money and better conditions of work. Now they heard him use that tongue over John. Elland maisters were frightened of the mob that men like Abe could raise—but they understood how men with little work and high rents to pay needed to be heard. With Abe and the angry John outside, the Elland clothiers turned back to the matter in hand. Joe let go of his held breath and looked at the men confronting his father.

Men Joe knew, men who came to his father's workshops to talk business, to buy or sell, to work or set up new machines, these were the men gathered in the low-ceilinged dark room where Mrs. Wilkinson served up flagons of ale. Not many spoke. Three or four listed monies which seemed large to Joe, only used to spending small amounts of change for the bread and buns he bought for his mother. One talked of £150 owed to him. Mr. Cadney brought everyone's attention by hitting the table in front of him with a small gavel,

"Neighbours, here we have a list of monies owed by Mr. Thomas Mellor—only three or four men—if these calls are to be believed. As you know it will be better for all if he keeps on trading to make the money he needs to pay you. But, as you know, it's up to you if you need the money more quickly than that. There's much trouble just now what with the war, the terrible harvests, and the changes from the mills in the valley—will the money come back if you press for it now—or will you get more by waiting till trading improves? Let the debts stand for later payment. Can you show your agreement with a show of hands?" He lifted his head to scan the room. Hands were raised and he picked up the wooden gavel. With a smile at the frowning traders he said, "This is a public place and it is known that Mr. Mellor needs to pay back these monies. He will attend to improving his position—and pay them as is listed today. I close this meeting." He tapped the table with his gavel.

The lawyer gathered up his papers and turned to James, sitting on his left. Joe had closed his eyes as he heard the gavel fall. He heard the rustle of papers and opened them to see the men relaxing and turning away from the table with its three seated figures.

"Thank 'ee. Thanks be to thee, Mr.Cadney." James spoke in a low voice, warm with gratitude and relief. Mr. Cadney had managed a stay of execution for his nephew. He had bought time for Thomas to pay his debtors.

Uncle James wrung Mr. Cadney's hand. He spoke for his nephew struggling to contain his dignity. Thomas felt keenly the loss of standing amongst his fellow towns people. He was proud to call himself a clothier and proud to raise his family as his father had done before him. His hopes of trading as successfully as his kin, Benjamin Mellor of Stainland, of John in Halifax, and Joseph over at Dungeon Mill, were taking a battering in this Inn. As the men relaxed Thomas drew a gulp of air in this stifling, overheated room. Reassured that his neighbours were relieved to see him surviving, he felt that he could rise above this setback. Uncle James backed him. His ambition for himself, his family, his continuation of family tradition, his hopes for the future, in the shape of his son standing close behind him—all would survive this setback. He would fight another day. He would succeed.

Capital, or the lack of it, sometimes intruded on best intentions. Thomas had to borrow outside the family. He owed £150 to a man who himself owed money and needed to pay urgently. Mr. Cadney, busy behind the scenes in Halifax, knew the whole complex business web would collapse if men called in their debts too hastily. Others thought that calling in debts was the moral duty now the war was won and Napoleon dispatched to his lonely island. Monday's meeting was arranged to allow business to continue. The smaller creditors persuaded the largest one to wait. Each accepted payments made over a longer time in smaller amounts to enable continued trading. Thomas was free to trade as long as he paid these smaller amounts. Joe did not understand the financial complexities—but he felt the sun dancing through the beams above the dusty windowsills and relaxed his jaw. As his father and uncle rose to leave, he stuck close behind.

Outside in the warm afternoon sun, Joe noticed his father, head hanging down, lost in thought. Surreptitiously he slid his hand into his father's. Uncle James was touched when he saw the boy's kindness.

Thomas and Peggy had done a good job with their children, he thought to himself.

"Well Thomas, not too bad then. We can survive. Take an office in Halifax. It'll increase your sales—and your contacts with all the merchants. That way you'll get more money to pay off these men."

James waved at the Inn behind them where the townsmen had stayed drinking together. Bending closer to Thomas he continued, "We'll go up Saturday and look for a room. Bring the boy with you. He should see how we go about business." Uncle James nodded affectionately at the boy holding his father's hand.

Thomas smiled at his uncle, the man who had taught him the wool business. He saw an older man, wrinkled now, but still seeing the best in people, still smiling at life's ups and downs. His eyes softened, feeling the warmth of this upright, reserved and loyal uncle. Uncle James was with him all the way, standing by him in bad times as well as the good. To Joe it seemed natural that his grandfather, old Joseph Mellor, was not there but to Thomas that had been a hard blow. Joseph Mellor, woolman of Elland, was too ashamed to attend and see his son crushed by fellow clothiers.

"Aye, Uncle. We'll be there—the boy and me. We'll be there." Thomas extended his hand to his Uncle and they shook vigorously. With his free hand James enveloped his nephew in a hug—and Thomas, after a brief moment of leaning in—moved back and turned, taking Joe briskly up the hill to Greetland.

On the walk home, Joe dared not ask what it had all meant but Thomas was no longer silent. He talked to Joe about the office he planned to rent. He talked of the bales of wool that he had sold after the shearing in May. He chatted about the hay bales now standing in their barns, of the cattle and the sheep on the moor. Joe skipped along beside him and, at the top of the hill, just before they reached their home, he told his father of his experiments with the cogs and wheels and axles he had found in the workshop. Thomas had little interest in machines—the cloth was his love—nor did he share his son's love of inventing—but he found Joe's questions useful when he was examining new machinery in other people's workshops. Joe touched everything, poked everything, crawled under everything, took them apart and put them back together. He made toy carts roll down the hills faster than all the other boys. His father, a landsman, was always interested in the animals who grazed the land, always engaged in the sheep who gave his family their wool. He never understood his son's fascination with making things—but he was proud of thinking so unlike his own and he listened patiently to the long and complex details that Joe loved to recount.

Back at the squeaky gate with its unoiled hinge, Thomas stopped and looked at his son.

"Lad," he said. "No telling thy mother about that angry John. It fears her hearing of such ill-feeling. She was afeard enough last week. Abe Hanson has that man under control. He won't cause us any more trouble—but nothing to Mother. She will turn it over and over in her mind and worry. We don't want that, do we Lad?"

"No, Father," Joe replied, wondering what worrying his mother meant. She was the one who always sorted things out. She was the one they all turned to when things needed changing. Any bullying boys got short shrift from her defensive tongue. Troubled neighbours always found a listening ear in her kitchen, a cast-off coat for a child's winter warmth, a bun or a pudding to fill a grumbling belly. Joe thought it was his father who worried, not his mother. His mother had been scared in the first instance of that man shouting in the yard, but she had stood up to him, spitting at him as he moved away. His mother protected them all; she kept away demanding, angry people.

Perhaps, aware that his son did not share his view of Peggy's fragility, Thomas took his son's hand again and they walked into the kitchen together. Thomas told his wife that Joe had been a stalwart boy. The meeting had gone well, he said, and he was going to open an office in Halifax—upon Mr. Cadney's and Uncle James' advice—to recruit more business. Joe kept quiet while Peggy wondered whether her husband was telling her everything. Easier in her mind that Thomas was talking again, that he looked at his son with pride, and that Uncle James was working alongside him, she thought that this was the worst it would be. The war was over two years—the French emperor Boney, a prisoner on the remote island of St.Helena. Wool prices would rise again, she hoped. She turned her mind towards the never-ending task of feeding her hungry family and told Hansie to call everyone to tea.

Afterwards, Hansie took Joe to the hay barn. It was her favourite hiding place, warm, dry and sweet-smelling. She loved the kittens playing chase, jumping from bale to bale as she lay on the platform above the vast barn doors. She watched as the men drove the carts laden with summer harvest through these doors in June.

"Joe, what happened? How was Father?" she asked her brother when they had climbed the ladder to the loft.

"Silent mostly, Hansie. The room was dark. Maisters were there. So was a dark coated gentleman called Mr. Cadney. Uncle James kept close and there was talk of money—lots of it—£150 I think. Someone wants that much from Father but he's going to pay in little bits, over months. Father's going to get more money by taking an office in Halifax. He didn't want me to tell Mother about a nasty man who shouted at us."

"Oh, Joe, there's lots of maisters needing to pay money. I heard Mother talking about bankruptcies down in the Town when we went to the herbalist for some cold remedies. Pieces of cloth are not selling so well in market. What will happen if Father has more trouble?"

"Don't think he will, Hansie. They settled it, the legal man and Uncle James. Ouch," Joe wailed as the kitten dug its claws into him, leaping up the bales to its hiding nest in the high straw. Pulling the tiny tabby off his trousers he gently threw it down in the hay behind him. "I don't think we need to worry, Hansie. Father will sort it out."

"I hope so," said Hannah rather doubtfully. She had heard the women talking at the water pump and they talked of more trouble than most of them had known before. Cottages on the hillside stood empty; children were going without food. Men were 'playing' and following Abe Hanson over the hill to his meetings demanding better wages and shorter hours in the mills. Hannah did not know what the trouble was but she feared her Father was 'catching' the trouble—like an illness.

Joe suddenly picked up one of the kitties and made to throw it. She ducked and then nipped in to give him a pinch. A tussle ensued until he stood triumphant and climbed back down the ladder, widely grinning at her discomfiture. Ruefully she acknowledged that her days of beating her little brother were over. She followed him down the ladder, leaving behind their cares over money troubles.

PART II—Chapter 13

Family Arguments
June 1819

*62. Families would often eat outside for Midsummer Feast
(WYAS, Calderdale Library, Halifax.)*

Two summers later, in July 1819, Hannah and Lizzie were twelve and nine. Their brother, eleven-year-old Joe was asleep in the tiny room above the hall entrance. The girls, in their bedroom were looking out over the garden. It was late on a warm June evening; the family sitting outside for supper, were entertaining a visiting cousin, the Reverend Tom Mellor. Cousin Tom weekly rode to visit his widespread congregation; he prayed with them for their health, and offered guidance if they were suffering money troubles, as many were. The epic battle of Waterloo, four years earlier, had not brought peaceful prosperity for working folk in Yorkshire, nor indeed in other parts of Britain. After a strenuous day of visiting, Tom called on his cousins in Greetland—for a more frivolous evening.

It was summer and like all school children of the time Hannah was out of school—harvesting needed many hands and children's hands were as useful as the adults'. In the fields above the houses, men scything the grass needed drink to refresh themselves. The girls carried it up from the farms and cottages. They helped rake the cut grass into piles for the men to build stooks of hay. The hay was dried in the field and later gathered in carts to be taken to stone barns for winter fodder. Dairy cows needed milking—and the holes the sheep forced in the stone walls needed repair. Three or four weeks later wheat and oat crops needed cutting and gathering. The summer months called every hand to field work. Weaving and spinning, fulling and dyeing, all were held over until the farm work eased; wool work began again in the long winter months—as did school.

Away from school, Hannah missed the stories of faraway places, the exercises in writing, the playing with numbers, and the help she loved giving to others in learning their letters. At home, she had less time to think; she attended to her younger sisters—keeping the four little girls, and Brother Joe, out of trouble. After his unusual trip to the Savile Arms, Joe was more thoughtful, less eager to play tricks. Hannah listened with jealousy of his talk of school, realising the greater time he spent on his studies, and the wider book learning he was gaining. She had to learn to sew, to sing and speak French whereas he learnt about the History of Greece and Rome, about geometry and algebra. Joe, like his father, was an action person; he could not understand Hannah's enjoyment of book-learning. But the pair of them were avid listeners to adult gossip. When they were not supposed to hear both would make themselves as still as possible and absorb all being discussed. They learnt about town troubles and family disputes. Tonight though it was the girls, Hansie and Lizzie, following family arguments from their bedroom window.

The Reverend Tom found the Mellor home welcoming and, with its lively children, fun and entertaining. There he was no minister, more of a family man turning over family affairs. Today, however, Tom had sat with a long face over tea and scowled in his Cousin Thomas' direction. Eventually Peggy told Joe to go to his room and Hannah to take the girls—Lizzie, Nancy and Harriet—upstairs to bed while she nursed Baby Momo. Before they went, the girls tidied away the supper things while making jokes and telling funny stories. The adults laughed, but shortly, and Hannah felt the tension between the cousins.

Upstairs the girls changed into their nightdresses—and the two older ones peeked out of their window at the adults perched on the benches beneath. Father was leaning forward and shaking his head. Peggy was looking at both men with exasperation as she nursed her baby. The girls knew she hated arguments, always steering the children from arguing with their Father. Peace at any price was her motto—and she firmly closed her mouth when her husband became angered over his business dealings and, more importantly for her, with townsfolk and relatives who let him down.

As the light closed in and dusk deepened the listening girls heard Cousin Tom explode at their Father;

"Thomas, you cannot expect people to sit back and watch their families starve. It's more than human nature can endure—to hear little ones begging to fill their stomachs while the parents sit at home 'playing' because no one gives them any work—because there is no work. You cannot ask it of anyone, least of all Yorkshire folk. It's against the Lord's commandment."

Their father retaliated, with great fierceness, though lower than his cousin, the Baptist Minister.

"Of course, they can't sit back, Tom! They need to go over to Oldham, to Manchester, to go on their travels to find work. They can't take it out on the clothiers and mill owners. We mun' make our living as best we can—if there's no work, then we need to go looking for it, get off our backsides and find it—like I've done by opening my shop in Halifax. There's plenty of work in the mills, so them with no work must get out of their cottages on the hillside and come down the valleys to the mills. The good Lord knows it's hard enough these days to make a living out of wool but we must keep going, keep on. I thought it would ease when the Iron Duke put old Boney away at Waterloo but things have gone from bad to worse. The price wool fetches is even worse than during the war but I keep going—round the villages, tapping up customers at the Piece Hall every Saturday—just like Father did before me. We manage—not good just now—but we don't go smashing up property—that's just wrong."

Cousin Tom, exasperated at Thomas' view, started talking about the Good Lord's commandment 'to love your neighbour as yourself'. He talked about the early church sharing all their goods and wealth. He urged his cousin that if one man fell then all were affected. He even quoted that 16th century poet and divine, John Donne,—'Send not to know for whom the bell tolls. It tolls for thee. If a clod of earth is washed away, then the whole land is diminished. No man is an island, even unto himself.'

Nothing cut through to Thomas. He repeated his opposition to mass meetings, to riots and charters for workers.

Cousin Tom realised he was hitting a raw nerve with his usually mellow cousin. Times were tough for everyone—and Thomas was no exception. He too had to find the money to pay his rent. He had to keep his creditors at bay, week in and week out. When he lost a customer then he had less money to feed his family and pay his weavers, combers and spinners. The shadow of Cousin George's hanging persisted among his customers. Riots meant a certain decline in his business.

The man of God realised he was asking too much care for others when Thomas himself was struggling.

Thomas the clothier turned to the fate of George in his doomed battle against mills and factories, against new machinery, against mill-owners like William Horsfall—and their friends, the magistrates and landowners. Hansie listened more intently. She had never forgotten those dreadful events of April seven years ago even though no one in the family ever talked about them in front of her or Joe—fearful that their terror would return.

Her father hissed at his cousin, "Well it be sure that challenging authority did no good to Cousin George. He should never have murdered a man in cold blood, not even that vile William Horsfall. Look how his friends ran riot—and it did them no good. Even the traitor, that scoundrel Richard Walker, won no gold for his turncoat evidence. He's on his uppers, or so I heard in the market today. He says he never got the reward he was tempted with. Rioting does no good to anyone."

Thomas ended triumphantly with his arms firmly pressed on the table, his hands stabbing at his food.

"Amen to that," said his cousin, relieved that he did not have to attack Thomas' views on at least one subject. Like most people around Halifax, both men thought George wrong to have murdered in cold blood but his real wrong was to be caught. The trial had been a set up—the magistrate, Joseph Radcliffe, knew what result he wanted—and he got it. Transportation to New South Wales in Australia for the followers; the gallows for the 13 ring leaders. Hannah and Joe knew it had been a dreadful time in the West Riding but no-one explained what had happened afterwards. Hannah's ears were peeled to catch all she could. Brother Joe needed to hear this too.

"Now," said Cousin Tom, "Abraham Mellor has followed the same path—he was found guilty of poaching a sheep last week—and he's been sentenced to transportation to Van Diemen's Land, that island off New Holland or Australia as they be calling it now. They send so many convicts out there. They say it'll be for 7 years—but he'll not come back—they never do—but at least it's not execution. The authorities know the people won't stand for that. They're running scared, but not scared enough to give 'em Reform like they're demanding. They are afeard the valleys will rise if they are too harsh in their punishment."

Hannah heard her father reply, "Not so scared they won't bring up the Militia from Kent to run rings round the people asking for help. The authorities will bring this country to order—and they need to—but it'll cost people around here. I don't know what's to be done, Cousin."

"Nor I." Tom Mellor replied. "Wasn't Abraham a friend of yours in childhood?"

"Aye, he was. Many's the time he and I scrumped apples from the orchards. We roamed the moors as lads. He knew all the birds and where they nested. He aimed his catapult and brought down a partridge or pheasant, with none the wiser. That went into his mother's pot— and they needed it—with his father dead, there was no money coming into the house. Recently he won't tell me what he does—the least said, soonest mended, he says. I'll miss him. And he canna' write—so no letters to his old Mother. Can't imagine what she'll do without him." Thomas sighed as he thought of Abraham.

"You raising your boy Joe, to be straight and true, Thomas. He'll never go to bad like Abe."

Thomas reflected that it was hard to keep the young lads on the right path—when times were so hard—it wasn't clear how any family could keep their young following the good road.

His cousin offered him words of encouragement,

"Just do your best, and keep the young in the straight path, like you and Peggy do with all your little 'uns. But….., we have to try to make things better for their future. At chapel, people talk about Reform of Parliament—they want to send men to London that talk of our interests, of Yorkshire wool needs—not just men that talk of their land needs—of their rolling acres. Good craftsmen need the vote in Parliament—without that nothing will change."

Thomas groaned, "That's ridiculous, Cousin Tom. Members of Parliament will never change. Look at the money thrown around in the last election bribing people to vote. And if you think it's bad up here, I've heard from your chapel friend, Thomas Langdon that it's even worse down in West Country, in his old stamping ground of Honiton. They throw around so much money to get elected that no one wants to stand for election—it bankrupts them—they still stand though. Parliament is only for the landed, for the rich. Ordinary folk'll ne'er get their voices heard. To get heard you must make money—like Benjamin Mellor at Stainland. Then, as often as not, folks forget where they've come from—with their fancy carriages—their attendance at Square Chapel in Halifax—and a big house."

"Precisely my point, Thomas. When people get rich—by God's good grace mind you—not by their own unaided efforts—they should look after their kin, not turn their backs on them. They should care for others—that's the creed we all follow—in church as well as chapel." Minister Tom was certain that he was bringing his cousin round to his point of view.

But this was dangerous territory.

Minister Tom Mellor was a good preacher and he cared well for his flock. With his teaching and preaching his roadside chapel congregation was swelling. He and others had put up the money to build a Particular Baptist chapel in Rishworth, the small hamlet to the south on the road to Oldham. 12 'seed corn' congregation members had preceded him from his 'parent' congregation at Salendine Nook, in the higher Colne valley. Lately Tom had opened a thriving school and now his members numbered nearly 100. By long and hard work, by powerful preaching, he had increased his ministry. Cousin Thomas Mellor, the clothier, was working as hard and as long as the minister. He too heard tales of hardship and eviction but for him, if he failed, then his income failed whereas Tom had a small amount of money given him by the chapel folk—so failure would not throw his family into the workshop. Minister Tom wanted people to share; Clothier Thomas could not see sharing bringing him happiness or prosperity. This coloured each one's view of how to resolve the present difficulties in the West Riding. The young listeners above did not understand the differences dividing their opinions.

Thomas and Peggy Mellor had baptised their children in Elland parish church, the established church as the law demanded; Peggy followed her parents attending a Wesleyan Dissenting chapel every Sunday. Thomas saw himself as a wool man, a trader, a manufacturer—and he saw his future lying with other prosperous merchants—not with the poorer sort of weaver struggling to sell his pieces in a market increasingly dominated by mills and bigger enterprises. His cousin shared weekly chapel meetings with exactly those poorer weavers, combers and mill workers as well as with the more prosperous manufacturers who were funding his income. Clothier Thomas felt the woes of the struggling middle people: Cousin Tom the minister felt the pangs of hunger of his poorer congregation.

Thomas, wanting to feel on the moral side of the debate, continued arguing,

"Church teaches us to mind our own business, Cousin. God helps those who help themselves. A man must follow the Good Book and the Ten Commandments—as thou well knowest. 'Tis against the law to smash up machinery—and to run riot in our towns and fields. 'Thou shalt not steal' says Moses, and 'Thou shalt not kill." It's madness to think men can smash and steal their way through tough times—however bad those times are." Thomas spoke curtly and, with hard eyes, stared belligerently at his cousin. The minister knew he'd gone as far as he dared.

The girls heard their mother stand up and suggest more beer for the men once she'd put the baby down. Thomas scraped his boots on the stone flagstones under the bench and turned towards his departing wife.

"Indeed Peggy, we need a jug. Put Momo to bed and I'll find it—it'll be good for Cousin Tom to have one before his ride home." Thomas gave this invitation a steely tone.

But Minister Tom took it at face value. "I need a glass—the warm weather has put a thirst on me—and then I'll be on my way. It's a full moon and cloudless—it'll be easy to find the track home." He smiled up at his vexed cousin.

The listening girls heard their father stand, push the bench back and plod into the outhouse. Silence was kept, until he returned, with a flagon of ale. Two mugs were set on the table and their father splashed ale into each mug. A bench creaked as he sat back down. Both men spoke more quietly. The girls could hear no more.

Their mother's skirts brushed against the stairs as she brought the baby up to her cot. She shushed the sleepy babe, rubbing her back to return her to deep sleep. A few moments later she softly moved away, pulling the door close, so the babe did not wake. She crossed the landing and put her head round the girls' door.

"Mother, what were they talking about? Why were they arguing about stealing and smashing? Why do people want to do all that?" Hannah was worried about the talk of violence and was insistent in asking her mother to explain.

The violence she had seen seven years before, on Greetland Moor and above Dungeon Wood continued to give her nightmares. In her mind's eye, she saw the crowds, the soldiers, the guns on the Moor. She heard the whispered horror once the rifles had fired from the wood. She flinched at the picture of William Horsfall's horse plunging wildly. In reading her stories of far-off lands, of exploration beyond the ice in North America, across the sea with Captain Cook she buried these memories but tonight, all too vividly, the overheard discussion was bringing them back. She wanted to know why anyone would shatter the peace that she clutched so tightly.

"Why do they do these things, Mother? Why?"

"I don't truly know, my poppet. New mills, new machines—homes with no gardens, no closes. High rents—high food prices too. Old weavers up on the Moors with no work. Mill owners undercutting crafts-folk—cloth pieces sometimes better from the manufacturers—though never tell your father I said that—bad wages in the mills—clock time ruling everything—so much different and so little any better. Great speakers—like Abe Hanson—stirring people up—thousands pouring to the hillsides to hear them—and the magistrates running scared, calling up the army to help them. Children crying for food—none of it is good—and none know how to make it better." Peggy paused for breath—she knew how bad things were, but could see no way to ease their effects. Indeed, she thought calls for different ways were making it worse for working folk—when landlords threw them out for speaking out. She sighed wearily.

"Hansie, tha' mun work it out yoursel'—as the years pass. 'Tis a bad muddle now—but we canna stop change, that's for sure. So shush now. Settle down and get a good night's sleep. Good night my poppets, sleep tight—and mind the bed bugs don't bite!"

"Oh Mother, we're too old for that now."

"But not too old for a butterfly kiss?" their mother replied smiling at them both.

So saying, she bent over each girl and flickered her eyelashes over their soft cheeks. If she could, she gave each of her children these butterfly kisses every night. Hannah and Lizzie were getting so grown up that they went to sleep at the same time as she did—and the butterflies were harder to come by. Tonight, it was as though they were still two little girls; they hushed as they listened to her skirts swishing across the floorboards and against the doorway as she pulled the door shut behind her.

"Hansie, what would you do if you had no work?" Lizzie whispered anxiously to her sister.

"Me—I'd go places—travel the world—no riots nor stealing for me. I'd go to Manchester—or London. I'd find something to work." Hannah was learning geography at school and knew the world was expanding fast. She heard of discoveries being made by British sailors, about spices from India, about tea, coffee and cloth that great ships brought to Britain.

Lizzie, much less confident than Hannah, could not bear the idea of leaving home. She loved the moors, loved walking up and over the hills and feeling the cloudy mist on her face. She muttered a sleepy good night and snuggled under her coverlet—even in summer the temperature dropped low on a cloudless night. Soon her even breathing told Hannah that she slept. Hannah lay awake, pondering that strained conversation on the benches down in the garden. She wondered how she might travel to faraway London—where, they said, the streets were paved with gold. She told herself stories of the fine carriages she might own, the clothes she might wear—and the bone china tea cups with which she would entertain her friends.

Later she heard Cousin Tom unhitch his horse from the ring by the mounting steps. She heard him talk encouragingly, with humms and ahhs and 'my beauty', to his strong grey horse. She heard her father call good night and a safe ride home. He went in, and she heard the bolts shoot across the door. The horse's hooves clattered out the yard and her father's footsteps stumped up the stairs. Warmed by these familiar sounds, she fell asleep. Trouble there might be, but Hannah slept, safe in the knowledge that her parents were protecting her.

PART II—Chapter 14

Newsgathering in Halifax
August 17th 1819

*63. Illustration of Peterloo Massacre in St. Peter's Field
held in Manchester Library*

In the quiet of the next morning, Hannah, up as usual with the sun, took her night chamber pot to empty in the garden privy. Drawing back the bolts on the kitchen door she pushed it open. She felt the gentle rush of chill air and saw the dawn-light etch outlines of shadow across the dew-spread garden. Everything was sharp and clear; the valley filled with song birds calling. Passing along the flagged path, she brushed against the lavender releasing a hint of fragrance into the sleeping dawn. She was alone; the noises of the day were still to come, the bustle and dirt still asleep. The world, washed clean of its distress, waited to welcome returning life, a fresh start from the chaos and muddle of the previous day. Dew lay heavy on the webs spun across her father's blackcurrant bushes, diamonds glinted on the blades of grass beside her path. Today, now, Hannah felt the promise of newness, of adventure as yet untold. She longed to explore this wonderful world.

Abruptly, three year old Harriet intruded; she trundled down the path, dragging her 'blankie' behind her.

"Hansie! Pick up, pick up Harreee! Harree ride!" Harriet had few words, and poor pronunciation, but she got by well enough. Using gestures, she made herself very clear and the family, particularly her eldest sister, understood exactly what she wanted.

Hannah bent to lift her little sister and, as she straightened herself with the toddler in her arms, reached to pick two purple plums hanging low above her head. Baby Harriet felt bed-warm snuggling into the line of her neck. Helping the child extract the stone from her plum, Hannah took her inside for breakfast.

In the kitchen their mother was tending the flame in the cooking range and gave Hannah the big kettle to fill from the pump in the yard outside.

As she took the kettle, Hansie told her mother, "Today I'm going up to Halifax. I want to find cotton cloth for the babies' dresses—to make them Sunday best calico smocks—light and easy to wash and dry."

Hannah settled Harriet in the high chair that sat behind the door ready for whichever child needed to be kept out of mischief. She gave her a crusty toast.

"Thou hadst best be quick, my girl. Autumn turns into winter all too fast. Last year was different—we were blessed with a long warm Autumn, but this year, who knows—winter may nip in quick and sharp."

Peggy brought her pot to the table where 6 small bowls were lined up waiting for their dollops of porridge.

"Bring the milk standing in the pantry, Hansie! Before thou drawest the water!"

"Milk and water both coming up!" Hannah whistled as she moved to the pantry. She was pleased with her idea of going up to Halifax— Baby Momo was growing so fast, and the dresses handed down from her four older sisters were threadbare, greatly patched and heavily darned. She would ask six year old Nancy to come along with her. Nancy loved an outing—and already had a sharp eye for patterns and colours. Hannah, well used to darning and mending, took a practical view of choosing cloth for dressmaking; Nancy, free of her older sister's chores as the eldest daughter, looked for an effect and confidently chose with surprising aplomb. This morning sister Lizzie was in one of her 'dull' moods and would be happier helping their mother at home.

"Stop that whistling," Peggy spoke sharply to her daughter. "It's not the sign of a modest young lady. Thou mun' watch thine step, my girl— else there'll be no husband!"

"Who needs a husband, Mother? I don't. I'm going to travel the world."

"Hannah, that's plain silly. Every girl needs a husband—else it's a lifetime at the beck and call of others, of creeping into places where one's not wanted, of not knowing where thou canst live—Governess to spoilt children, companion to a cranky older lady, shop worker to some other family business—or even down mill with its long factory hours— all at behest of others—and nothing to call thine own."

"No Mother—somehow I'll be different. I'll travel—make myself rich—somehow."

"Well until that time comes, young lady, thou hadst better mind thy 'ps and qs', and remember your manners. We don't want people talking behind our backs."

"I always remember my manners, Mother, always." Hannah said very hotly. She hated being thought rude or careless with other people's feelings.

She flounced out of the kitchen setting the empty black kettle in the hearth. Seconds later she was back with a flagon full of milk. She set that on the table next to the row of bowls and swung the kettle off the stone hearth and out into the back yard. Her mother heard her working the pump, up and down, crashing against the wood covering the pipe thrusting down to the spring in the earth below. The water swooshed out, tumbling into the kettle. It paused, in silence, till the next push sent it swooshing forth again. Once full, the kettle was heavy, and Hannah brought it back in with a lop-sided walk before heaving it onto its hook over the fire.

A succession of children traipsed into the kitchen requesting their porridge. Hannah suggested that Nancy put on her stout boots if she wanted to go up to Halifax market to choose cloth. The six year old twirled around the kitchen singing, loudly and tunelessly, about little pigs going to market! She ran into the outhouses where they stored the boots. Joe was in charge of cleaning them after any bouts of heavy rain had covered them in mud. Hers stood, bright and mud free, alongside Hannah's much bigger boots. She still needed help with her laces but, being asked to go with Hansie made her feel grown up; she rejected help from her mother and stuck her booted foot at Hannah as she sat, on the back-door step, lacing up her own boots.

Booted and ready, both girls gave their mother a kiss, grabbed a basket and left the kitchen. They clattered down the garden path to the front gate—still squeaking on its hinges—as it had two summers before. The girls turned right, down the steep hill to Elland Bridge. A day's delight was ahead of them—wandering in and out of Halifax market stalls as they pleased.

Nancy ran on ahead. She skipped and called out to friends; "We're off to market, up to Halifax for dress cloth."

Hannah called after her, "Save your energy, Nance! Going at such a pace now is fine—it's downhill and early—just wait till it's the end of the day and we're coming back up the hill."

Her sensible exhortations fell on deaf ears. Nancy was so excited to be out with her big sister that nothing dampened her spirits. The girls followed the road, down to the parish church. They heard the river, small in its summer trickle, dropping over rocks and boulders in the river bed. They saw birds darting through the trees clinging to the steep banks. Hannah had half hoped a neighbour, in his cart, would pass them on his way to Halifax—and offer them a lift. No one passed. Over the bridge, they started climbing up through Skircoat, past the Green and on upwards towards Kingscross Lane and the market.

Where Kingcross met Paradise Road, Hannah knew her father's friend, Joseph Baines had his cloth-pressing business. His wife ran her father's public house at the end of Paradise Road. Hannah knew that they could call there for any refreshment should they need it. A responsible sister, Hannah was heartened by the feeling of being able to share her burden of care if little Nancy became hurt or overtired but she was in a hurry. She wanted no delay to her shopping.

Hannah tried to hurry past the Baines workshop. It was cotton she wanted for her dressmaking—soft muslin for Sunday smocks—not woollen cloth from Mr. Baines. As they passed however, Joseph Baines came out with his son, John and three more little children—all younger than Nancy. Hannah and Nancy had to pause to exchange greetings. Joseph was a commanding figure in Halifax. He helped his father-in-law with his public house. He knew everyone—and had an eye for good business. He was prospering at the centre of Halifax. But today he came towards Hannah and Nancy with a heavy frown, waving his staff at them.

"Hannah and Nancy, What on earth are you two doing here, alone?" he shouted at the girls.

SPREAD EAGLE INN, OLD MARKET, HALIFAX.
Now destroyed.

ANCIENT HOUSE, WOOLSHOPS, as in 1840.
Now covered with plaster and otherwise altered.

64. Contemporary illustrations of Halifax workshops and inns
(WYAS Calderdale Library)

"We're just shopping for cotton, Mr. Baines. Mother sent us. We're here for the day. Harvest is nearly done and we're not needed in the closes." Hannah was surprised at the anger in Joseph Baines voice—and at his interfering with their business.

"There's terrible slaughter over at St. Peter's Fields, over Manchester way. Hundreds dead, people fleeing, the military charging down protesters. No one did wrong; the military charged defenceless families. Our Yorkshire's not safe, not safe for anyone, let alone two young girls. Get back to your mother now—no shopping today." Joseph Baines was talking fast and waving at the girls.

Hannah paled. She remembered the meeting on the hillside above Greetland. She felt the fear that ran through her as the shots rang out above Dungeon Wood—she held Nancy's little hand much tighter. Was this what her father had feared last night?

She asked, in a strangled whisper, "Is this a riot? Are they banging up machinery? Will they be coming to get us?"

Joseph Baines realised that she was shaking with fear. He turned and pointed towards the public room in the Inn behind him.

"Go in to see my Jane, dearies—and son John. Come in. You can't go home in this state of worry." He shepherded the two children through the public bar into the back of the Inn and called out to his wife. "Janie! Janie, I've two bairns here as need a scone and jug of milk. Take care of them and send them on their way."

"Coming," Jane called from her kitchen. "Coming, girls."

As she entered the dark lobby between the outside yard and her living quarters at the back, she saw Hannah's terrified eyes and shaking hands. Nancy was looking puzzled rather than frightened. With a questioning look at her husband, she wrapped her arms round both children. "What's up, Husband?"

"They be visiting the market for cotton cloth, Janie. They've just heard about the massacre at Manchester. I told them to go home quick—but looks like they need a little something before they do that. I'll leave them with you—they be two of Thomas Mellor's family— he's a good supplier of mine. Look after them."

Last night, Hannah had heard with dread, the argument about rioting, reform and breaking up machinery. Today the anxiety she had suppressed in the dark of her bedroom came screaming back at her in broad daylight. Her father's friend, Abraham being transported was bewildering enough, but now hearing that soldiers were out with their rifles shooting people was terrifying. Soldiers might turn down this street at any moment. Shooting could start again.

"Tell me we're safe, tell me there's no more shooting." Hannah's voice shook as she implored Jane Baines to make things quieter, calmer.

"Come into the back with me. I'll explain as best I can. Come in the two of you!" Jane Baines had four small children and she saw these two in the same light. "I'll give you a snack and we can work out what to do."

Hannah and Nancy followed her into her kitchen. She sat them down at the kitchen table and brought out scones and oatcakes for the children to nibble. "Take your time girls. There're no soldiers here.

We're all safe." She patted Hannah's shoulder and gave her a little hug. "You're a good girl, you're taking good care of the little one here."

"Thanks, Mistress. Do you know what happened?" Hannah whispered up at her.

"Not as much as I'd like but I've heard enough in the tap room to know what's gone on. Yesterday there was a huge meeting at St. Peter's Fields on the edge of Manchester. It had been planned and families went from all over Lancashire—and even some from our side of the Pennines." Jane was talking in a low voice, calmly and slowly as though it was all a normal day's happenings. She understood how to calm frightened children giving them a truthful outline in an everyday normal voice. She gave the children distance from the disaster that had taken place in Manchester the previous day.

She continued with her story.

"Men were haranguing the crowd from their carts. Soldiers were in the lanes outside the fields—waiting for an order. They were waiting on horses. At a signal they charged the crowd to capture the speakers. They crushed and trampled people in the crowd. Everyone screamed. More soldiers arrived—more shots—more charges—more people falling. People ran. Many hid. The soldiers charged all day. People ran away—hiding and not telling anyone that they were hurt in St. Peter's Fields. They don't want soldiers coming after them."

Hannah was watching her horrified. "But children were hurt too?"

"Indeed, whole villages had come—thousands upon thousands— all wanting to tell out how hungry people were, how much they needed higher wages—but no one brought weapons, no one wanted to riot."

"Did people die?" Hannah's voice was low and tremulous.

"I'm afraid so. Our own English soldiers, our own English government, killed our own hungry people. It's shocking. I can't believe it happened."

"Are we safe? Are people safe in Elland?"

Hannah and Nancy were wide-eyed. Nancy could sense the fear— but could not see where it was. Hannah had a vivid picture of fallen bodies, of snapping rifles, of voices silenced and sullen.

In answer, Jane Baines picked up her youngest child and handed her to Hannah to hold. She told the eldest, John, named after her father John Jackson, the publican, to go find something to play with Nancy. She knew the power of a soft warm baby who laughed at all games of peek a boo; she knew too that children playing become less anxious. It was time for these two to have some relief from their fear. Cuddling a baby calmed most fears.

Her husband Joseph popped his head round the door.

"Are the children alright?"

Jane nodded and walked over to him. "I'll be back in a moment, children. Don't worry about anything—just play." She bent close to her husband and together they moved out of the room, closing the door behind them.

"Hannah, the elder girl, is shaking with fear," she told him. "We need to get her back home safely. She fears the soldiers coming at her— and I reckon I do too—vicious murdering thugs. Children on their own, walking the high roads, they're not safe today—anyone could decide they were dangerous –and shoot. Where oh where is justice?" Despite her calm manner of talking, Jane herself was as scared as Hannah. She knew, from taproom conversations, how angry people were, how bewildered and shocked. She knew how many families were struggling with hunger and homelessness. Those two girls needed to be home with their own. She looked at her husband.

Joseph, being more phlegmatic, thought the girls were safe enough; he had seen no soldiers in Halifax that morning. However, he knew he had to keep his wife calm in this matter. There were enough neighbours who would agree with her—and curse him for exposing youngsters to danger.

"I'll get the taproom boy to run down to Skircoat, to Mellor's work-shop. Someone from there can come up to get the girls and take them back to Elland. Or would the girls go with him? And then it's Mellor and Turner's responsibility." Joseph Baines knew Thomas Mellor worked with the Turners, steady craftspeople who adapted to challenges with-out fuss. The girls would be safe with them.

"Thanks, Husband. That's sensible. I'll persuade Hannah 'tis safe to go with Ned Walker—he's a talkative lad who keeps his head. He'll accompany them to the Skircoat workshop. I had wondered about Mellor's Halifax room—but he is often not there—and that would be even more bewildering for the girls—Skircoat workshop is always working—that's safe—and quieter too." She turned and went back to her kitchen, calling across the yard for Ned, the stable boy.

An hour later Ned Walker accompanied the girls to Skircoat. They greeted Job Turner, Thomas' partner in the workshop, with relief, then waved a cheerful goodbye to Ned who had kept up a flow of jokes all the way down the hill! Job told them to sit and watch him finish off his weaving—and then he would take them back to Greetland.

65. Copley Toll-house beyond Copley Bridge on way up to Greetland
(Author 2019)

Hannah's confidence was returning; she persuaded Job that they could walk up from Copley Bridge on their own. With the new toll roads to Huddersfield recently opened no one now went the old pack horse route by Copley, so they would see no soldiers marching anywhere. Keeping off the main road, they ran down to Calder river on their own, crossing by the little bridge and climbed back, through North Dean woods, and up the hill.

Their house looked solid and secure. Inside there was panic. News had travelled and Peggy was frightened the girls had met disaster. They stepped into the kitchen and she scolded them fiercely.

"Stupid to go cloth shopping. Bad, bad idea—I should never have let thee go—especially with Nancy. Tell me what happened."

Hannah, by now much calmer than she had been outside the Bull Tavern, recognised the fear in her mother's voice. She bit back a tart reply—and sat down, airily suggesting it had been very interesting and good fun. Her mother pursed her lips at this 'fairy tale'. She banged down a plate of scones.

"Less nonsense, please, young lady. Thee be well-favoured girls. Come eat this."

Nancy babbled away retelling some of Ned's jokes. Gradually her mother understood how Joseph Baines had rescued her girls and by the time bedtime had come, she had recovered most of her equanimity.

When he came home, Thomas told his wife it had been a big fuss about nothing. He was disposed to regard the St. Peter's Field meeting as a challenge to the authorities.

"People don't get shot for nothing. They must have been throwing things at the soldiers. Our girls would never throw anything at anyone, let alone at soldiers. They were always safe in Halifax," he reasoned with Peggy.

Nevertheless, when he next saw Joseph Baines, he thanked him very cordially for caring for his two girls. He asked what he made of the stories flying round—some of which enlarged the damage by hundreds. Joseph heard much in the taproom and was a good source of information.

"It looks like a bad job, very bad. The military have had their own way—and no one is going to prosecute 'em—but the newspapers are writing about it—and it's being talked about in Parliament. Nothing'll come of it now but someday there'll be a reckoning. Someday, the working people of the North will be heard. Someday, the vote will come to them—someday."

As he ended this speech, Joseph Baines shook his head over the probable length of time change would take.

"Meanwhile we must get on with work," he said. "You got any cloth for me to finish, friend Thomas?"

The talk turned to business. Thomas Mellor returned to his first thoughts that the authorities were right, that riots and protests should be curtailed. Hansie, his eldest daughter grew on, wondering how to make things better, so that everyone had food and shelter. She dreamt of freedom to live in orderly harmony. She debated endlessly with her brother what they should do. Thomas' eldest children were trying to find their own ways through the troubles that surrounded them, trying to work out a balance between family survival and the prosperity of their neighbours, to balance the common good with individual opportunity.

PART II—Chapter 15

Delia's Birth
19ᵗʰ March 1820

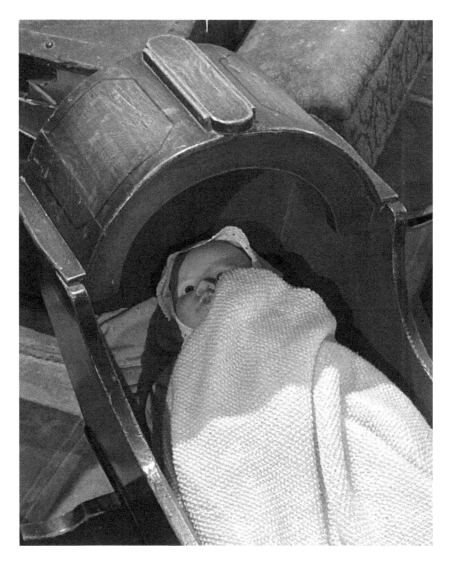

66. Baby crib at Weaver's Cottage, Colne Valley Museum, Golcar
(Author 2019)

Towards the end of the following winter, Hannah stood, annoyed, outside her parents' bedroom. Minnie, the village midwife, whom Hannah remembered well from baby Momo's arrival three years before, had hustled the girls, Lizzie, Nancy and Harriet, down the stairs and out of the house.

"Out of harm's way with your prying eyes and ears," Minnie shouted.

Hannah, being the eldest and fully 13 years old, was expected to help. She was needed to carry sheets, towels, clothing up and down the house. She carried messages to Cook to boil more water in her tub on the open fire in the back scullery. Minnie was in command, Hannah an obedient and unthanked servant. In the dark of a mid-March morning, Father had risen early and left for Halifax where he was to meet a new customer from Manchester. Hannah was on her own, Minnie shuttered in Mother's bedroom. Baby Mary, or Momo as Harriet had called her when she could scarcely talk, was a handful—she climbed everything, opened every door, and tasted every liquid standing in jugs around the house. Hannah had to have eyes in the back of her head.

The previous night Mother had been slow and tired. Hannah heard her pacing her bedroom long before Thomas clattered out of the yard on his horse. The wind whistled in the chimneys, screeching through every crack and crevice; the house was cold. Practical Hannah attended to shawls, blankets, fleeces—anything to keep a babe and mother warm. After this babe Hannah hoped there would be no more; Mother became tired and had little time for cooking her delicious pies and puddings. Father, Hannah knew, wanted another son—and Joe wanted a brother. For herself she wanted more time to herself—with a baby in the house there was none to spare.

As she reached the landing for the third time that morning, she turned and saw toddler Momo scrambling up behind her.

"Momo, take care. Where will you be if you fall? Mother can't cuddle you better, not today. Take care."

Mary was just learning to make words, mostly no it had to be said.

"No, No! Want Mama, want Mama!" She was standing on the third step and raised her arms to her sister above. "Carree, carree Momo!" she implored as she raised her arms, teetering on the stair.

"Momo, hold on, hold on tight," Hannah spoke quietly so as not to shock the child. But Momo rocked herself and sat backwards— too narrow a step for sitting, even for a two year old. She fell back, letting out a howl of rage and hurt as she bumped down the two steps! Dropping the towels, Hannah jumped down to pick up the noisy, but undamaged infant.

"Momo, hush, hush! You silly billy! Let me put cold water on the bump. Shush little one, shush. We mustn't let Mother hear—not just now. Hush!"

Minnie popped her head out of Mama's room and shouted, "Clothes Hannah, clothes. We need the baby's clothes!"

Hoisting Momo onto her hip, Hannah rushed back to the kitchen and grabbed the clothes spread on the clothes horse standing in front of the newly installed kitchen range. She ran back upstairs and burst into the darkened room. Her mother, hair straggling out on the pillow behind her head, smiled weakly. Under the bedclothes, cradled in her mother's arms, Hannah saw a little dark head busily sucking away.

"Hannah come and look. She is beautiful—so wonderful—all her toes, her fingers—all perfect—and a good sucker already!" Though exhausted, Peggy was as excited by this new arrival as she had been at the birth of every one of her other six children. She tucked down the blankets so Momo and Hannah could see the baby more easily.

Smiling up at Hannah, she said, "Thank you so much. You've looked after Momo—and the others—so well. Now we have such joy from this latest wonder. Before she came, I only remembered the dark broken nights, the work in washing, but with her here it is so wondrous. Your father wants to call her Delia—a strong Bible story for such a wee one—but I think it's Princess Adelaide in his mind what with the tragic death of our beloved Princess Charlotte three years ago, and the rise of that bloated scoundrel the new King, George 4th. Father wants to keep alive the old values, the old ways. So Delia it is!"

Momo reached out towards her mother but Hannah kept hold of the struggling toddler. Peggy took a pudgy little hand and stroked it against the baby's cheek.

"Baba," said Momo, awestruck. "I want Baba."

"Sorry Momo, no. Mama's tired but there's tart waiting for you downstairs." Hannah said, turning the child's thoughts to her stomach.

Momo brightened and gulping back her tears she told Hannah she wanted to go now.

"Clever girl, Hannah," said a now smiling Minnie. "Go tell the others. They can come up shortly but first, I want to clean things up here. Then I must be off—it's Mrs. Brown's time too—and it's her first—she'll need more help than your mother here." She shepherded Hannah and Momo out of the room.

Hannah had fallen in love with that little head, so busy suckling for her life. She shouted down the stairs to her sisters—but there was no answering call.

She burst into an empty kitchen and rushed to the back door, grab-

bing a pan on her way through. Outside, she banged the pan to alert the girls—who she suspected were probably resting on the flat-topped rock above the house and barns. The girls heard the banging and knew the baby had arrived. They scuttered down the rocky path and tumbled into the kitchen, breathless. Hannah had put Momo in her chair and was taking the tart out of the oven.

67. Child's Victorian High Chair Colne Valley Museum, Golcar (Author 2019)

"Is it a boy?" Harriet at 5 still remembered her anger at a new sister when she was 2½.

"No Harry, it's a girl called Delia. You'll have to be nice to her—no sticking pins into her when no-one's looking." Hannah remembered only too well how obstructive Harriet had been when anyone looked at her new baby sister, Momo.

Harriet was indignant, "I don't stick pins into babies now. I didn't mean to then either—but she should have been a boy—I wanted a boy—Joe's too old to be any fun as a brother—I wanted a boy to go hunting with!"

Nancy, the most clothes-conscious of the girls, asked Hannah, "What does she look like? Is she beautiful—or a bit of a prune?"

"She's beautiful, Nance—perfect in every way—fingers are long and fine—she's sucking well—so no trouble keeping her round and bonny."

Lizzie, the quietest of the girls, stood watching at the door. She hesitated to push herself into the scrum around the tarts. Hannah worried about her bashful sister, watching out for her when she became withdrawn.

"Come on Lizzie, there's a tart for you—the baby needs to be welcomed—this is her 'nice to see you cake'. P'haps you can look after her—and she will be your special little sister?"

"But she won't like me, Hansie. She'll not want me—I won't be able to make her feel good."

"Lizzie, what nonsense. She's just a baby who wants cuddling, keeping fed and warm. You can do that easily—you've had enough practice." Hannah was exasperated at her younger sister's diffidence. Even as a babe Lizzie had been quiet and undemanding. She watched the other children as they banged, boxed, ran and tripped. They argued fiercely and fell in and out of arguments within moments. Hannah wished Lizzie was more robust, like fierce Nancy or independent Harry. She divided the tart into eight pieces.

"Here's a piece of each of us—and two for Mama as she is feeding the baby!"

Eleven-year-old Joseph burst into the room.

"I heard the pan banging down in the town. What's up?"

"What do you think, Joe?—The baby's come—you take no notice of what's happening in this house!" It was Nancy's turn to be exasperated by her older sibling—and she shouted at him roundly.

"Oh is that all? What is it?," he turned to ask his ally, Hannah.

"A girl called Delia," four girls chorused. Momo waved her arms at him from the high chair.

Joe could not hide his disappointment. Like his father he had wanted male reinforcements in this household full of girls. "Papa will be disappointed. Too many girls already. Hey, can I have my piece of tart?" Joe grabbed his piece and ate it speedily.

Hannah was fiercely defensive of her new sister.

"Joe that's rubbish. Girls are useful—boys just get dirty and make more work. Those breeches of yours were clean when you left this morning—just look at them now." She shook her head at her boisterous brother who tumbled from one scrape into another—but who always came to her if his troubles became too big for him to handle alone.

"That's enough, Hansie…. But there's still too many of you!" said Joseph as he turned to leave. "Give Mother my love. I'll be up to see her later. Now I must go to the goathouses—that stupid billy goat got his head stuck in the netting around the field edge. I must release him before he does himself damage."

"No, Joe. Wait Joe! Go and see the babe now. She's truly bonny." In vain Hannah called to his retreating back.

"I'll be back in time for tea. I'll see her then. Give her my love." He rushed out, snatching his jerkin from the chair where he'd thrown it as he came in. Hannah knew he would, like his father, be back in time for tea. She sighed.

It was tough being the eldest. Her parents expected her to lead the others—if they misbehaved it was her fault; if the jobs were not done, she had failed. She chivvied the little ones, and they tried to wriggle out of their jobs. They argued, she pacified—and then she retaliated and that caused trouble. She wanted to be outside, creating, carving, making. She had to be inside, cleaning, washing, darning. She had not read Mary Woolstoncraft's book of twenty years earlier, 'A Vindication of the Rights of Women', but she still questioned her place in the larger community. As a 'wife-and-mother' she would fill the role which the Bible commended for women but, her mind wanted wider horizons. She rebelled against a world which gave Joe scope to roam the country-side—but kept her and her sisters at home.

These feelings conflicted with her present joy at the arrival of tiny Delia. Instantly her heart sang at the sight of that dark little head, so busy in its business of living. She loved cuddling, soothing, jiggling, bouncing babies on her lap. She revelled when she sang them rhymes and tunes from long ago; when the babies giggled with happiness at games of peek-a-boo. This time she was going to love this babe—last time her job was to deflect Harriet from her jealousy of the incomer baby Momo. Now Nance and Harriet loved having the walking Momo follow them in most of their games. Hannah was free to dote on what she hoped would be the last of her sisters. A few weeks later Delia's flailing little arms tried to catch the beams of light falling from Hannah's candle and so Hannah named her 'Lucy', for the goddess of light. Ups and downs thought Hannah. Nothing in life could be perfect—confined to the house nevertheless she would flourish with babies in her care.

Pulling her mind from this 'daydreaming' as her mother called it, Hannah called her sisters to tidy so they could go up to see Mama and the new babe. For once they all worked calmly together; quietly they went upstairs and knocked at the door. Minnie answered, with a threatening finger laid across her lips, "Not now girls, not now, your Mother's resting." She tried to push the door shut in their faces.

"Oh Minnie, let them in. They're such dears. They've been so good, so quiet. They must see their beautiful little sister." Mother called from her bed.

The girls filed into the bedroom, taking care not to tread unwarily on any unexpected pile of clothing. The crib stood beside the bed. Their mother had a hand slowly rocking it back and forth. The girls stood over it, taking a good look at the new arrival. She made Momo, whom they all still saw as a baby, look so big, so grubby. Baby Delia was on her side, tightly wrapped in her shawl and breathing in a quick irregular up and down movement. No one touched her—they all knew that sleeping babies were 'good' babies. The Mellors had become a family of six girls and one boy; a lively family rooted in their land, in its wool, its animals and its produce. Hannah smiled to herself as she saw her sisters hanging over the babe in her crib. They were a goodly tribe, she thought.

But time did not stand still. Delia, born in March, thrived. Not much else thrived in Elland and Greetland during the next four years. The price of bread rose, rents rose, wages tumbled and wool prices fell. Working men and women struggled. Manufacturers with mills and big workshops survived these pressures. Smaller businesses often failed. Thomas' troubles mounted. Harvests failed across the country. Thomas did not talk to anyone about his difficulties. His astute father-in-law, Joseph Thornton, kept himself aware of the ups and downs of business in Huddersfield but Halifax though only seven miles away was a closed shop to him. Mr. Cadney, the lawyer who had helped Thomas stave off those earlier creditors could have told him what was happening. Thomas' father, old Joseph Mellor, had an inkling of the trouble but neither of these shrewd men talked. Nor did Uncle James. He too was in trouble. Peggy knew her cheery optimistic husband was growing more silent, knew he had less time for the babies, knew he was urgent for young Joe to grow up and help him. He kept silent about pressing creditors, declining sales, and rents at the Piece Hall outrunning incomings. Over the next two years his talk declined further, matching the decline of his business.

Then, Thomas told Peggy he was not going to renew his lease on the counting house in Stafford House in Halifax. He paid his last annual rent at Michaelmas, at the end of September 1822. At the end of the day he came into his wife's kitchen and gave her a speech.

"The counting house ain't bringing in enough customers, Peggy. We must cut costs. I'll sell from the Skircoat workshop –that's less overheads. Business is bad. Them organising rallies and protests up on the moors promise a brighter future but how can they when wool prices are down, bread costs so dear? Old friends have turned to poaching—

and been transported to Van Diemen's Land for their pains. It ain't right to transport a man when all he's doing is feeding his family. They try petitions to Parliament but that brings nowt. I canna' see the end. Trouble comes whichever way one looks." Thomas lifted his shoulders in despair. He turned away from his wife's questioning eyes.

She came to stand close to him and spoke soothingly, lifting the back of her hand to stroke his careworn face. She knew how much her husband wanted to satisfy his father's ambitions.

"Tis hard to see men shipped off in those dreadful hulks. They were bad enough when they shipped slaves across the Atlantic—but now they're shipping good honest Britons across the world to New Holland. Your Dadda doesn't know the half of it all." Peggy had heard talk around the water pump that transportation of their sons was stripping families of any capacity to earn money, robbing them of their pride as well as their food.

68. Sorrow of Transportation—Picture shows contempt felt towards 'convicts' whose crimes were often caused by poverty and despair. (Calderdale Archives WYAS)

As for Thomas' own troubles, his wife knew Mr. Cadney had staved off the creditors five years before but she did not know that Thomas was borrowing more money, nor that the old creditors were demanding bigger repayments. She did not know whether he was selling at a profit, nor indeed whether he was selling at all. He was quiet amidst the swirl of family life; his business troubles unvoiced, silently speeding them to disaster. Peggy dreaded what she did not know, what she could not see.

In the Huddersfield market her father, Joseph Thornton, was doing better with his 'fancy goods'. Cloth for waistcoats and breeches was fashionable and in demand. He kept his mouth tight shut about family connections to the Luddite George Mellor. Without the Mellor name and, with his own high reputation—no one stopped doing business with him over that tragedy—as they had with her Thomas Mellor, George's cousin. Joseph Thornton did not know how badly his son-in-law had been affected by the general fear of violence and of violent riotous men.

One night in the spring that Delia turned three, Thomas paced his office for an hour after midnight. Peggy heard and came downstairs in her nightgown. She tapped on the door and asked to come in. She had a suggestion to make, which she feared would make her husband very angry, but which seemed to her a good way of reducing their costs.

"Husband," she began timidly. "Dost thou think now would be a good time to bring the girls back from school? Hannah is finishing anyway and the others, apart from Harriet, are not as interested. We could save a lot. I managed without schooling—the girls would be fine."

Unexpectedly Thomas, the great optimist, the great planner, the great schemer, sat down heavily. He laid his head between his hands and leant over the table, staring blankly down at the bleached wooden surface. He looked beaten. Peggy thought he could be crying. She moved over to put her hand on his shoulder—but he shrugged her away.

"Peggy, t'was my dream for the girls to be educated. Hansie is coming home with so many stories, with so much to tell from the books she reads. Harriet is learning her letters so fast—she is copying Hansie well. I wanted them all—even little Mary and Delia to read as well as Hannah. What life will they lead with no learning? What honest, hard-working husband will they find with no education?"

Peggy stiffened. "Husband, I hope thou dost not think thee made a bad bargain with me having no learning. What was good enough for me, will be good enough for them, my man."

Thomas hastened to reassure her. "No, no Pegs. I never made a better bargain than when I married thee—all thy work, thy management of our customers, of the household. I wouldn't change anything about thee." Thomas looked up at her and saw her troubled eyes searching his to see what he meant. "The world is changing, my Pegs; it ain't like it used to be. Look how my Dada did so well at Halifax Piece Hall—for twenty or thirty years—and now they can't let all the pitches in that grandest of cloth markets. We could never buy a little cottage of our own—not like he and Mother did eleven years ago—to reduce the work as they aged. Beating Boney at Waterloo was supposed to bring better times—but it hasn't—we're worse off than before—and none knows how to change it—certainly not me!"

"Husband, 'tis not all bad. Young Joe is turning out smart—soon he'll be making his way as apprentice. The girls are neat semptresses and they can earn from home if needs be. Hansie'll make an excellent housewife—and she helps with all the little ones. We've got a full quiver Thomas—we should be counting our blessings—not finding the trouble that fills the world." Peggy felt that Thomas now took pessimism in great gulps, as previously he had taken optimism. She stayed calm in the face of trouble, on the outside at least—and she tried to infuse her husband with some of her practical coping strategies—but the price of wool and the competition from the mills were crunching so many clothiers that Thomas was truly frightened that he too would be crushed. He could not be comforted and turned away, trudging upstairs in the dark, on his own.

The next morning, he stomped over to his workshops. He stood counting the bales of unwoven wool, the pieces of unsold cloth, the baskets of spun wool waiting collection by the weavers. He could not go on; something had to give. He turned on his heel and went back to Peggy, working in the scullery.

"Thou hadst better do it. Tell the girls that school is out. It'll sound better coming from thee. Tell 'em."

He left the house, walked out the yard, banging the gate shut behind him. He spent the day up on the moors. Peggy let him in at the end of the day. He looked beaten, and despairing. She led him into the back parlour, brought out his favourite meal of kidney dumpling—and sat with him while he ate.

"Come to bed now. It will be better in the morning. We have each other. It will be better one day. Come to bed." Slowly, stiffly Thomas rose from his chair, followed her to the stairs, and together they climbed upwards. The children slept on, unaware of the changes that were coming.

PART II—Chapter 16

Devastated Harriet
Winter 1823

69. Early nineteenth century school on cobbled road

A great howl went up from the back room where Peggy was giving the younger girls their morning porridge. Sixteen year old Hannah was helping toddler Delia, her 'little Lucy Locket', mop up the mess around her bowl. Lizzie and Nancy were long gone—down to Elland to keep their grandmother Mellor company, to help her care for Grandpa Joseph. Harriet was kicking the stool and yelling at her mother.

"I want to go. I must go. You can't stop me. I want my friends. I'm going!" Her face contorted with misery Harriet was pulling her mother's skirts. "I must go. I told Becky I'd see her in the lane. I want to know what happens next. Mother, you must let me go."

Peggy stood stolidly beside the table with her hand outstretched, holding the porridge ladle hovering over Harriet's bowl. She spoke calmly despite the noise of the shrieking child.

"Harriet, stop. I can't talk whilst thee makest this noise. Stop. Stop now."

She had not expected this outburst from sensible Harriet, a child who watched and listened, and fitted herself in to family life, the least likely to cause upsets. Her sisters railed against the rules; Harriet slipped away from confrontation and did what she thought best without further talk. That way her behaviour was scarcely noticed, let alone obstructed.

This was different. Harriet wanted to go to school and yet here was an order countermanding that desire. She loved school. She loved her teacher and she loved her friends. She could not understand why she was being stopped. She was shaken with fury and misery at the thought of all she was missing. She gave another howl of anguish and subsided against her mother, with huge gulping sobs shaking her frame. Briefly her mother stroked her distraught child's face pushing back her hair into its pins, and then smoothed down her own crumpled skirts.

"Go along now and splash water on thy face, Harriet. I canna have thee making such a fuss. Thou wilt do as I say. Run along and play with thy sister Mary. She's not crying about naught—keep her company whilst I deal with the washing. 'Tis Monday and that means wash day work. I need to get on—no time to lose. If I catch this wind, the clothes will be dry before dinner. Get along with thee—let me be."

"Please, please can I go to school tomorrow then?" Harriet clung to her mother and looked pleadingly up into her tightly closed face.

"No Harriet. No more school. Thou wilt be learning housewifery at home. Thou wilt help in the wool sheds and stitch and sew like a useful young woman. 'Twill be fine—once thou stop hankering after school. More use to the family– no time-wasting books—just good cooking and caring so we can all manage."

Harriet persisted by holding fast her mother's skirts and tapping into her mother's own anxieties, "Dost Father know, Mother? Does he want me to stay at home?" She was testing the parental alliance at a touch point—like all the children she knew their mother was less supportive of the schooling that their father was so adamant they should have.

Her mother snapped back. "No cheek, young lady. Your Father has indeed said no more school."

Harriet felt herself drowning, the breath being punched out of her. "But he always wants to know about school—he always asks—he can't want it to stop." The bewildered child stuffed her handkerchief in her mouth, fearful of the effect her wracking sobs might have on her angry mother.

"That's no way to be talking, young lady. What your father and I decide is happening, will happen—and no arguments from you. No school—and that's that. Off you go—and come back later to help in here—when you've remembered your manners, that is."

Peggy unhitched her daughter's clinging hands and turned into the back scullery where a large tub was coming to the boil on the back-room fire. Noisily she lifted the lid and forked in mounds of white clothes with her long ladle. She stood back, with her hands on her hips, watching the bubbles from the tub overflow onto the stone flags, her face grim.

Harriet watched and then crept out of the kitchen and up the stairs to the room where she and Mary slept with toddler Delia. She hid under the bed and sobbed out her misery. Half an hour later, cold and miserable, but now silent, she eased herself out of her hiding place. Spreading a shawl on the floor she bundled into it some clothes. She pulled together the corners of the shawl and tied a clumsy knot. She took her cloak from its hook behind the door and with the bundle over her shoulder, crept down the stairs and out the front door. No one heard her until the door shut with a loud click that startled her. She ran down the garden path, through the squeaking front gate turning down the hill to Elland. Hannah heard the front door click shut, and glancing out the parlour window, saw her little sister running wildly down the lane. Before she could decide what to do she saw her father run out of the hay barn, leap over the gate and turn speedily down the hill to catch the straying child before she reached the fork in the road. He grabbed her and marched her back up to the house.

"Never, never do that again." He spoke sternly. "Go back in and apologise to your Mother."

Harriet slid, slowly and sullenly, back into the scullery.

"Sorry, Mother," she muttered to her mother's back—not caring whether or not she was heard.

Duty done, she turned and went back into the front hall where Hannah was waiting for her. Holding out her hand to the crumpled little figure, Hansie smiled at the tear-streaked face and said, "Come in here Harry. I want to explain."

She led the little girl into the front parlour tucking her onto her lap as she sat down in an armchair beside the fire.

"Hansie, why won't Mother and Papa let me go to school? Why are they keeping me away from my friends? Why can't I learn my numbers and my writing?" As she spoke, Harriet sat up straight—stiff and belligerent. A strong sense of grievance filled her voice as she went on,

"It's not fair. You like school. You're sixteen and you still go to school—you've had all that time—and I've got to stop. It's not fair. I think Mother's stopped me going—Father never would. Mother's just lazy and wants more help in the house."

Hannah was troubled. It was true that she loved school; it was true that she was sixteen and had had eight more years at school than Harriet was going to have. She also knew how hard it had been for her parents to make this decision. Their father delighted in asking the children what they did at school. He helped them form their early letters, helped them work out their take-away sums. Hannah had always known not to ask her mother for help with schoolwork—although she turned to her for help with darning and stitching. Peggy felt uncomfortable about being un-lettered but was proud of all she could teach her daughters and angry when Thomas appeared to value book learning more highly than the skills she passed on—at the kitchen table, in the vegetable garden, in the scullery and pantry, from her medicine chest and even at night when she passed on the stories she had heard as a child. But even she wanted her girls to be schooled. This no school business was as upsetting for her parents as it was for Harriet.

Hannah had known she would be finishing school. She had been preparing, thinking about what would come next. The other girls had had no inkling that their lives would change so radically, so suddenly.

When Hannah had seen her father shut up Stratford House in Halifax for the last time: when she heard Cousin Adam Mellor declared bankrupt at the Rose and Crown in Huddersfield; when she overheard arguments about food prices and shortages, about mills laying workers off; when she saw maisters turn away weavers, fullers and dyers from their barns and sheds—then Hannah worried. At home she watched the bales of wool coming into their barns—and counted out far fewer. She heard the machines in the sheds close down earlier each evening. She saw fewer men coming to work. Job Turner was the only man working at the Skircoat workshop.

Job was old, no one would take him on—if he was turned off then it was the workhouse for him and his family. Everyone dreaded the workhouse—people took every action possible to keep out—its grim food, its unrelenting, mind-numbing work of stone splitting, its harsh rules, its separation of children and parents, of men and women, its thin coverings and bitter shivering—all horrors widely told, and even more widely feared. So Job worked on with Thomas—with not enough work for one man, let alone two. Money was short. Schooling cost money. With money short, school fees had to stop, as did the cook in the kitchen. No money, no school, no help in the house. Hannah recognised these harsh facts of life in Elland.

She sighed as she struggled with this knowledge. Her little sister demanded answers. Hannah put her hand to the child's lips.

"Shsh, Harry. I can't think how to say what I must if you keep talking. It's hard, all of this—it's very hard. None of us like it, not even Mother nor Papa. It's not what any of us want. Shshsh Harriet and listen."

Harriet stopped her catalogue of woe. She felt the worry in Hannah's voice—and as Hannah always helped when she was in trouble, she began to be anxious for Hannah. If Hannah said things were hard, then Harriet had to listen.

Hannah spoke slowly and carefully. "You know Father's wool business gives us this house, these barns and workshops. The closes, the sheep, the goats and the gardens give us our food—but it's the wool that pays for our clothes, our schooling, our winter fires. Wool today is not fetching a good price, bread prices are sky high. Papa has to pay rent for the house and for the men's wages. But people aren't buying in the Piece Hall, nor in the Cloth Hall in Huddersfield. He has no money. Mother cannot buy what we need—our remedies from the chemist, our sugar or our tea."

Harriet followed these words carefully and then, with a big smile on her face, declared:

"Let me find my purse. I'll give Mother all the coin I have there. Then we'll have enough and I can go back to school."

Hannah shook her head sadly. "Harry—it's not that easy. Your purse amount won't make the difference we need. And what happens when it's all spent and you can't give her anymore. You are a kind and thoughtful girl—but I'm so sorry—'tis not enough."

Hannah felt for this sister who so wanted to go to school. She recognised her love of stories, of studying distant countries, the accounts of voyages, the listing of plants, the music she played, the embroidery she executed. Both sisters had made good friends—with girls whose fathers were shopkeepers, woollen manufacturers, farmers and clothiers.

"So what will happen Hansie?" What will we do now there's no school? How can I keep on learning to read? Will Papa find more money one day?"

"Possibly Harriet. He paid for Joe to take up his apprenticeship with Uncle Joe Fox at Rastrick. That's one less mouth to feed and, after seven years Joe will be able to set up as a maister on his own account. He's learning to make machines—everyone wants these so maybe there'll be more money in that line—that will help Mother and Papa. And we girls can do some millinery, some needlework from home if needs be."

Hannah herself was not convinced by this argument as she saw other expenses arising for Joe—and her sisters—which might eat away any additional money—but it was important not to overload her little sister with too much.

Harriet was thinking hard. "If I carry on learning here at home, then I can make money by teaching other children to read and write. Can you help me Hansie?"

"That's good thinking Harriet—but first I may have to find work as a governess with a rich family."

"Mother would never let that happen." Harriet objected fiercely. "You are far too necessary in helping with Momo and Delia. She couldn't let you go."

"Maybe I could find work in the mills by the river. I can't bear being trapped inside but if it brings in money for food then I must." Hannah had already begun enquiries about a place in the mill, but, like her father, she found that the name Mellor rang unpleasant memories for mill owners. They still remembered that George Mellor had assassinated William Horsfall, the Marsden mill-owner, as he was riding home from Huddersfield market twelve years before. They refused to take on a 'trouble-maker' from that family.

Hannah and Harriet stayed in the parlour for another 15 minutes. Hannah tried to comfort Harriet for the loss of something so important, tried to make light of the situation. She did not convince the angry little girl that it was either right or fair but she did explain the impossibility of changing the decision.

Harriet remained angry with her mother—angry that Grandfather Joseph Thornton had kept her at home as a child, angry that there was no money. Uncle James Mellor and Grandfather Thornton had similar views about book learning—both thought it more important to feel the wool, to work the machines, to watch the trading—and both thought that girls should not bother their 'pretty little heads' with useless book learning. Harriet realised this was a dividing line in the family—but now she was forced to see how it affected her. She was no longer a detached outsider but a sufferer. She was angry that Papa's wool trading was failing. In her anger she turned to Grandpa Mellor.

Grandpa Mellor, a silent man with his wife and son, shared stories with this grand-daughter. Like his son, Thomas, he always asked what was happening at school. He played games with the children—but particularly with Harriet who often found herself on her own—the older girls employed in the parlour stitching while the babies were too young to engage her. A competitive man, Grandpa Mellor, never let any child beat him at the game he loved, draughts. Last winter Harriet had proudly held him to a draw. During their chats he told her stories from his past; explained the gossip and jokes she heard in the Town. He told her stories from the Bible—of Cain and Abel's huge fight, of Noah saving the animals, of Jacob and Esau squabbling over their father's inheritance, of the success of Joseph bullied as a younger brother, being sold into slavery in Egypt, of becoming the Pharaoh's great commissioner for food, of his rescuing his brothers during another great famine. Taciturn Joseph Mellor saved the words from the stories given to him in his childhood and passed them on—from his chair beside the fire—to his thoughtful grand-daughter Harriet.

But Grandpa Mellor was ill. His armchair beside the fireside was empty. He was wheezing and coughing upstairs in his bedroom. There was no more story telling in that little cottage for his lost little Harry. Grandma Mellor was kind but had no time for childish talk. She got her grand-daughters baking, cleaning, stitching. They loved cooking, particularly when she had sugar in the house and kneaded a sweet bun dough—as she did at Eastertide—but she had no time to explain what was happening around them. Harriet missed Grandpa's stories. She had used them to make sense of what was happening, to escape troubles she sensed rather than understood. Without her Grandpa's stories or her school, she was lost—and angry.

Hannah, sharing Harriet's yearning for books, had no idea she learnt so much from her grandfather. When Hannah herself had been little, Grandpa Mellor was as strong as an ox. He rode around the district seeking wool, employing weavers and fullers, bringing in harvests, tending animals in their closes at Banks in Upper Elland. He had no time to entertain his eldest granddaughter with stories. That time came later when he left his fields and workshops and sat in the chair beside the hearth. Hannah determined to strike her own path forward, to make money and build a future, had no time for the past. Little Harriet saw no way forward, no way to change her future; she heard Old Joe's stories of the past. Both girls shared a love of books and learning but neither could feel the losses of the other. Hannah remained steady and determined on her outward voyage. Harriet more afraid, less confident she could make her mark, depended on others to make her life; Hannah was determined to mould hers herself. The girls would face very different futures.

PART II—Chapter 17

Old Joe's Passing
April 1823

70. Empty Windsor armchair with quilted cushion
Colne Valley Museum, Golcar (Author 2019)

Ten-year-old Nancy ran down to Elland town. Eight year old Harriet ran ahead. After the sharp, dark days of February and windblown March, the weather was soft and mild. Daffodils began to unfold their bright trumpets in sheltered corners besides the barns and gates of Elland. The day dawned grey but as they ran, the clouds thinned and the sun struggled through the bare boned trees standing in their hedges besides the lane. The girls were visiting their grandparents in the small house where they had lived since Thomas and Peggy's wedding, eleven years earlier. When he left Banks, Old Joe had slowed down. Grandma Hannah stopped climbing up to the Moors. Terraces of small cottages climbed the side of Calder valley, housing workers from the mills alongside the river. Miners and their children covered the open fields with their quarrying of coal—and, in the place of sheep and crops, farmers like Uncle Joe Fox hacked out York stone for the pavements of London town. As they walked past, Nancy and Harriet ignored the slow, silent stares of the mining children with their coal blackened faces and small misshapen bodies bent double from crouching inside the hill.

Peggy had sent the girls with a big pie made for their grandparents. Old Joe laid low with his wracking cough since Christmas made her mother-in-law anxious for his health. Spring, it was hoped, would bring relief but the spasms of coughing were still wrung from Old Joe's chest. Before the winter, he had been a sprightly figure walking the lanes up to his closes to keep his sheep and tend his goats. By the end of March he had to ask his neighbour to help him with the lambing ewes. There was no sign that his energy was returning. The last time he had tried to go up to the ewes he had stumbled in the yard outside and had had to retire to his chair beside the parlour fireside.

Despite his reticence with his wife and son, Grandpa Joe was a favourite with Nancy and Harriet. He always greeted them with a big smile and teased them about how fast they were growing. Crossing the cobbles of the yard behind his cottage his voice boomed across to wherever their grandmother was working.

"Hannah, love, some girls are here to see 'ee. They'll not be wanting any pies from thee though. They'se here to scour the pots." He called out, keeping his face straight.

"Grandma—that's not true. We'll help with the pots but we do love your pies, we truly do." Harriet would call out, worried that his words would stop her grandmother bringing out her favourite cakes. "We're here to help—with the chickens, Grandma, with whatever. We truly are but we do like your teas as well."

"Hush, children, your Grandpa's only teasing. I know you're here to help—and I know you need some pies—that's why I bake them—to keep you all growing healthy. Now Joseph, shhh. Never tease those girls—it's not right on them. They believe you too easily."

"Hannah, they're fine. They know I don't mean it. So come on girls, a lovely big huggle for your Grandpa." Both girls would run into his strong, wide open arms.

But this winter the strong, wide open arms were wrapped around his chest, clutching the arms of his spoked Windsor armchair as he sat besides the kitchen range. Grandfather only left the kitchen to go to his room at night, when the fire had died and the embers glowing in the grate gave little heat. Since Christmas the big voice had fainted to a tremulous whisper and the hearty appetite had given way to tentative sips of tempting broths and soups. Their grandmother inspected his tray after every meal, and sighed as she saw the food uneaten, the bowl still three-quarters full. Grandpa Joe, so unlike his gruff and hearty self, sat dozing in his chair slipping in and out of half sleep.

The girls knocked at the front door, and hearing no welcoming voice, lifted the latch and walked in. Grandpa's chair beside the range was empty. Startled, the girls called out to their Grandmother. With her skirts brushing the walls, she came down the stairs into the kitchen. Her face was careworn and drawn. Seeing the horror on her grand-daughters' faces she put her fingers to her lips, and said, "Shh, girls. 'Tis lovely to see thee. Come in, come in and set ye down. I see thy mother's delicious pie in your basket. Set it on the sideboard, would thee? Grandpa's having a rest upstairs. He had a bad coughing fit last night and he needed more rest today. He's awake just now and you can creep up and say hello to him. Don't stay too long though—he needs his rest."

The girls put down the pie and stole up the stairs to their grandparents' bedroom. When they opened the door they saw their grandfather lying under his coverlet, looking thin and tiny. His hand, scrawny and knotted with big blue veins, was twitching at the white quilt spread over him as though it felt too heavy, too cumbersome.

"Grandpa, we're here. 'Tis Nancy beside thee, and Harriet on the other side." Both girls leaned over his bed and gave the thin face a brushing kiss. Grandpa Joe opened his eyes, crinkling them at the sight of the two hesitant but smiling faces.

"'Tis my naughty angels come to see me! Will they be working for me now? Will they be eating their Grandmother's pies today?" Joseph pleased to see the girls, put his hands back behind his head and held onto the bars of his bedstead. With an effort he hauled himself upright in the bed and told Nancy to pass him his jacket hanging at the end of the bed.

"It don't do to receive young ladies in my nightshirt. My jacket is right for such ladies of quality." He smiled at the girls as a coughing fit, brought on by his exertions, reduced his words to rough sounds. His wife came into the room and tutted.

"Joseph, man, it's not right to make too much work for thyself. Let me help thee." She moved grimly towards the bed to smooth the bedclothes around her husband.

"Let it be woman, let it be. I canna abide fussing now. The girls can help me—'tis them I need to see. Stop with the fussing. Go back and make them some tea. I'll send them down when I'm finished with them."

"Thee be sure, Joseph? It won't be too tiring for thee?"

"Course I'm sure woman. They'se my flesh and blood an't they—the flowers of my age. They'll see me right."

Turning to go, Hannah gave her husband a warm glance of exasperation. She shot the girls a hard look warning them not to stay too long.

Joseph started coughing and the girls waited patiently beside his bed. Nancy, the bolder sister, held the hand that was not holding the handkerchief to his mouth. He gripped her harder than she expected. After a few moments of anxiety, during which the girls feared the coughing would shake his body off the bed, Joseph ceased and lay back on his pillows. He gestured to the girls to rearrange them to help him be comfortable, giving them a weak thank you in acknowledgement of their efforts. They tucked in the pillows and waited for his breathing to ease.

"Nancy, you bold little 'un and thee Harriet with the fierce spirit, be good to thy mother,—and be kind to thy Papa. He's not as strong as he thinks, my girls. He has a big mouth and talks the talk—but inside he's a softie trying to look after everyone. Times are bad and he don't know which way to turn. I love thee two—we've had good games, good songs. Sing to me now—Psalm 23—The Lord is my Shepherd—thine too. Sing girls, please sing."

Each girl, either side of their grandfather held a hand and softly sang. They sang the psalm twice each picturing the shepherds tending their lambing flocks this springtime on the moors above; they saw his eyes droop in a restful sleep. They left him and crept back downstairs, subdued and anxious about their stick thin grandfather. His whispering voice, his reluctance to join in the song, this dropping into sleep— all spoke of a sick, weak man. They had never before thought of him as weak but now it was forced on them—their Grandpa was sick and weak.

When they crept fearfully back into the kitchen, their grandmother, kneading the bread dough in a bowl beside the fire, beckoned them over to her and enveloped them both in a big floury hug. They stood for some moments, as still as statues, fearful of what they knew must be coming. Harriet gulped back tears and pulled away. "Please Grandma, can we have some pie?"

"How could you?" said her older sister. "Grandpa's ill and all you can think of is your stomach."

"Hush Nance, Hush. 'Tis fine. We need to eat. We need to keep ourselves together and we need to do it the best way for each one of us. Come on Poppets—we won't help Grandpa by leaving that wonderful pie. That pie was baked with love by thy Mother—and it will give us love in eating it. Grandpa will insist that we eat, so eat my poppets, eat."

At ten, Nancy knew that old people coughed badly in the winter months. She knew that some didn't survive the cold and dark but…. She had never thought that Grandpa would one day be one of them. Today however she realised that one day soon he would not be welcoming her with his teasing. He was not a man of many words—he preferred the words he sang in chapel, the words he heard read out from the Holy Book. His own words were locked tight inside him. He shared them with a very few old, old friends. So those words he had spoken through his wracking cough were very special—Nancy would ponder them many times in the coming years.

With the pie eaten the girls set back their chairs, put on their cloaks and mufflers and turned to go back home.

Their grandmother stood with them in the porch as they stared out into the cold, twilit evening. "Tell thy mother that Grandpa loved the pie—I'll give him some later when he's more rested—tell her he wants to see thy Papa before he goes—but some things don't wait on men—and now is one of them. Give my thanks to Mother. Run along, quickly. Don't dally—it's lighter now but just as bitter of an evening. Off, go and run, quick now."

With a silent peck on their grandmother's cheek both girls ran out into the sharply dropping temperature of the early April evening as the sun sank down behind the hills. She watched them until they turned up near the church and disappeared from her view. Sighing she stepped back to her warm kitchen and slowly, wearily, climbed the stairs to Joseph.

The girls gave their mother the message from their grandmother. Thomas dropped by his parents every day. Peggy sent all the sisters to see him, armed with more pies. They came back subdued. Then she herself went down to her mother-in-law, in her time of trouble. Since

Nancy and Harriet's visit, Joseph had weakened. Young Joe, Hansie and Lizzie had all called in and now here she was with five-year-old Momo and three-year-old Delia.

Her mother-in-law was brewing a posset for Old Joe as Peggy entered the kitchen. Peggy moved over to give her a brief hug and asked her whether Joe was strong enough for her to pop in to him with the bairns.

"He is, my dear. He might be sleeping but if not, he'll be glad to see thee. I'll bring this posset up shortly and perhaps he might be tempted by thee offering it. He gets a bit tetchy with me—says I fuss."

"Well so you do, and so you must. If we didn't fuss no one would ever recover from sickness."

"There's no recovering from this my dear." Hannah spoke quietly.

Gently pushing open the door, Peggy slid into the room, a child held in each hand. Her father-in-law seemed to be a mere crinkle under his coverlet. He lay, with his head back on his pillow, his white hair, closely brushed and shining round his head. He seemed asleep but as she approached the bed he opened an eye and said, "Good to see thee my dear."

Like her daughters she took one of his gnarled hands in hers and stroked its back wishing she could ease the pain of his caught breath. The little girls stood, silenced by the solemnity of the moment, beside his bed.

"It's good to be with you, Maister Joseph. You've been a good father-in-law and a good grandfather. I thank thee, maister, from the bottom of my heart. My father Joseph sends his love."

"He's a good man, that 'un. Your girls too. I worry about Lizzie—so quiet, so distant—like me perhaps. Hansie is capable and has a great care for her brother. Those two will go far—look after my Thomas, Peggy. He's not the man he was—this money trouble has worn him away—unlike thee he puts not his trust in the Lord—he puts his trust in his own strong arm. And his arm's not so strong after all."

Peggy, waited patiently while Joseph spluttered out these brief words—snatching at every breath as he gasped for air.

"Shall I sing Joseph? Shall I sing?" Peggy asked the old man as he lay trembling after his coughing fit.

Joseph nodded and lay back, the breath rasping in his chest. Peggy sat beside him, holding his hand and singing the hymns she knew he loved—the Easter hymns of joy, the Lenten hymns of sorrow. She knew he heard as his fingers, under her hand, moved in time to the well-loved rhythms. The little ones joined her. After a while, his fingers ceased moving and he lay, lightly breathing in an irregular pattern.

Later that week, on April 12th 1823, worn out and saddened by his son's money troubles, eighty year old Joseph Mellor died in his own bed—no longer fighting for every breath, no longer wracked in every muscle. He had gone to his rest leaving behind a loving—and troubled family.

Troubles were mounting for Thomas and Peggy. Now they stood alone, without Old Joe behind them. Thomas felt his loss keenly. His mother stayed on in the little cottage that Joseph had bought years before. She kept it sparkling, full of flowers—and warm baking smells. The children visited, demanding their usual pies, but—without Grandpa's big laugh shaking across the cobbles, their visits felt empty. Grandma smiled and cooked as before, but with a shadow behind her, a sadness in her eyes. She and Old Joe had managed well. They had had their arguments. She had stopped talking to him when he moved them out of Banks. But, she had relented and at the end, she could tell him that she loved him, that he had been a good man, a caring husband, an upright 'maister' in all his dealings. He had died saying 'Thank 'ee' to those around him. Those thanks helped them through the next hard years.

PART II—Chapter 18

Disaster
March 1824

71. Shackled prisoner-debtors were held indefinitely until their creditors were paid or were persuaded to let the debt go—but it cost prisoners to feed themselves in prison and they had no means of making an income. Wealthy 'friends' could bail people out if they had the resources and debtors had good claims on their generosity.
From site of law.jrank.org

It was a sad little Christmas in 1823, the children's first without their Grandpa Joe. Thomas was preoccupied and distant. Peggy kept the household going, kept things normal. The girls, with the energy of children, forced the household to pay attention to the present. Hansie and Lizzie visited neighbours and helped with the wool-work at home. Nancy joined them when she tired of helping the little ones. Young Joe came home on Sundays for his family lunch. The rest of the week he lived at Rastrick with Uncle Joe Fox learning his trade as a joiner and wheelwright.

In February in the midst of a long cold winter, Delia soon to have her fourth birthday, was in the back room. It was warm and toasty while outside the frosty sun was shining in a clear blue sky. In the front room she heard her sister Harriet sweeping up the crumbs from under the table, banging against the chair legs as she pulled the chairs in and out. Delia, working so much more slowly than her bigger sisters, was still engaged at the table, painfully scratching her letters with her dip-in pen. Her sisters had been released to do their household chores; she had not finished and was not released. Papa insisted, despite their objections, that they should copy Hansie's letters in an attempt to make the same flowing style. During the months after school ceased, as they lay in the dark once the candles had been taken downstairs, Harriet complained, bitterly and frequently, about missing school. Her complaints were heard and Hannah spent an hour each morning teaching them how to write letters with long loops soaring above, and swooping tails dashing below the lines ruled out on their pages.

As Delia smelt the warmth of cinnamon from the buns proving and rising in the kitchen next door, she dipped her quill in the inkstand and tried again to make a neat line of 's' across her page. Yet again she pressed too hard, ink spluttered out from the nib, and dropped in blobs as she lifted it from the inkwell; her work was messy, her fingers ink-stained. She rolled the blotter over the page and despaired. She would never write as neatly as her bigger sisters. In the front room, Mary had finished her lessons and was sorting through the threads for her samplers. Harriet was still sweeping. Delia was alone and cross.

Then, next door, Harriet stopped her sweeping. Delia looked up, putting her head on one side to listen. From the yard behind the house, two burly men strode over the garden and turned up the path to the front door. Delia heard them banging. She went to the parlour door and pushed it open, just a tiny crack. She peered through and saw Harriet open the front door and two men, push past her, speaking roughly and loudly.

"Where's your Father? We've come for him. On King's business."

Harriet hung her head and mumbled that she didn't know. She dropped her dustpan with its load of sad little dust, turned and ran to the back, calling to her Mother. The men stood, huge and brutish in the hall, not waiting outside in the porch as most visitors did before they were invited in. They stamped their muddy boots on the clean rug and blew onto their cold hands. Delia, behind her crack, shrank back. "Who are they and what are they doing inside our home?" she thought, terrified at the violence she saw in their movements. She heard her mother come through the kitchen door and saw her brush her floury hands against her cooking apron. She had been helping the young maid.

"Good day, gentlemen. What can I do for your kind selves?" Peggy asked as she entered the hall. Delia stood, frozen and unnoticed behind her door.

"It ain't you Ma'am that we want. It's that dratted, conning husband of yours. He owes money—and we want it now!"

"I'm sorry but he's not here just now. If he does owe anything—I'm sure it's an oversight. He's very particular. He's out of town today seeing some men about a wool delivery. Why don't you call another time?" Peggy spoke calmly as though rough men in her hall were a normal occurrence.

"Woman, we've heard that story before. It's just a put off. We want that money and we want it now. We're not going anywhere—till we have it—have your husband—whichever—his choice. So, no more blathering." The bigger man leant over Peggy while the smaller one leered at her.

"Oh dear, oh dear. I can't help you. He's not here."

"I'll oh dear you, lady. I bet you're as thieving as he is!" The big man, Bill, sneered at Peggy.

"No, Bill, I wouldn't say that," Jez the smaller man, intervened. "This lady here looks kind and gently, wouldn't you say. That wicked husband of hers has been pulling the wool over her eyes, I've no doubt." He cracked his face with a menacing grin.

Peggy drew herself up, and spoke coldly, clearly. "Good sirs, I would ask you to remember you are talking about my husband—who has never pulled the wool over my eyes, nor over anyone else's."

Normally Peggy avoided confrontation but this was an attack, in her own home, on her husband—the pillar of their family. However silly she thought Thomas was being in private, in public she defended him—and all the family—fiercely. The children, many a time, had seen her belabour the local toughs who gave them grief in the lane outside their home. At home however, that fierceness was turned against the children's own bad behaviour. The children were proud of their mother but minded their tongues in any dispute with her. Now Delia was awed by the sight of her standing up to these thugs standing oafishly within their home.

"Hoi, hoity toity. That's all very well. But fine talk don't wash with us. Yer don't know the half of what 'e owes—and to good men like our master. Your man will have stashed it away from honest folk—and set it aside for 'is own glory. Nah, 'e ain't backward in spending 'ere in this house. There's plenty'll pay good money for all that's stashed 'ere." Bill crossed his arms across his large chest and glared at Peggy.

"We're staying put 'til 'e comes, that we are." Jez aped his superior's stance and pushed his face up against Peggy's. He raised his arm over her shoulder. She did not move.

"You will not stay inside this house, gentlemen. If you must wait, then wait outside in the lane. I'm sure when my husband gets back he will give you all the assurances you need." Uttering these words Peggy moved to the front door and held it open. Unwillingly, the men backed out, knowing they were exceeding their authority by bullying a woman and her children.

"I don't believe yer for one minute but … we can wait outside—watch out for any goods being moved so they go to their rightful owner—not into 'is pile. C'mon Jez, we're leaving this den of thieves—for now."

Delia heard the slow boots of the men tramping down the garden path, through the squeaking gate and into the lane. Her mother closed the door behind them. Harriet and Mary came out of the front parlour and rushed to Mother.

"Are they gone? Are we safe? Is Papa going to be safe?" they besought their mother, muffling their cries in the heavy cloth of her skirt.

Delia ran into the hall. She too rushed into their mother's skirts, great sobs of fear shaking her body. Mother was shaking. She stood still while the girls clung to her. Then, with a shudder she turned and brushing her hair from her eyes went back to the kitchen. Harriet rushed to the front door and pushed the bolts across. Three bewildered little girls crept after their mother.

In the kitchen, the housemaid was looking at Mother oddly. She had her hands on her hips and an insolent curl to her lip.

"So—I aren't the only one getting no money! With all your talk of God you should be ashamed of yourself. Denying others what is rightfully theirs. Debt is a sin against the Almighty. With all your fine words about looking out for people, you should be ashamed. Well, I know trouble when I see it—I'm out of here—and will be adding my name to the list of those owed money." The girl's voice had risen as she had seen Peggy's white face, and her cowed body. She stalked out of the room, throwing her apron onto the kitchen table.

The little girls stood at the door, stock still. Never had they seen their mother so shaken, so beaten. It was she who always saved them from trouble. Here though trouble was hitting her, violently. Peggy sank onto a stool. She buried her head in her hands, and let her breath come in hard, gulping sounds. She was shaking from head to toe.

After a few moments of shocked silence, Peggy lifted her head and saw the three children. She opened her arms and they rushed in. Holding each other tight the family slowly wondered what to do next.

"I wish Joe and Hannah were here." Peggy sighed through the handkerchief she had drawn from her pocket. "They would know what to do—they're so clever."

"I want Papa," moaned Delia. "I want Papa—he makes things better."

Thomas was a great hero to his seventh child—he came to her with a smile, a little bag of sweets in his great coat pockets. He took her up to bed. He took the older girls up to the moors—though they noticed this was less frequent since Grandpa Mellor had died. Recently he was short-tempered giving even Delia brusque answers. Frequently he spoke harshly to Peggy, especially after she had paid visiting traders for mending her pans, her ironwork in the kitchen, or the chimney sweeping. Wool men visited less than before—and Peggy herself had fewer smiles. In the evenings, the children heard Peggy imploring her husband to explain his trouble—and then the door would bang and he would be out in the lane with Peggy left behind, silent and shaken. Today Delia trembled when she saw these ruffians doing as they pleased, attacking her home, and destroying it with their boots, their sticks and their rough words.

Peggy shook her head. "Papa can't sort this. It's too big. We need the others. We need Grandfather Thornton, Brother Joe and sister Hannah." She sighed as she patted the shaking Delia on the back.

"I don't know what's to become of us. I don't know where we'll go, what we'll do. I can't have my bairns in the workhouse. I can't. Please let Papa bring home money for these dreadful men. Please let them go away and never, ever come back." Peggy was talking as much to herself as to her children.

In the town Peggy had heard talk, for months past, about clothiers in trouble—going bankrupt. She had heard of families evicted, of mothers begging food for their children. The mills took whatever trade there was—but even they were not employing as many as they had during the French wars. Wisely, in the marketplace, at the water pumps, even at chapel, she kept her mouth shut about what she was seeing in her own workshops. She trusted blindly that merry Thomas, with his big ideas, his laughter, his quickness with figures, would manage, would prosper—like so many of his cousins—John in Wakefield, Benjamin in

Stainland, even his minister cousin Tom in Rishworth. Peggy thought her father could help but Joseph Thornton did not know that Thomas' business was in such trouble. He had good information from Huddersfield merchants—but fewer contacts in Halifax who might warn him. Peggy pulled herself up—now was not the time to collapse. Now was the time to plan—if trouble was ahead, better be prepared.

"Harriet, go down to Grandma Mellor. Tell Hannah she is needed back at home—but don't say anything about the men outside to Grandma. Mary, you go to the top close and bring Nancy and Lizzie home. But no talking to anyone, absolutely none at all. Delia, come upstairs with me and we will do some packing—while there's time." Peggy spoke with more assurance than she felt.

Delia was relieved. Her mother was back in charge. Her mother would stop those nasty men, dressed in their dirt brown garments. Hansie, the big sister who kept her safe, was coming home. She would explain. She was the eldest girl—now sixteen, almost old enough to marry and set up home on her own. Even bustling Joe, at fifteen, energetic and fascinated by his growing knowledge, recognised Hannah as the one to be relied on to sort family troubles.

Her father often used to joke that his girls cost him the earth. Delia could not understand how earth, the earth on which she stood and ran, cost anyone anything. Had Papa meant these men, coming into their house, shouting about thieving—had this been the cost that he meant in what she had always thought was a joke. Her home stood on the earth. Was her home what it cost to raise a large family of girls? Was it her fault—as the last girl instead of the long awaited second boy— that these men had torn into their lives so hideously while the crumbs were being swept up? She went upstairs with her mother and together they searched for clothes to put into a bundle for her father.

Later, Delia looking out the window in fear of the ruffians still leaning against their garden wall, saw her father come wearily up the hill, leading his horse who appeared to be limping—probably with a lost shoe. She wanted to run out, to warn him about the men at the gate. They pulled out their cudgels as they saw the man coming home.

Delia was terrified. The men rushed down the hill towards Thomas. They raised their arms, threatening him. He gave no resistance. They stopped and stood talking. After some debate they turned and, with one on each side of him, Thomas walked through his own garden gate. He led his horse into the stable in the barn behind the house. He took some moments to throw a cover over the horse's back, to fill the bucket with water and to push hay into his manger. Bolting the stable door, he moved back across the yard to the kitchen. Delia watched no longer. She rushed down to the yard and planted herself firmly in front of her father, between him and the 'rough men'. The men raised their cudgels threateningly.

Thomas caught up his baby girl and held her high so the men could see what they were doing to the sobbing child.

"My darling, thee shouldna' be here." Thomas patted her back. She sobbed and clung tighter.

"Make them go away, make them go, those horrid men." The child screamed.

Peggy, hearing the screams, ran out and gently eased her frantic daughter out of her father's arms.

She looked Thomas in the eye. "Is it true, Husband? Dost thou owe money?"

Avoiding her look, Thomas stared at the ground. "Tis true, wife. Tis true. We're done for. No money—huge bills."

Peggy, hugging Delia close to her, turned in despair.

"Thomas—thee hadst such grand ideas—and now all dust. How can we cope? What's to be done?" She threw this over her shoulders as Bill and Jez closed in. They grabbed him by the arms and told him he was coming with them. They were arresting him.

"One minute, gents. One minute. I'll come. A quick word with my wife first—just a quick one, please."

Chastened by the sight of Delia still shaking and sobbing in her mother's arms, the men relented. Thomas was allowed a quick word, and a moment to take the bundle from Peggy.

"My dearest wife. I'm so sorry—I thought Mr. Cadney had managed to quieten things down—but James has gone too—he went last week. Get thy father. I dinna' know how it'll turn out—but it will turn out in the end—in the end I will make enough money to pay. I will. Please get thy father—he will help." Thomas stood close to his unyielding wife. Stony faced, she no longer believed his optimism. Her father was different, cautious, unburdened with debt. He would indeed sort out this mess.

Bill advanced on the unhappy pair. "No more loitering. We're taking you to the lock up."

This woke Peggy from her trance. "No, no don't take him." She reached up to his troubled face and touched his cheek. "My pet, Thomas, have a care for thyself. Have a care."

As the thugs grabbed Thomas and pulled him out of the yard, he gave her a despairing look backwards—and she blew him a kiss in the air. She stood watching as he was bullied down the road, until they were out of sight. Peggy who had checked any tears in front of the bailiffs, now let them flow, silently down her cheeks. Delia, still held close in her arms, patted her face, trying to stop them. Mary and Harriet crept out to stand by their mother. They too looked after their father disappearing round the turn in the lane. As he disappeared their sister Hannah came up the hill with Nancy and Lizzie. Passing their father with his gaolers close beside him, they stopped and cried out. The bailiffs pushed him on past the three girls, ignoring all their questions. They heard their father shout, "Go to your mother, quick. Go home and help them there."

Bewildered, the girls stepped on faster, up the hill to home. Seeing her mother, shaken and ashen-faced, Hannah shepherded them all into the kitchen. She put the kettle on the fire and sat everyone down round the kitchen table. Once food and drink had been put in front of them, Hannah herself sat down and asked her mother what had happened. Peggy told her, in a flat expressionless voice. Hannah knew enough about debtors to know what faced her father. Once a creditor was unrelenting in his pursuit of a debt, there was no mercy. Her father would be taken to London to face trial, his goods seized; he would be thrown into prison, with no means to pay any debts, for an unending sentence. Meanwhile the family, unable to pay their rent or any other household bills, would be thrown out of their home and banished to the workhouse—there to eke out a rough living, separated from each other, doing back breaking, grindingly dull stone splitting for 12 or 14 hours a day. Mr. Cadney had saved them eight years earlier but, knowing that Uncle James was bankrupt and fearing that Mr. Cadney was unable to resolve anything from the creditors, Hannah knew the future was bleak.

"We must get Joe here. We must tell Grandfather Joseph Thornton." Hannah spoke to her mother, but she knew her sisters were listening. "Let Lizzie and Nancy go to Rastrick to Uncle James Fox and tell Joe to come home. And I'll go over to Lockwood—now."

"Hannah, no—it's too late—it'll be too dark to go over Ainley Top and through those woods. You go first thing tomorrow—but Lizzie and Nancy can get to Joe before it gets dark. They can stop over night with him or Sister Thornton and the three of them can return tomorrow morning." Peggy was frightened for her eldest daughter if she went walking through the depths of evening darkness in Grimescar Wood. The younger two going to Rastrick had less far to walk—and the territory was more familiar, closer—and less wooded.

Lizzie and Nancy quickly put on their mufflers, their mittens, their sturdy boots and winter cloaks and left the warmth of the kitchen. Hannah and her mother spent the evening talking about what to tell Grandfather Joseph and planning how to arrange the bedrooms if, as they considered likely, Grandfather brought himself and Abigail, Peggy's mother over to stay.

Meanwhile, Lizzie and Nancy quickly covered the two miles along the valley side to Rastrick. They walked into Uncle James' Fox farmhouse and demanded to see Joe.

"He's out in the timberyard," said their aunt, rising to her feet as the girls fell into her kitchen. She pointed to the hooks where they should hang their cloaks and then motioned them to take a seat on the settle bench besides the fire. Meanwhile her daughter Mary had run out to find Joe and her father at work on cutting timber.

When everyone had gathered, Lizzie and Nancy began to tell their story. They were stuttering and incoherent, partly because they had not seen everything unfold at the Mellor homestead, partly because they feared that their world was unravelling fast.

Young Joe, stood up, anxious and disturbed. "I'm going back to Mother, now. That's right, aint' it Uncle Joseph?"

Joseph Fox nodded. Family helped family when trouble came. He could manage without his apprentice while troubles were sorted. But his sisters shouted at him—"No Brother, no. Mother said to stop overnight and to come home tomorrow morning."

"I can't do that," Joe said stubbornly. "I'm the man of the family. I must be there."

His uncle and aunt rather agreed with him—but they could see that the girls were exhausted from the anxiety of the day. Their aunt told them it was fine for them to stay overnight and to return the following morning. Joe could cover the two miles more quickly as he was more used to moving in the dark night—and he might be able to do something to help his father. Reluctantly the girls let him go—and then, warmed by the family around them, they began to let go of their worries in their uncle's farmhouse kitchen.

Less than two hours after Lizzie and Nancy had left home, Joe burst into the back kitchen demanding to know what was happening. Peggy, switching from uncertainty and doubt now her two eldest children were with her, wanted a plan of action. She told the three little ones to go to bed. In the dying light of the dwindling fire, she and her two eldest children made plans. In the morning Hannah would go to Grandfather Thornton. Joe would go to Elland lock up to see his father, and from there onto Mr. Cadney's office in Halifax. Peggy herself needed to see their landlord of eleven years, Mr. Charles Pitchforth, to make arrangements for their rent. But first, her thoughts turned to her cold and lonely husband. She wanted to take food to the lock up in Elland. Joe and Hannah tried to dissuade her. They feared Delia's 'rough men'. Peggy was adamant. Her husband needed the food; she would not abandon him. She made up a parcel of pies and bread, found his hair-brushes, pens, paper and small Bible, put on her cloak and stepped into the cold January night.

PART II—Chapter 19

Elland Lock-Up
March 1824

72. "Whoso keepeth the law is wise"
Written on the wall above the town lock up—drawing taken from Lucy
Hammertons' Book on Olde Elland published privately in 1901 with 70
copies—held in Elland Library (Author 2019)

At the bottom of the hill, in the square round the Inn, Delia's hated 'rough men' halted. Big Bill retained hold of Thomas' neck collar keeping his right arm in a tight lock, while Jez searched through his pouch to bring out a big heavy key, the key to the town lock up. He opened the solid, creaking door and Bill gave Thomas a hefty shove. Thomas fell awkwardly into the narrow space of the lock-up. Together Bill and Jez heaved shut the nail-studded door and slammed in place the cross bars. Jez turned the key in the padlock sticking it in the pouch hanging from his belt. Their hobnailed boots clumped over the cobbles towards the warmth of the public room in the Savile Arms.

Thomas rested against a stone ledge, the ledge that would be his overnight bed. He sat above the gaps through which the cold January wind nipped at his ankles. There was no room to stretch his legs. Cramped, cold and crushed, Thomas was stunned by his terrible imprisonment—in the lock up—where, as a boy, he had taunted the drunkards locked in to sober up. Only the old, the misfits, the idiots found themselves in the lock-up—and yet here was he, dragged away from Peggy, from his children, his workshops. No longer a 'Maister'— just a vagrant, an outlaw from decent society. He prayed his family would keep this news from his widowed mother—but feared they could not.

With purple rage roaring within, Thomas stood, violently hammering on the door that he knew would never shift. He yelled and pounded, kicking savagely at the unyielding solidity of the oaken boards; he collapsed back onto the ledge. Holding his face in his hands, great sobs shook him. He despaired. He had failed—what would become of his wife and children? No Maister, no work, no food—only starvation, death—the workhouse. Where did he go so wrong? Why him? Why not others—Horsfalls, Armitages, Cartwrights? Why? Why? What would his neighbours think? His mother? He thanked the Lord his father had been spared this humiliation by dying last year.

For hours, his mind spun around the choices he could have made differently. For hours, he thought of what might have been had his debts been more considerately handled by his so-called 'friends'. He raged and fumed; he shouted at feet he heard passing by. A man of the outdoors, he hated each moment he was forced to keep indoors, pacing like a caged animal from room to room. Yet here he was now, enclosed by four narrow stone walls. Darkness fell—even earlier than usual—a cloud of gloom and darkness from the March storm extinguished any hope of release that day. Sharp flurries of icy shards drove under the door and solidified his feet in frozen blocks. Pulling his knees up to his chest he perched on the sitting ledge. He huddled tight, clutching his coat tightly around him.

As he wondered how he would struggle through the small hours of this bitter night he heard some lighter boots come up and stop outside his cell. Peggy's voice whispered at him, but through the noise of wind and rain, he could not distinguish any words.

"Pegs, my dearest, what dost thou here? 'Tis not safe. They're only across the yard at the Arms. Pegs, I canna hear you—the wind's too loud, the rain too strong." Thomas' voice cracked with fear that Peggy was risking her safety by being outside the lock-up in this foul weather, and so near to the thugs who had taken him.

Raising her voice after looking carefully around her, Peggy put her lantern on the ground by the door. "I have some food," she said. She put her bundle on the stone beside the lock-up and opened it up. Under the door, she pushed three small parcels of food. Then she pushed under the pens, the paper, his Bible—and last of all a hair comb.

"Quick, take it up," she said loudly. Thomas did so, stuffing the parcels under his greatcoat. The lantern light was sharply gone. Peggy hearing the Inn door open, swiftly removed herself behind the lock-up, leaving no trace. Thomas sweated as heavy boots crunched towards him. His heart raced for her safety. Outside, Jez waved his lantern wildly back and forth, checking that the bolts were securely in place. Turning he shouted back towards the light-spilled doorway of the public rooms, "There's nought out here. 'Tis a bitter night. Good folk be safely tucked up—none to rescue our man. I'm coming back, sharpish." He stomped back across the yard and slammed the door shut behind him.

After a long pause, Peggy crept out from behind the lock up. The lantern, still shuttered in case light spilled across the yard, she held against the cracks in the door. Thomas was horrified.

"Shut it down. Thou wilt be seen." He hissed at her through the crack between door and door post.

"None'll come now," Peggy called back. "They're too cosy propping up the bar to come out again in this bitter cold. Here's a pie, wrapped in cloth—it's coming through in quarters. Quick, before any rats get it." She pushed an awkward shape under the rotten board at the bottom of the door.

"Got it, Pegs. Thanks. I don't know what to say—but thou mun must be gone now, gone quick—in case they come again." Thomas felt so ashamed; his wife forced to give him food through the gap under the door of the town lock-up. He could not find his words—certainly none that made any plan for dealing with the terrors of his situation.

"Be quiet, man. Listen. Tomorrow Hannah's going over to Lockwood to get my father and mother. Joe is going up to Halifax to talk to Mr. Cadney. I can manage the closes and the animals, and the wool men who visit. Dost thee know their plans?"

Thomas, feeling utterly powerless, muttered through his teeth, "They be taking me to London town, to the King's Courts."

Peggy drew a sharp intake of breath—that was worse than she had feared. She had feared Halifax gaol enough but at least she could visit there. London was near two hundred miles away, three days travelling by stagecoach. How could they function as a family with Thomas so far away? How would they know what was happening? Mail took its own time to arrive—and it cost. Only Joe and Hannah could read it—or write the letters. How would she know what was happening to her husband? Peggy dreaded the future she glimpsed—but, she had seven children to raise—so she put out of her mind all these difficulties—and talked briskly about the plans for tomorrow.

"We'll ask Mr. Cadney and my father about plans for London. In the meantime, I'll keep the business going—we will get it into my father's name, then our house and stock will be safe from the thieving rats of creditors. O Thomas," she sighed, no longer able to stem the flowing tears.

Thomas thumped the door in frustrated rage. "I'm sorry, Pegs, I'm so sorry. It's desperate, hopeless. I've failed you all."

"Thomas, stop that now—at once. This is no fault of thine. Times are bad. The whole town is suffering. It's come to Uncle James—and we know there's no finer clothier in Halifax parish. Stop—it does no good, neither to thee nor any of us. Life is as it is—and the good Lord sends trials to all—whether just or unjust. Take heed of Job—he lost all, yet he despaired not. We've got our health, thank the good Lord. We will survive. We have family to help each other." She stopped in full flow thinking she heard the door bolts being drawn back.

"Pegs, are thee there?" Thomas whispered through the solidity of the door barring his escape.

"Yes—but I must go. If they find me, they'll make it hard for thee. I don't know when we'll meet again—but it will come—and it'll be better times. Thomas, my dearest, fare thee well, farewell. Touch the door now and I'll touch this side. Farewell."

Thomas reached his own hands up the face of the dark, dank door. He whispered, "Fare well my Pegs, farewell. I love thee. Give my love to the children." Peggy heard the whisper linger in the air—but could not make out the words. She picked up her lantern and turned away, stepping slowly back up the hill.

Her Thomas loved being out. He loved riding across the moors. He loved meeting up with his acquaintances, his business colleagues. To confine him inside as sometimes happened in the cold swirl of snow deep winter was to give him a bear's head, full of grumbles and twitchiness. How would he cope in a cell, with no free movement? Peggy feared the loss of his optimism, the loss of his ability to direct his own course of action.

The next morning Joe, up early, left promptly to talk to Mr. Cadney. On the way through Elland he loitered by the lock up. He saw Jez and Bill lurch out of the Savile Arms. They strolled over to the town prison and pulled his father roughly outside. Thomas stumbled as he emerged. Bill cuffed the prisoner, Jez sneered. Joe paled. He had never seen his father battered by anyone. He had never seen his father turn out unkempt or ruffled. Today he looked like any common criminal brought out from the lock-up. Joe dodged away from his father's view, hiding behind a horse and dray unloading barrels into the pub's cellar. Instinctively he knew it would wound his father's pride to know his son had seen this public humiliation. Jez twisted Thomas' arm behind his back and prodded him with his whip forcing him to climb into the coach bound for London. Bill climbed in behind him and the two men sat either side of Thomas, giving him no space. Thomas could scarcely move a muscle. When he did one or other slapped him into cowed order. Joe saw his father cringe, saw him take a blow across the head. He hid back behind the dray and heard the orders barked at the coachman as the horses' hooves clattered over the cobbled street.

Bill yanked down the coach window and hollered up at the coachman, "Let's go. Fast man, fast. We've got a crim in here and we don't want no trouble from him—nor any highway chappies who might think they can rescue him. Any trouble from you though, and you'll see this." He poked out of the window a long cold barrel. Joe fell back against the wall in horror. The coachman took one look at the threatening shot gun and whipped the horses into a fast trot. Up they went, over to Rastrick and Brighouse and on down the Calder Valley to Wakefield and, from there, onto London. Thomas, a wretched prisoner, was leaving his Yorkshire Moors—and no one, least of all his bewildered son, knew when he would return.

It took three days of stifling, sickening, lurching coach rides to travel to London. Thomas, nauseated by Bill and Jez's overpowering stench, drank little, ate less. He had no wish to talk to these men who swore blasphemously every other word. He hated the priggishness of chapel folk but he believed that he should live quietly following God's Holy Writ. It was sinful to curse the Lord, sinful to call on his Name with ill thoughts and diseased minds. At night he slept in the lofts above the stables of the inns at which they stopped. Stable boys stole clothes from his bundle—and someone lifted the Bible which Peggy had slipped under the door his last night in Elland. Unused to captivity his muscles contracted painfully in the enclosed space of the rocking, bumping coach.

As they travelled south, the land became gentle—fewer hills, more green fields, fewer sheep, stonewalls gave way to hedges with ditches lining the roads. Townhouses clustered around market crosses, lofty parish churches. Thomas watched as more cottages and houses lined the roads. Leafless woods and thinning hedges became long, narrow front gardens. Muddy roads gradually became cobbled. York stone pavements raised above the road protected the skirts of passing women. Street callers sang out their wares. Urchins rushed to sweep up the manure left by every passing horse. Thomas heard the names of inns called out in Sheffield, Chesterfield, Derby, Rugby, Bedford, Ware, Barnet, Islington. He rattled through crowded streets. Houses closed in. Smokestacks poured heavy clouds into sullen skies. The coach lurched through the congestion of carts, carriages, porters, and street vendors that thronged London Bridge. It rumbled into the yard of the George Inn, off Borough High Street. Thomas was a prisoner in London. The King's Bench prison awaited him.

In Elland Joe knew none of these places, none of the indignities inflicted on his father; he turned away from the Savile Arms, shocked and fearful.

PART II—Chapter 20

Crisis in the West Riding
April 1824

73. Kings Bench and Marshalsea Prison in London—
held by janeausten.co.uk

Joe, shocked by the heavy handedness of Jez and Bill at the lock-up, walked numbly up to Halifax. His father was the man who sorted problems, who made things happen; this morning though Papa, bound by rough, ill-kept men, captive in a narrow coach was on his way to London. He ground his teeth foreseeing the taunting that would come his way. Joe, impulsive and hot-headed squared up to anyone who spoke ill of his family—many would jeer, and he knew that this time he could not fight. As the coach was driven over the cobbles away to Wakefield, Nancy and Lizzie, on their way back home from Rastrick, called out to their brother as he shambled away from the inn. They were giggling about 'Joe's sweetheart, Mary Fox'; Joe had no time for this silliness. Mary was a pretty girl but with all this trouble, no one was thinking of courting, least of all him who was bound apprentice to his uncle, her father, for another four years. Nancy, shocked by her mother's breakdown, was reacting by being 'silly'. The twilight walk to their uncle Fox had been exciting and the evening with their cousins in their farmhouse warm, and fun. The girls' spirits had risen—ordinary life had dulled their fear of the 'rough men'. Now they were agog for fresh plans. Normally plans took days or weeks to make; ideas were discussed, options pushed back and forth, talks went on and on. Life was sedate, measured. This new torrent of things to do was keeping the girls busy, running from house to house. Despite their fears, they were enjoying themselves. Joe had little time for this chatter.

He sent them back home to help Mother while he plodded on, across the river up to the Skircoat workshop to tell Job Turner what had happened. Job showed little surprise—he knew all too well the thinness of Thomas' income from the wool trade. Joe climbed on up to King Cross in Halifax and knocked timidly on the door of Cadney and Sons, Lawyers. Joe was setting in train business to save his father.

Meanwhile, at home, Hannah set out for her five mile walk down to Elland and then up and over Grimescar Edge and down across Longroyd Bridge to her grandparents, Joseph and Abigail Thornton of Lockwood. By eleven she had reached them and told them what had happened. Grandfather Thornton was shocked; normally he knew all the rumours about other people's business—but this news had not come through to the Huddersfield market. Too many people in Huddersfield themselves were in trouble for any thought to be spared for men of Halifax. Grandma Abigail, as soon as she realised her daughter needed her, busied herself to pack and leave for Greetland within the hour.

Joseph, who gave matters deep thought before he acted, told her to steady herself, to consider their best options.

"Take care, Husband. You will miss the moment to help, by thinking too much. Now is the time our Peggy needs us, so now is the time to go."

"I'm not changing my habits for a little problem. This event needs turning over. I need to find out in the market what is happening. If you want to get over there quickly then pack up your stuff and go back with Hannah. I'll follow on when I have a better idea of how things stand. I'll see my own lawyers—and then, when I've seen Peggy, I can go and talk to Thomas' lawyers—Mr. Cadney I think it is."

Joseph Thornton spoke quietly and deliberately. Abigail knew he thought things through with immense care. He had a fair idea of what he could expect to find, and a fair idea of what he might need to do; but he would never act until he saw his way, both into analysing the problem and onwards into solving it. This approach infuriated Abigail who responded with her heart and let her head catch up later—but she recognised its worth in difficult situations and complied with her husband's suggestion that she and Hannah should return together—in the Thornton's little pony trap with their man, John Carter.

Hannah went upstairs to gather her grandmother's things for a week's visit; she found the trunk and carefully folded in her grandmother's clothes, putting paper and lavender bags between the folds. Joseph harnessed his horse and rode off to Huddersfield town while John Carter drove Hannah and Grandmother back towards her daughter's Greetland home. Reinforcements were arriving for the beleaguered family.

The next weeks passed in a whirlwind of activity. Plans were made, and unmade, before being remade again. Joe went up to see Mr. Cadney.

Mr. Cadney came to talk with Peggy. Grandfather Thornton came to talk with his daughter. He went up to talk to Mr. Cadney. At the Skircoat workshop Job Turner worked on, slowly reducing the number of bales standing in the barns; Peggy visited friendly clothiers and arranged quick, short orders to be fulfilled. Back in the Greetland house and barns, she brought in wool from the farmers, and sent it out to weavers. All her business dealings were small and required no credit. It was known that her father was backing her and so she made a small income—and her father guaranteed the rent on their home. They were safe from the workhouse.

When Joe told his mother about the indignity inflicted on his father the morning he was taken to London, Peggy recognised her son's anxiety at losing his active, masterful father. She spoke gently to him as he shuffled from foot to foot,

"I expected no less of those thugs. They live among felons, they work among felons, their eyes are tainted by felonious dealings. They could not see the respectability in thy father—and if they had—they would have jeered and derided it. I'm glad thee hid—to see thee watching would have reduced his spirit—but … he has a keen sense of who he is, and of the values he lives by. He will be digging deep while forced to be in London. We must dig deep too—keep our silence in the face of village taunts, work hard, pay everyone on the nail—and work with Grandfather and Mr. Cadney. They be the only men who can get thy father released—and sadly even that will take months—legal business moves at the pace of a snail."

Joe now stood a head and shoulders over his mother but she could put her arm round his waist. He was too big for one of her best cuddles—but she put all her love into that embrace—and Joe went out, strengthened.

Grandmother Thornton never went home. She found herself too useful. The weeks slipped by. She busied herself in the kitchen with vegetable cutting and peeling; she prepared jams and preserves when the fruit came in from the harvest. In the parlour, she kept her sewing box—which Joseph Thornton had been commanded to bring over from Lockwood, the second week of her 'visit'. Linen, small clothes, pinafores, aprons, everything it seemed was piled into that box—she pulled out the correct colour thread, asked one of the girls to thread the needle as her eyes had lost their sharpness, and stitched the household back together again. Peggy, busy with the woolmen and the farmers, hardly noticed how much was being repaired and improved in the back parlour. Hannah did though—much less time for her own 'bottom drawer' sewing. She brought her grandmother old clothes to be cut down into patches for quilts. She rifled through the girls' clothes to see where they were wearing thin—and then she would sit sewing with her grandmother in the back parlour, until the light grew too dim to see their neat stitches.

Grandfather Joseph stabled his horse at Lockwood as often as he could, but he rode daily in pursuit of business in Huddersfield on his own behalf, and then up to Halifax at least weekly on his son-in-law's behalf. During his journeys he called in on his wife and daughter in Greetland—and was sometimes persuaded to stay the night. Peggy noticed that he became sharp with the younger girls. His patience with childish fights, never long, was becoming shorter as the worries piled up. He took Joe with him on a three day visit to York where he hoped smarter lawyers than Mr. Cadney, with more experience of London courts, could pull more strings for Thomas down in London. That proved a vain hope and he decided he had to make the long trip down to London to see how to improve Thomas' time in the debtors' prison. Joe besought his grandfather to take him—but Grandfather Joseph was insistent that he could best work on his own. He was a bit afraid that the sight of his father incarcerated would be too much for Joe but he was more afraid that he himself would not manage the business as well if he was in charge of an impetuous fifteen-year-old.

Daily, Peggy was occupied in the woollen business. She visited weavers in their cottages on the moors to chase her orders. She called on Job Turner in the Skircoat Green workshop to find out how many Halifax people were coming to him for cloth. She knew Thomas would need customers to be there when he returned. She encouraged Job to know that he was not on his own, that the Mellors were behind him as he worked on alone. She toiled in the closes enlisting neighbours to help at harvest time. She had little time for the family of girls at home, supervised by Hannah, and guided by the wisdom of her mother. After the excitement and drama in the winter, household life settled into a new pattern for the summer, and winter of the following years.

Grandmother Thornton's joints continued sore and aching. Sometimes her bad nights made her crotchety with the little children. When Grandfather came to tea, or stayed the night, Hannah kept the little ones as quiet as she could. Joseph could not tolerate any rudeness or mess with food. He expected the children to be seen, and not heard. Lizzie became almost speechless when he was around. Harriet withdrew to the back parlour with her quills and paper, keeping silent as she avoided Grandfather's criticism of girls 'wasting time' on learning. Nancy, always ready with her smiles, would charm him with offers to fetch a beer for him, or to move the screens away from the fire if he seemed too cold, or putting them between him and the fire if he looked too red from the flames. Nancy was his favourite. He was never short with her. Hannah made sure that Mary and Delia went up to bed as soon as they showed any sign of being tired. When Grandfather put on his riding coat and called for his riding boots, the household breathed a little more easily. With him away there were fewer arguments, fewer tears. The girls were grateful for his efforts but they missed their father's hearty jokes, and continual hopes of 'when I become rich'.

Delia, haunted by the memories of the 'rough men' who had taken their father away, often needed soothing at night. Hannah would tell her stories of her own escapades as a child. She would sing songs, and unroll waves of ships, explorers, foreign lands until her little 'Lucy Locket' would lie asleep curled up in the bed she shared with her two older sisters, Mary and Harriet. That soothing though failed to stop the nightmares that shook Delia in the dark nights following Papa's arrest.

Hannah, with her plans for escape into the big wide world, had to draw back. She focused on the house in Greetland, on her five sisters at home. Joe worked in Rastrick with his uncle. He was learning his carpentry trade. Hannah did what so many dutiful daughters did—managed the household caring for the frail and the young. Her dreams did not vanish. At night she still saw herself travelling, making her way—but for now she had to button up her ideas, her stories. She, with Mother and Grandmother, had to keep the family together. That was their job. Without Thomas it was essential that they work together. The family survived—but with less laughter, less joy in their steps.

PART II—Chapter 21

London Exile
1824-1828

74. Kings Bench Prison next door to Marshalsea shared common practices—both imprisoned debtors—some for many years. With wealthy friends a debtor could be spared harsh imprisonment and rent rooms in the surrounding area under 'The Rules', a captive still but spared the chains and squalor of the gaol allocated to the poor with no friends— locked up with convicted scoundrels and felons.

Thomas woke after another noisy night, sleeping in small snatches surrounded by the stench of his London prison. As with the mass of huddled wretches, his hair was a tangled mat, his clothes mere rags on his back. He dared not change; he needed to save his few scraps, to keep them from toothless men who grabbed anything and everything. At first he had tried to wash in the mugful of dirty water allocated by the gaoler each morning. He gave up even this small gesture of normality as the water standing in the buckets was covered in a greasy film. The prison was damp, dark, full of violent curses. Rats scurried over men lying listlessly in the stinking straw spread over the cold flagstones. Thomas, a newcomer, a gullible 'foreigner from up North' was fleeced by con men who gathered daily in His Majesty's King's Bench prison for debtors.

On his arrival, three weeks previously, he had been thrown into the common prison. He could not pay for his lodgings, nor for food. On his first night fellow prisoners had robbed him of his greatcoat, stripped his pockets bare, thumped and kicked him as he lay, teeth chattering, on the stone-cold floor, desperately trying to sleep. He tried to stop his ears to the swearing, tried to ignore the coughing, the spitting, and the belching that continued all night but his fear of the leering, lurching bully on the floor next to him kept him flinching every time that lout raised a limb. His three-day journey from Yorkshire had been friendless. The prison was worse than friendless; this world was peopled with enemies.

On the way down, Thomas had hoped that Joe would come to London with news of his release. Within days of arriving, he was sunk in despair, and appalled at the idea that his son might see him in this abject state. Stolen were the paper and quills, as well as his Bible, which Peggy had smuggled into the lock-up; he had no way of letting anyone know what was happening. A pompous, fat bellied lawyer in grubby black robes assured him that all would be well if he would release a little capital into his official hands. This man was supposed to be representing him in his trial; he had visited him but once, to demand funds from Thomas' empty pockets. No funds for him meant no trial date for Thomas. The setting of a date for his hearing receded into the distant future.

Thomas, an independent 'maister', a Yorkshire 'clothier' was a spokesman in Elland and Greetland. People turned to him for advice; they waited for him to bring their wages. Here, chained to a ring on the wall, no one spoke to him except to curse. He crept the small distance of the chain avoiding the tattered bodies lying nearby. His clean-living conscience was appalled by the foul blasphemy pouring from every mouth. He shrank from all vile touch; he turned his face to the wall. He refused to listen, to share jokes or stories. He shut himself in, into his own head, his own thoughts, his own mistakes. He saw no way out, no light at the end of this tunnel. He was lost and ashamed. He lost weight. He took no care over clean water, nor did he sieve the foul gruel dolloped out by slatternly women from huge urns. Fleas and bugs jumped on his skin. Rats ran over his body at night. The stench of urine and fresh excrement nauseated him. He wanted it all to end—but saw no way of making it end.

One morning, six weeks later, thin sun struggled to penetrate the grime covered windows into his hell-hole of a prison. Thomas closed his eyes to bring back the pure, clear air of his beloved Moors, the sounds of the heavily wooded valleys around his home. He withdrew from the bodies shifting uncomfortably nearby. He was lost in his own head. But a man stood over him. He was forced to look up—and to his horror—he saw his father-in-law, booted and shod in his riding dress, standing twitching his whip against his thigh. Skeletal men crawled over to him and reached up to his coat, fingering the quality of the cloth. Joseph Thornton held his handkerchief close to his mouth. The stench was over-powering—urine, faeces, sweat, suppurating sores, wet cloth. Along with a rush of shame that Peggy's father should see him in such a terrible place, Thomas felt a wild leap of hope. He scrambled to his feet. Joseph held out his hand to support him and called a gaoler to unlock the iron ring. Released from its heavy weight, Thomas stumbled. Joseph caught him and together they moved across the crowded hall towards the stairs.

Joseph, realising that Thomas was struck silent, started speaking, "I'm sorry lad. I truly am. Peggy sends her love—as do all the bairns—and your mother. All are well. Mother is staying with Peggy and the children—and Peggy is keeping small amounts of business going."

Thomas was overwhelmed. He was unprepared for this news from his old life. Tears started to his eyes; his tongue stuck to the roof of his mouth. Joseph Thornton continued,

"We could get no news. Peggy told us you had paper and a quill. We hoped to have a letter. Mr. Cadney has heard nothing through his lawyer friends in London. We didn't know what to do—so I came south. What has happened? Why this filth? This depravity?"

Thomas, despite Joseph's helping hand stumbled on the stairs. He coughed and brushed back the hair from his eyes. At the top, the turnkey waved them into a small room, the same one where he had first been questioned at the start of this horror. He looked helplessly around. He could not put his thoughts in order. He refused to name the horrors he had seen, the blows he had received. He could not tell his elegant father-in-law why he was dressed in such rags.

"I have no money, none at all—it was all stolen on the way down here. So was my paper and quill pens. You can't survive here without money—money to pay the gaolers, the men with the food." Thomas halted this tale of woe. He felt ashamed, that it was all his fault, that if only he had behaved differently none of this would have happened. He refused to tell Joseph anything about the gaol itself, about the thumping, the cursing, the thieving. Stonily he shut his mouth and hung his head. Even his breathing was laboured and rasping. Joseph looked at him, bewildered. This was not the man he had seen six weeks before. This Thomas frightened him, a wretch whom he could not understand.

The prison governor, seated behind a big desk, coughed and motioned Joseph to come outside with him.

Outside the room, with the door closed behind them, the governor muttered conspiratorially to the well-heeled gentleman friend of his prisoner. If he played his cards cleverly, calculated the greedy governor, this debtor might yield him good money. At first, he had considered

Thomas a lost cause, a derelict of society with no means to support himself in prison—of no interest to the many sharks who preyed on the defenceless in King's Bench Prison. Now that he saw he had friends with money he began to work out how he could 'milk' this situation.

His smile oily, the governor brought his face close to Joseph Thornton's. His breath was stale and beery as he leered at him,

"They often bin like that my friend. Give 'im time—they often don't know what's happened to 'em. After a little time in 'ere they learn 'emselves how to talk agin. This son-in-law o' yourn' ain't used to it. 'E's taken it bad. 'E'll come to—just you wait a little. Come back tomorrer—then 'e'll have words for you—I'll make sure 'e do."

Joseph looked with distaste at this threat from the loathsome gaoler. He was distressed by the stench and the violence, and by the iron chains chafing on Thomas' leg. He knew gaolers expected back handers. He knew bribes were offered on behalf of prisoners, and, once offered, were readily taken by the gaolers. He did not know how much he was expected to give to rescue Thomas from this state of beggary. To hear it said that Thomas would speak more on the next visit gave him a way to improve conditions for him.

"Sir," he said, quailing inside himself at the use of this title for such an unpleasant, uneducated man, "I carry no 'sovereigns' but I expect to carry some when I return. I'll be back tomorrow morning—in the meanwhile take my relative to a better room. Give him some bath water and some food and get him help to spruce himself up."

The governor would have preferred a sovereign in his hand but he reckoned that the upright Yorkshireman was a man of his word. The Guv made his reckonings. The stiff Yorkshireman would return with sovereigns the next day. He would part with them—to his own sticky palm—but only if he saw improvements in his relative's behaviour. If he, the Guv, was to extract many sovereigns from him, it was wise to show him how much better he could make his friend's life.

He motioned Joseph back into the dark office. He barked at the turnkey who stood beside Thomas, "Take 'im upstairs to the top back room. Give 'im some hot water and some razors. Get 'im presentable so 'is friend 'ere is pleased."

Joseph, turning his back on the Governor, rested his hand on Thomas' shoulder. "I'm going to see some lawyers for you. I'll be back tomorrow and we'll talk about where you might live while all this is going on. You cannot stay down below. 'Tis a bad business but there's no business too bad that we canna' set it right. I'll be back and I'll talk to this 'gentleman' here about further arrangements."

He could not keep the scorn he felt for the blackmailing governor out of his voice, but that rogue was content. The scorn meant Joseph knew he would have to be handing over money—and didn't like it. The governor knew that he could extract more money from an angry man than he could from a man who kept his calm. Joseph was angry—so for the governor that meant more money. Business in a debtor's prison was good for sharks who preyed on those in distress. The Governor was only one of the many shark. Joseph realised that the turnkey taking Thomas upstairs would also need bribing. He reached in his pocket for the loose change he had put there this morning.

As the turnkey pulled on Thomas' arm to move him across the room, Joseph touched the burly man and put a crown in his hand. "You will keep him tidy, won't you? See to a decent meal. This should go towards paying his expenses." The turnkey nodded and Joseph told Thomas— "I'll be back tomorrow. Keep your spirits up. Pull yourself together for Peggy. She depends on you. God be with thee, Thomas. God be with thee."

Giving the Governor a curt nod of the head, Joseph moved towards the door to the outside world. He expected to be let through into the crowded courtyard where the better-off prisoners were exercising in the feeble sun.

The Governor laughed at him. "We need to open up do we? As a fine Yorkshire gent you need to go, do you? We must wait for Sam." Joseph stood, isolated and uncomfortable in the dark room. Sam moved across the room, clinking the keys at his belt. The Governor, who had turned his head from Joseph and appeared to be deeply engrossed in his papers, scarcely raising his eyes said to the turnkey.

"Oh Sam, this time we must 'umour the gent. This time we'll let 'im go, shall we Sam? But don't forget to come back with somethin' good for us tomorrer, somethin' gold, you fine gent. Sam, use your keys and let the gent go."

Sam picked up the large bundle of iron keys that swung on a metal hoop hanging from his belt. Painstakingly he examined each one until Joseph thought he must shout with impatience at the time Sam was taking. At last he selected one and fitted it slowly into the lock. The door, heavy with bars and bolts, creaked and had to be pushed firmly open to release Joseph from the room. Joseph moved disdainfully past him, relieved to have escaped.

"'Ee's an 'aughty gent, that 'un, Sam—a wery 'aughty gent. 'Ee'll soon change his tune when 'ee comes back tomorrer—when 'ee learns 'isself how much it'll cost 'im to 'elp his relative." The Guv turned his attention to Thomas, standing in the corner. "Go on Sam—take the prisoner up to the top room. 'Ee's making my office stink. Quick now—'ee's clouding my eyes with his dirty self. Get rid of 'im, Sam—sharpish now."

Sam pushed Thomas up the stairs to a garret room in the attic of the building. He thrust him into a bare room—with an iron bedstead, a rackety chair—and a dirty chamber pot for his toilet needs. It was cold and had no means of becoming any warmer. Draughts howled through the windowpanes, paint peeled off the walls, damp seeped through from blocked gutters outside. Thomas felt cold but no longer so alone. His father-in-law was coming to see him tomorrow. He would use the bowl of water, and the dirty towel to clean himself so that Joseph thought better of him. He began to work out what had happened to him. Sam shut the door loudly, turned the key in the lock and clumped down the stairs. Thomas remained a prisoner—but at least now he had a room to himself and was a little cleaner.

Meanwhile Joseph Thornton crossed the Thames on the crowded London Bridge; he turned up past St. Paul's and walked on, to the offices of a lawyer recommended by Mr. Cadney. There he learnt how debtor court cases went—slowly he heard—and very expensively. He learnt that debtors with money from friends could stay in the area around the prison, called The Rules. Debtors with friends could avoid the noisome and stench ridden public prison where Thomas had been held until his visit that morning. Joseph would make it his business to arrange finance so that Thomas could live in a more comfortable way. Then he learnt that one creditor alone could pursue the court case, vindictively— even unreasonably—on his own. One creditor alone could deprive a man of his liberty. Other creditors could agree a dividend to be paid as trade allowed but one man alone could push against a reasonable settlement—and Thomas had such a creditor. As long as he pursued his claim Thomas would be imprisoned.

Depressed by this news, Joseph returned to his lodgings, avoiding the dirt in the street gutters and turning his eyes away from the sellers and callers in every corner and alleyway. For himself, he had always avoided borrowing money from anyone—but then his business was more specific than his son-in-law's. He made 'fancy goods', cloth that went into men's suits and waistcoats. His woollen cloth had never sold to the army—it was too fine—but to the many growing wealthy from the expanding cotton business in Manchester. When the war was over and the army stopped buying in bulk Joseph' business stayed steady. Thomas' business saw a big drop in trade. He borrowed to buy machines which might enable him to compete with the new mills lining the Calder River. Sales after the War never picked up for clothiers. The family money was insufficient to keep Thomas solvent, and against his better judgment, Joseph Thornton had sanctioned Thomas borrowing money for more machines. Prices in the wool trade never recovered to pre-war levels. Bigger mills produced more cloth at lower costs than did the old weavers of Calderdale. Thomas' trade was doomed. Debt and eventually bankruptcy seemed inevitable. In London, Joseph was learning that there was no easy way through.

Armed with these painful facts, Joseph went to a quiet looking tailor's shop and ordered a respectable coat and pair of trousers—and three clean shirts for Thomas. The following day he returned to the gaol and, with two gold sovereigns, he paid the Governor so that Thomas could lodge with him. He paid for food and water. Then he asked to see Thomas again.

Reluctantly the Governor called Sam.

"Bring down the man Mellor, Sam."

Joseph intervened, "I'll have you call him Maister. He's no common criminal."

"Whatever you wish, Mr. Thornton. Sam take Mr. Thornton up to Maister Mellor. Is that the right pronunciation for you, Mr. Thornton, or should we be more careful?" The Governor sneered at Joseph—who ignored all slights. "It appears that Mr. Thornton 'ere, Sam don't reckon we've taken good enough care of his relative. It appears that he ain't thrived in our care, Sam. Take 'im up, after you've seen the colour of 'is money, Sam. There's no trusting these Yorkshire types with money. They keep it close. They don't understand how much it costs to feed men 'ere in Lunnon town."

Joseph spoke coldly to the turnkey. "Sam, I quite understand the cost of eating here in the city. Here is a sovereign to cover your costs. Now bring Maister Mellor down-stairs and we can talk business."

"Oh Mr Thornton, you forget the largeness of my family. One gold button ain't enough to give 'em care. One more though will surely make 'em love your relative."

Sam waved a hand in his face, and with a grimace of disdain, Joseph put another coin into the dirty palm. Sam turned on his heel and left the room. Joseph looked enquiringly at the Governor who smirked and said; "Don't you worry yoursel'. You can see your relative in a jiffy. Just wait and see."

"But I can't wait all day. I want to see my relative now."

"All in good time, my friend, all in good time, Mr. Thornton. We don't do things in a hurry down 'ere in Lunnon Town. We do things in style, knowing how to give things proper attention you know, not hasty nor ill-mannered as it might be in the country."

Joseph gritted his teeth at these aspersions cast on his country background. He knew how much trade Yorkshire sent across the seas to Europe, to Russia, to America. He knew the money Yorkshire men made. He despised men who made money through bribery and preying on others. But he was shrewd, and he realised that every time he showed the Governor how riled he was, the price of those bribes went up by another sovereign. He kept his mouth shut and his face expressionless.

Ten minutes later, Sam returned and pointed to the back stairs. Joseph moved across and climbed up behind him to the attic. Sam bent to undo the padlocks on the door and shoved Mr. Thornton into the small airless room. Thomas had made great efforts. He had pulled a strong comb through his hair. He had used the water left by Sam— and the razors—and he presented more tidily and cleaner. Joseph threw onto the bed the clothes he had purchased the previous day in the City. Thomas took them and, behind a screen, put them on. Now he looked like Thomas Mellor of Greetland and Skircoat. Joseph Thornton looked at him approvingly.

"Sit ye down lad. Sit ye down and tell me what happened."

Patiently Joseph Thornton listened to the sad tale of humiliation and loss. He heard how Jez and Bill had kicked and yelled at him, how inn servants had stolen his money and possessions. He heard how the prisoners had robbed him at night of his top-coat, his best breeches. He heard of the thin, poisonous gruel and the filthy water. At the end he wondered how Thomas had stayed alive, rather than wonder how he had come to such a filthy mire. In his turn he told Thomas of all that was going on in Yorkshire. He spoke of lawyerly delay, of confusion and ignorance in Halifax and in London. He passed on Elland news—of others being sued as bankrupts, of Uncle James. He talked of rocketing prices of grain and of soaring rental costs—and of the stream of new mills being built on both sides of the valley. Children were crying to their mothers for food. Joseph had no idea how people would manage.

As Joseph stood to go, Thomas put out his hand to his father-in-law. "I cannot thank thee enough. Yesterday I thought death was better than this hell. Today you have brought back to me a sense of family, a sense of being loved, of belonging. I cannot thank thee enough for the visits, nor for all the arrangements. I thank thee for myself—and for Peggy and the children."

Normally undemonstrative Thomas took his father-in-law by surprise when he wrung his hand up and down and when tears rolled down his face.

"Tush, tush young man. You are family, as you well know—and families stand together. This is a bad do—but then times be bad in Elland. Others are in as bad a place. We'll get you out—have you back home before we can say 'Jack Robinson'." Joseph looked to have a tear in his own eye.

"I'm talking to lawyers mostly on this visit but before I go home, I'll come and let you know how things are going."

"Not so fast I fear" said Thomas "—these lawyers charge by the minute and they write longer and longer sentences so their fees go higher and higher. Have a care how you talk to them."

Bidding each other farewell the men parted, one to walk the streets towards the Inns of Law beyond St. Paul's Cathedral, the other to walk slowly across his small room, looking out of the grubby sky-light at the murky sky, darkened by the multitude of smoke rising from chimneys across the metropolis.

It took four years to realise the dream of returning to Yorkshire. Four years when Thomas rented a room, courtesy of Joseph, within the area of the Rules surrounding the Kings Bench prison; four years of paper piling up in lawyers' offices, of wrangling and arguing over small details. It was four long years away from Yorkshire, from his beloved Moors and his lively family. Thomas was an unwilling prisoner in London and felt humiliated that his father-in-law, and his wife were carrying on the business that he himself should have been driving forward. Thomas was belittled by his exile in London.

PART II—Chapter 22

Single Parent Family
1824-1828

75. Woman making oat cakes in Yorkshire house
Book of illustrations held in WYAS, Calderdale Library, Halifax

In Yorkshire's West Riding, Joseph Thornton and Lawyer Cadney worked a good deal. They transferred Thomas' workshop tools, his bales of wool and cloth, to the home and barns in Greetland rented from Mr. Waterhouse since 1813. The Skircoat workshop remained empty, unused save by old Job Turner, Thomas' longest serving craftsman, who kept 'his hand in' with small jobs of weaving for himself and his wife. Creditors could not gain the Greetland house—Joseph made sure the rent was paid, each quarter, in full and on time.

The Mellor family were safe from Poor Law Guardians—those fearsome grim-faced elders who put children to work when their parents could no longer feed nor clothe them. The littlest children in the Workhouse had to break stones all day to 'pay for their keep'—and that keep meant little sleep, hours of heavy labour, and small dollops of thin, grey gruel for supper. Adults fared no better, older people preferring death rather than incarceration in cold, harsh interiors with unrelenting rules and inhumane restrictions. In addition to paying Peggy's rent, Joseph Thornton made her a small allowance to cover the costs of his wife's keep in Greetland. The Mellor children were saved from the Workhouse.

Peggy managed the wool-shops. Hansie ran the household. Her grandmother, Abigail Thornton, a quiet reassuring presence, sat beside the hearth in the parlour. She listened to her granddaughters; she told them stories of their mother as a girl. She knitted their stockings and their winter blankets. She bit her tongue when her daughter berated anyone—which was often now she was working so hard at the business. The girls heard Grandmother Abigail's sympathy but knew not to depend on it. Their mother was the queen of the household and woe betide anyone who did not do their jobs as required. No kind grandmother could shield the young people from their mother's tongue, or her high standards.

Grandfather Thornton continued to journey down to London; he spent days in Huddersfield cloth hall and in his small mill. He was fit and active but, in the summer of 1826, two years after her arrival, Abigail Thornton quietly passed on to her rest in the Lord. It was almost as though she was too tired to wake up any longer, too tired to battle with her aches and pains, too tired to gainsay the sweetness of rest.

Her strength deteriorated slowly. Over the two years since Thomas' imprisonment she passed from pottering among the vegetables that grew just outside the back door, to sitting at the kitchen table chopping those vegetables for the pot, and then finally to the rocking chair beside the fire in the back parlour. Shortly before she died in July 1826 she kept herself upstairs in her bedroom—Hansie climbed three times a day with a tray of carefully prepared food arranged on decorated fine china plates and set on pretty white linen crochet mats to tempt her frail grandmother. But quietly, slowly, without drawing any attention to herself, Abigail Thornton was fading into her final sleep.

One July summer's evening, Hansie was sitting beside her grandmother with the window open to let in the birdsong, and the ring of the church bells as the ringers rehearsed next Sunday's peel. Her grandmother loved the quiet of the countryside as it garnered in its workers and freed itself from the bustling noise of the long day. That afternoon her grandmother had said, to her two eldest granddaughters as they bathed her gently on her bed, turned her over to pull out the crumpled sheets, and brushed her snowy white hair off her face, "Thank ye, thank ye. I do appreciate all you do for me."

"We love doing it Grandma—it reminds us of when you used to make our beds fresh for us when it was hot and sticky in the summers of long ago. You pushed our hair out of our eyes and gave us clean nightwear when we were ill."

Lizzie had always welcomed the quiet reassurance that Grandma Thornton brought to her troubled dreams and told her grandmother how much those words had helped when she was little.

"Ye twain were good bairns." Abigail sighed, "This dying business is taking an awfu' long time. 'Tis time for me to go, time to be taken back by the good Lord. I want to slip away out of the window, up to the moors through the wooded hillsides."

"O Grandma—we don't want you to slip away. We want you to stay."

Hansie heard her voice crack as she said this—like her grandmother she knew the end was near—and wished it far off.

"Whisht, girl. It comes to us all—and it's time for me—I want to go. There's no point going on and on. It'll be better for all that way. Sit ye beside me and do thy quilt stitching, my girl. Time to put that into your bottom drawer."

Hansie sat silently, working and watching while her grandmother slept. Later Abigail stirred and opening her eyes saw Hansie stitching slowly in and out, in and out, round each patch, brushing something out of her eyes.

"Tis for the best, my poppet. I'm tired, so tired—it's God's time— I'm content. I've had a good life—a good family—and thee my darlings, thee must bring goodness into this trying world—the Good Lord will strengthen thee."

"We will Grandmother," they both whispered to her.

Hannah sitting quietly on the upright chair beside her grand-mother's bed stitched on as the sun dipped down behind the trees on the hillside above their house, and the light in the bedroom dimmed. Her grandmother shifted her head, closed her eyes, and slipped into shallow breathing, with her hand twitching at the coverlet. Hannah stitched, unspeaking, while Lizzie went in and out taking the tea tray downstairs. Later they were both beside the bed and their grandmother made a strange sound in her throat. They called their mother and one by one all the girls slipped into the bedroom. Each one gave the now restful, but papery pale face, a kiss and stood, waiting watchfully. Soon their mother bent close to her own mother and feeling the now stilled chest, the now silent breathing, looked at her daughters and said: "She is gone. She has slipped away, out into the night, as she wanted. She is at rest with the Lord. Bless ye the Lord."

Hansie and Lizzie stayed together beside the bed until the room was so dark they could no longer see each other. Then they left, and Hannah went outside for a long, sad, sobbing walk through the darkness of the summer night.

After Abigail had been buried in Huddersfield parish church where she had married some fifty years earlier, her daughter Peggy, who had had little time for her mother's quiet presence in the parlour with her constant tatting and needlework, missed her more than she could have imagined. The household became more quarrelsome—there was no one there to listen, or to calm down heated voices. Peggy had no time out of her business decisions, her coming and going in the wool trade—so more fell on Hannah—and she felt tied. Tied against her will by the needs of her tribe of younger sisters. She loved them and knew where her duty lay—but she thought to herself, why did duty have to be so burdensome, why did it have to clip her own wings so tightly?

A month later, in the quiet of the front parlour, Hannah sat, by the window, stitching her quilt. It was nearly done; it had taken her a full year to complete. In the centre she had stitched a rectangle of cloth and surrounded it with narrow lengths of different cloths marching round and around until it covered her whole bed. This morning she was stitching an H and an M in the corner of the quilt—and the date of the year, 1826.

She liked things plain—too fancy and it all became a muddle. Hannah was practical. She loved the clear, early morning before the day had begun. She heard with pleasure the morning service sentence, "The night has passed, and the day lies open before us." Hannah knew the night brought worries and could bring terror. The day though was for work, for action; she welcomed action. Here in completing her quilt, she saw the possibility of change, the possibility that her horizons could expand. 1827 would be a better year. She would turn twenty and their baby sister, Delia would turn 7. Hannah would teach her sewing, teach her plaiting, teach her to read her books. Perhaps the court case would finish, perhaps their father would come home, perhaps … but perhaps not. Carefully she embroidered a slender stem leaf stitch over her initials, H and M and 1826—and sighed. She had hoped that her father would be home by the time she finished; she missed her grandmother.

76. This quilt was stitched in Durham in 1830.
Photo from Patchwork by Averil Colby (1958).
Published by B.T.Batsford Ltd.

It was August now, two and a half years since their father had been taken to London on that dreadful January day in 1824. Days earlier, Uncle James Mellor had been taken to court for bankruptcy, then his partner James Walker was served a writ and, nine days later Thomas had been seized and taken to London on a summons to appear before the Kings Bench in March. That time was bad for Elland families, for the West Riding and for the wool trade—food prices were high, harvests failed, the wool trade faltered. Two years later it did not feel as though anything much had improved—although it was true that the town was not seeing so many bankruptcies.

Her ageing grandfather, Joseph Thornton, journeyed back and forth to debate with the London lawyers, trying to make deals with the local creditors. None of them wanted to broker a solution, to compromise—the lawyers earning money from every delay, the creditors obstinate in thinking they would get their money back by enforcing the law of restraint on Thomas Mellor. They believed he had money hidden away; they swore his father-in-law could pay them out; they were convinced that Peggy Mellor was hiding vast profits to deprive them of their just rights. Nothing would shift them to the reality that there was no pile of money, that none in the family could pay back the capital invested in new machinery and workshops—that the Thomas Mellor family was, unlike Benjamin Mellor of Stainland, never going to run a big mill employing many people nor pay a good return on the money invested in machinery. Thomas Mellor could not push his business through those harsh years of depression and poor trade—especially not from the confines of prison in London.

With these reflections, Hannah stitched with, great care, her initials and the date of completion. She sighed as she knotted off her last stitch; she took a deep breath as she surveyed her beautiful quilt spread out in front of her. She walked round it, stood back and tilted her head examining again the cloths she had used from old dresses. She stroked it, then folded it, with lavender bags pressed between each fold, and wondered where she would take it in the years ahead.

Hannah tucked her needle in the little felt needle-work book which Delia had made for her birthday token last year. She was about to carry the quilt upstairs to the chest outside the bedroom she shared with her sister Lizzie when Harriet and Delia burst into the back parlour, arguing heatedly.

"Hansie, tell Delia there's a coach of four headless horses with headless riders. I know there is—I've heard the village wives talk about it coming out at night. I know it's true—but she won't believe me." Harriet panted this out utterly convinced of the truth of her statement.

"It can't be true." Delia argued assertively. A practical child, she could not see how anything could move if it had no head. She was determined to banish fear from her life—those rough and burly men in their brown jackets two years ago had terrified her. She could not bear the thought that apparitions of headless horses and humans would scare her as much as those bullies. Her bigger sister, Harry—who invented stories about the fairies of trees and water—and who dreamt of magical resolutions to any problems—insisted again that the headless horses and their riders leapt out of the inn halfway down the town of Elland, galloped through the streets to the bridge and then returned to their barn.

Hannah could see the points of both indignant girls. She felt the power of stories to instil fear but she did not want little Delia waking at night and creeping into her big sisters' bed because she had had another nightmare about 'rough men' in brown jackets riding into her room on headless horses.

"Harry, keep quiet. You must see you're scaring your little sister. She's not old enough to understand old wives' tales of horror. Have you ever seen the Headless Horseman? .... No, I thought not," she continued as Harriet hung her head and shifted uneasily from foot to foot. "Surely you can't say it's truly true until you've seen it for yourself?"

Harriet grunted shamefacedly—she knew she had been trying to scare Delia and she had been infuriated when that literal little girl had argued with her about needing a head to move. It seemed possible that Delia would outsmart her clever older sister with this practical logic—and Harriet wanted to keep her superiority. But all the girls dreaded Delia's nightmares—and tried to reassure her so she wouldn't wake them in the dead of night, with wide eyes, and the soft padding sounds of her bare feet on the cold wooden floor of the landing outside their bedrooms. Hannah gave Harriet a sharp look and Harriet mumbled, "Sorry Delia" and went back to the kitchen where she could smell a pie being cooked for tea.

"I am right aren't I, Hansie? People can't move without heads, can they? Harry was making it up, wasn't she?" Delia was questioning despite, or perhaps because of, Harriet's quick submission.

"Well, I'm not sure she was making it up, Delia. There are people in town who tell that story to scare others. Some even swear they've seen and heard the headless rider pass them by, and then pass them back again, after galloping down to the bridge—but none of us in this family have ever seen it. The Good Lord protects those who bless him by keeping such superstitions at bay. If you say your prayers well enough every night you will never see them. I certainly never have—nor do I want to—so I keep saying my prayers—like you should too."

Hannah was talking to Delia as though quieting her own fears about this Elland legend. Delia however was staunch in her own logic— "Whatever people say, I still can't see how anyone can move without a head." Hannah was pleased with this staunchness and wondered how it fitted with the fear that Delia showed at night.

Delia, unlike Harriet and Hannah, never painted pictures in her head of things that she did not know. She built practical stories about what she saw around her every day. She believed what Hansie read to her in her favourite books of Robinson Crusoe, and Pilgrim's Progress, and the Travels Gulliver made in Lilliput and Brobdinag—but she never saw any of those adventures as happening to her—and so she was unperturbed by strange events like meeting up with people immensely big, or very tiny; by solitude on a deserted island, or by the swamp of despair encountered by Christian, the pilgrim. Later in life she began to see Christian's adventures in a more personal light but then she was strong in her conviction that God would help her through any such passages herself. Delia was trusting and much beloved as the youngest child—and she felt that people—apart from 'rough men' in brown jackets—would be good to her.

"Come with me Delia. I've finished my quilt—look here I've just sewn in my initials—and now I want to put it away in the chest on the landing."

Hannah unfolded a small corner of her quilt and Delia peered closely at the H and the M—and at the date. "What will I be doing when you start using this, Hansie? Will you have children then? Who will look after us if you're looking after your own children?"

Delia had just uncovered a glimpse of a future which she didn't like very much. How could she ever live without Hansie—Hansie to feed her, to cuddle her, to bandage up her scratches, to read to her in the evenings. She needed her big sister and could not contemplate living without her. Hannah knew that Delia, her littlest sister, was very anxious about being unsafe and away from home and so hastily said "I'll never leave you my little Lucy Locket—not if you don't want to be left. You just tell me, and you can live with me as long as you want."

Delia was happy with this assertion and climbed the stairs to help Hannah put away her precious quilt, much more content than her big sister—who feared that growing up would bring unwelcome changes to them all. The quilt went into the bottom drawer along with the lavender bags—and with it went Delia's fears and anxieties.

Hannah was left with her own hopes and fears. Would she find the adventure she craved? Would she be able to travel as she dreamed? Hannah dreamt of living life as someone in charge, someone who did not depend on men to make her choices for her.

For the next two years, Hannah saw her mother working in the shops, negotiating with wool merchants and weavers. Hannah saw the grey beginning to escape from Peggy's tied back hair—the hair which she used to let down in the evenings, when no one came to their house for tea, for the children to play with as they went to bed. It was Peggy's glory—as was her beautiful cream-complexion skin—and both were fading under the relentless pressure to keep her family fed and clothed, to keep the workshop busy and the wool sold.

Hannah took on the role of mother to the rest of the children—it was she who mended their clothes, who tended their scratched knees, who baked them plentiful supplies of muffins and tea-cakes and oatcake biscuits, to keep at bay the pangs of hunger that these fast-growing girls had to assuage every day. When he was home, she tried to keep Joe fed and tidy in his clothes, but he was indignant that any mere girl should 'help' him.

"Leave me alone, Hansie" he would tell her. "I'm grown now and can manage my own affairs."

It was true that he was working, apprenticed as a joiner, to his Uncle Joseph Fox of Rastrick. Peggy had been adamant that he was not to join the wool business. She insisted that Joe broaden the family finances and had sent him to work in a more reliable business—hence apprenticeship to Joseph Fox—her sister Hannah's husband—who was trading in wood as a timber merchant, working in wood as a carpenter—and selling York stone from his land. Joiners were in demand—as were stone masons.

For Joe however it was not just the financial sense it made to work in a less troubled industry—he loved working with his hands and he loved making machines work. As a boy he had spent hours watching his father's looms, the spinning jennies, and the water wheels turning the axles to keep everything moving. He had sneaked into workshops when the hushed machines were being repaired, to watch how they did it, and to listen closely to the talk. He knew machines were crucial in keeping his father's woollen manufacturing afloat; he knew they cost him more money than he could find. He still remembered his flamboyant cousin George, the cloth shearer from Lockwood, who had been hung by the law in his fight against the threat of new machines. Despite George's bravery, despite his anger, despite his leadership of other angry men, Joe knew the future lay in machines. He himself was good with machines and he was content that his uncle Joseph Fox was teaching him the business of construction.

His sense of independence was satisfied by being away from home—and he would not allow his sister Hannah to bring him back to a sense of being young and immature by her caring reprimands about his clothing or his eating.

Hannah watched her mother keep the business going, saw her make decisions—and knew that Papa had never let Peggy take those decisions before his arrest. Now Peggy ran the business every day—her father Joseph Thornton was too old to keep the business going as well as negotiate the mired legal affairs—so Peggy was left unhindered to run the business on her own.

Hardened weavers, coming down from their houses on the moors, knew that when she had given them a price she would stick to it, knew she meant what she said, and most important, knew that if she said she would pay on a particular day, the money would be given to them, in full and without question. She did not consider grand schemes for expanding the business; she was happy if she bought and then sold the wool transformed into cloth at a small profit. Joe helped with the summer farm work in their three closes up the hill—and Lizzie and Nancy tended the cattle, the goats and chickens that roamed in the yard. The little girls, Harriet, Mary and Delia—had their chores around the house—and were expected to help Hannah keep the food on the table, and the linen clean and mended.

Hannah, had learnt life evaded her dreams, particularly life in Yorkshire where trade was so variable, harvests so unpredictable, and work could vanish overnight leaving families hungry and roofless. She had learnt all too well that Joe was Thomas' right-hand man, that he saw the future in his son—not his daughters. He loved his girls and, when Hannah was young, had played with them enthusiastically—but when there was trouble—as there had been—it was Joe he needed beside him, not capable Hannah. Hannah would not be disloyal to her absent father—but she wondered at the injustice of people dismissing strength in places where it was not expected to lie because it was feminine.

Peggy took the family to chapel every Sabbath—to the Wesleyan chapel in Greetland—which Thomas belittled for its hypocrisy in putting business before God. Their cousin, the Reverend Tom Mellor, from the Particular Baptists at Rishworth, rode over to see how his cousins were doing in their troubles. Many of his parishioners had money troubles—and little food to put on their tables. He feared for his cousins.

Minister Tom argued that the Government should do something about the men out of work. He knew mill owners needed to keep business going but he joined with those agitating for Reform of Parliament. Landowners and gentry would never help working people while there were no working-class votes in Parliament. MPs elected by the few who owned land, not by the many who toiled long hours in the factories, were not in a hurry to change the Representation of the People in Parliament. It would take another 105 years to grant every adult, including women, a vote. Minister Tom wanted a universal voting system then. Like so many Yorkshire men he joined clubs, he spoke from the pulpit, he argued with mill owners and mill workers. He thought what was needed was 'an effort to get things straightened for they're sorely crooked.' His argument continued that 'working families were ill off; they were poor and pined, thrown out of work by the frames and machines. They could get naught to do and could earn naught. Must they then', the reverend asked, 'must they lay themselves down and die?' He quoted these words of Sam Bamford, a machinist who taught himself his letters and argued persuasively that working men needed to be heard by the Government—at first violently, then later in tones more accommodating to the established order. The Minister was ardent for increasing the voice of working people.

Many non-conformist friends and manufacturers like John Fielden the Quaker and Richard Oastler, the steward of nearby Fixby Hall, were arguing along these lines. Charlotte Bronte, the daughter of the Irish parson from Haworth a few miles to the north of Halifax, listened to these conversations, and later, recorded them in her book 'Shirley'. Her father, Patrick, had once been on the side of the 'industrious classes'; once, it was said, that he buried, at night and in secret, those poor men sentenced to hang in York gaol in January 1813 after the Luddite riots. In age he had hardened and kept a gun beside him day and night to scare rioters. He had no patience with the long-winded morality of Dissenting Ministers—but he had not forgotten the poverty of his native Irish homeland and pitied those sanctioned by the magistrates when poverty drove them outside the law. He wasn't the only one to take the side of the poor. Reform was the talk in many inns across the West Riding.

Peggy, with her need to do business with all sorts—gentry, Tories, mill owners, toolmakers—did not join that debate. She kept her thoughts to herself to keep her family afloat in such disputatious times. Her girls heard the arguments for Parliamentary Reform—they listened—but no-one argued in public. It was too hard to run a business and support rebellious views. Her own father, Joseph Thornton, closed down all such arguments. He was a small mill owner and saw only the difficulties of staying in business—without giving himself the extra burden of worrying about national politics.

The reverend Tom, their cousin, understood these dilemmas and, in his visits, spoke only of family matters—never politics as he had with Thomas—however urgent they seemed to him. Peggy was grateful for his discretion and valued his religious opinions as a personal guide through her troubles.

Hannah was learning to mind her voice. She did not want to make herself odious to her neighbours, or her mother's customers and suppliers. She knew she had to find a husband but still she dreamed of adventure. Outwardly she behaved like a well brought up young girl of limited means—but inwardly she raged at the restrictions placed on her by society and by her dearly loved family.

Like Charlotte Bronte and so many other girls living on the edge of poverty Hannah felt caged by the restrictions imposed by her life of service. Without money she had no alternative but to 'serve', to resign her dreams of independence, to reconcile herself to marriage to a reputable business family—who might give her some of her dreams—fine china, quality rugs, sturdy, capacious furniture. These goods were filling shops in Halifax and Huddersfield; they were beginning to fill the houses of their neighbours and friends. They were making home life a little more comfortable. Books and ideas were freely discussed. Hannah heard with wonder of far off places, tales of pineapples, bananas, oranges—as well as greater supplies of tea and coffee and sugar. Hannah, with her reader's eye, saw the feast laid out for those of adventurous spirit and she longed to sample it. But she was too loyal, too loving of her sisters, too weighed down by her mother's urgent need to keep food on their table and shelter over their heads, to spend time bewailing her lot. Hannah never wasted time complaining about things that could not be changed.

77. Shibden Hall Wheelwright workshop, WYAS

Her brother Joe, on the other hand, knew poor trade restricted his life chances. He saw his father crushed by the need for finance and by the impossibility of paying for that finance when trade with London, America and Europe, yielded low prices. He remembered his cousin George, hung for taking on the system that destroyed lives; for proclaiming Luddite ferocity against the machines ripping the heart out of their economy. He heard tales of Mellors across the West Riding being transported to Australia for their political arguments, for minor attacks on the landed and rich. They disappeared, leaving their families struggling to beat starvation and ostracism from their communities, while more fortunate neighbours, backed by more money, prospered in bigger mills in crowded valleys. He saw the men of the uplands, the wool men, the weavers and clothiers of Halifax and Huddersfield struggling to keep business going, struggling against rising wage costs, defending themselves from hunger. He didn't like what he saw, the inequality and the rigid divisions across society, across churches and chapels. He vowed one day to change things for himself.

He loved his work with wood and machinery—not with the wool of his father's life. He aimed to prosper employing labour—rather than as a craftsman who sold his labour. While his sister Hannah was looking for her feminine way out of their family's troubles, he was looking to join the coterie of prosperous merchants, traders and mill-owners filling the cloth halls and taverns of Halifax and Huddersfield.

While these young people dreamt and strove, their father Thomas remained incarcerated in the 'Rules' area of the King's bench prison. As long as his creditors refused any compromise in the money they demanded he was detained. He lost his self-respect, his pride in his achievements as a Maister, as a clothier. He missed his Yorkshire neighbours—and his bustling home with its bevy of six girls—and the quiet support of his only son. He had to wait another two years for freedom—and a return to his beloved Calderdale. Money—or the lack of it—imprisoned him and clipped the wings of his ambitious children. It hardened his wife Peggy as she managed in Yorkshire. In London he became listless.

PART II—Chapter 23

Release in Wakefield
July 1828

78. Summer meadows in Colne Valley (Author 2017)

Winter turned into spring, then summer—and autumn brought back winter. In January 1828, Joseph Thornton felt a glimmer of hope in his endless negotiations with the London lawyers. The creditors sensed that a little money into their coffers was better than no money—even if they had to forfeit the pleasure of diminishing an old opponent.

After Joseph buried his wife in St. Peter's, Huddersfield, he travelled less energetically. He rested longer at his home in Well Green in Lockwood, near the places where he and Abigail had shared their youth. He travelled less to the Cloth Halls in Huddersfield and Halifax, and hardly ever to London. His travel was always 'for business for Thomas' but Peggy thought it was now an escape from loneliness.

By April 1828 the creditors accepted part settlement of Thomas' debts enabling him to plead insolvency at Wakefield Quarter Sessions. They agreed an achievable price for their dividend. Thomas was transferred to Halifax Gaol for three months where he worked out his sentence. In Halifax he had no freedom to move as he had in the Rules—he was closely confined—but the law entered a plea for insolvency at the quarter sessions at Wakefield on July 28th. Till then he was housed in a small room at the top of the gaol house for gentlemen debtors, untroubled by the felons and drunkards in the common gaol down below.

During those three months Peggy trudged twice weekly over Copley Bridge and up past Skircoat Green to the prison in Gaol Street—a six-mile round trip. She brought him food—and gave him money to buy in beer so he didn't have to drink the foul water that made so many ill. Later, when she had contented herself that the now morose Thomas had lightened his mood and would no longer frighten the girls she encouraged Hannah to visit taking with her the younger ones.

One day in May—with leaves unfurling on the trees covering the Calder valley hillsides—Delia bounced up the hill besides Hannah while two sisters—Harriet and Mary dawdled behind. Halifax, with its narrow streets, its crowds, its shops and taverns, was an exciting place for a little girl who spent most days in the courtyard and barns around her own home. Harriet and Mary, now 13 and 11, were quiet as they walked. They could remember their father—and wondered how he would welcome them knowing he had brought so much calamity to the family. Eight-year-old Delia had no such scruples. She laid all their troubles at the doors of the 'rough men' who had invaded her home four years ago. She didn't remember her father as a real man—but she heard tales of this important personage who had tossed the other girls around, who had ridden a good horse around the valleys, and who was a 'maister' among other 'maisters'. She was excited and untroubled by her planned visit.

Hannah rang the bell of the Gaol keeper's lodgings and, with the sound of keys clinking on a ring, and of one large key scratching the key hole, the heavily studded oak door was slowly opened and a surly individual with a long brown apron and a dirty neckerchief tied around his throat stood on the threshold barring their entrance.

"What's your business?" he grunted at them.

"We've come to see Thomas Mellor," said Hannah a little unsurely. The three girls stood closely behind her as the doorkeeper glanced over them with an unfriendly glare.

"Expecting you, is he? You'se bringing in things you shouldn't?" he demanded of them.

"Indeed not," said Hannah, holding out her basket with its bread and pies and cakes for the surly man to see.

"I'll be having some of that, my lassie," he said, putting his filthy calloused hand into the basket and turning over the packages of food.

"But it's for Father, and my mother will be upset that he's not got it," Hannah told him.

"Nah, she won't be. She'll be glad old Ben 'as 'is due rewards. Old Ben deserves all that comes 'is way—'tis a hard life, that's for sure—and all good people want to help Old Ben." He pulled the basket away from Hannah and set it down on a shelf behind him. Then he opened the door a little wider and with a nod of his bull-like head indicated that the girls should pass him and tread up the stairs ahead. They squeezed closer still to Hannah and held their breath as they passed him—the stench of alcohol and sweat was overpowering—and once on the stairs, they moved quickly.

Climbing the stairs Delia's eyes widened in horror as she saw what was hanging above the doorway through to the yard behind—a large iron blade, eighteen inches long, four inches thick across its top and dropping nine inches to a one inch cutting edge.

"Quick Lucy Locket—don't stop—don't worry about that—it can't hurt you—its's safe hanging there—none is going to get it down." Hannah spoke breathlessly as she pushed all three girls away from the sight of the fearsome axe, urging them out of its sight up to the top room.

Harriet asked Hannah as she panted up the stairs, "Is that THE AXE? Is that what they use to kill thieves and murderers? Is it the Guillotine that was used in France? Will they use that on Father?"

"Yes. It is the axe—but no-one uses it now—and it never went to France—it only went to Scotland for a bit before being brought back here. It's never going to be taken down—it'll never be used on Father—he's never going to feel it." Hannah herself felt rather uncertain and jumpy after the loss of her basket to that dirty old man at the door. Her voice did not reassure her younger sisters.

"I don't like it. I really don't." Delia was now full of the fear of the 'rough men' and wondered why this Father she was expected to visit was still surrounded by them and why she was coming near them again.

"You're safe, Lucy Locket," Hannah reassured her. "Father's not going to be here for long—and soon we will be able to have him back home."

The three girls had to take Hannah's words for it—they climbed quickly and quietly so as not to bring any closer that foul-smelling individual in his tatty brown breeches and dirty smock. At the top were four doors—all with big padlocks in the hasp holding each door shut. Hannah stopped, unsure what she needed to do to gain entrance. The little girls were shivering against the bannister above the stairs. Then, at the bottom, they heard a thumping sound and the banisters shook.

"Stupid girls clattering up them stairs so fast. This is a prison, aint it. No one comes in or goes out without old Ben letting them in or out. You mun' wait for me, that you will—and I don't do nowt in a rush these days."

The girls stood frozen, waiting with pounding hearts as Old Ben climbed, slowly and heavily, wheezing and puffing, till he reached their landing. They shrank away as he stood four-square in front of one of the doors wrestling with his bunch of keys. He turned the key, lifted off the padlock and pushed the door open.

"Visitors, you scoundrel, Thomas Mellor. Look right to them. I'll lock you in—and come and let 'em out in my own good time. In you lot go now—be quick."

The girls went in as quickly as they could. Inside they saw a bare room with one chest against a wall, a single upright chair, a narrow iron framed bed, and a stooped man with his back to them looking out the window. Old Ben slammed the door shut and they heard him heaving on the padlock and turning the key. They were trapped. Delia whimpered and Harriet and Mary went white. Hannah held Delia's hand tightly and said, "Papa? Papa?"

The figure at the window turned and Hannah recognised the old familiar face—although much of the light seemed to have gone out of its eyes as he looked her over.

"Papa, Mother sent us up with a basket of pies but that man has taken the basket. He says he needs it. Will he give it back to you? Mother'll be upset if it doesn't go to you—she says you need fattening up?"

"Hannah, my dearest one. Hannah come here—so I can see you properly. You've become as pretty as your mother once was. Leave the basket—you're not to worry about it—I'll try to get it back so your mother can be happy—though I don't need feeding up, not now I'm nearly home."

Thomas Mellor gave his eldest daughter a hug and a kiss—and then turned to the three girls standing awkwardly beside his narrow bed—the only space for them in the little attic room.

"Come here you three—are you Harriet? I can't believe you've grown so much. You must be Mary—and this is our littlest—my little Delia. I can't credit you've all grown so much—I've always thought of you as babies when I saw you in my mind's eye. Come, come here and give me a hug." And Thomas held out his arms expectantly. Harriet and Mary tentatively embraced him but Delia hung back, shrinking from yet another strange man. Her father was fast becoming associated in her mind with all the 'rough men' who made her scared.

"I'm strange," Thomas said. "Never mind, Hansie. Let her watch, let her be—till she gets used to me again—she was only four when she last saw me and she probably doesn't remember me. Well, well you two girls must sit on the bed with Hannah. Little Delia can sit on the floor next to the chest. That's where I keep my clothes."

Relieved, Delia scurried over to the wall and sat with her back to the chest, looking away from her sisters with their legs dangling from the bed, and away from that strange man, perched on his wobbly upright

wooden chair. She sat down, pulled up her knees, and eased her head down so she couldn't see anything. She tried closing her eyes but they kept opening when she heard that strange voice. She was terrified—and horrified by Hansie's kiss. It felt like betrayal—Delia was determined to give nothing to this bristly stranger.

79. Figure drawn on the walls of Halifax Gaol around 1800. Re-discovered in 1896 and printed again in local paper in 1975 at time of demolition – (WYAS – Author 2019)

After a while, she looked around. She looked at the wall beside her and noticed loose paint which she prised away. More paint flaked off and she prised further. Gradually her hole in the wall of paint grew bigger and she saw marks underneath. They looked like pencil marks and intrigued, no longer paying any attention to that troublesome man, she began to see pictures of a man wearing a powdered wig—and then she found a second man drawn under the paint. Deeply engrossed in her detective work she forgot about being imprisoned; thumps at the door ricocheted around the small room. The grating padlock being unlocked scratched her ears—and she shrank back against the chest. Hannah stood up quickly urging the other two to stand. Thomas flattened himself with his back to the window.

"Hansie, look what I've found." Delia unfolded her stiff legs and pointed to the drawings on the wall beside the chest. Her father looked where she pointed and laid his fingers across his lips.

"Stand up. Quick," he said.

She did, and just in time. When old Ben pushed open the door he saw Hannah and two young girls hastily tidying their skirts near the bed, Thomas up against the window and that whining little child who had shrunk away from him, standing stuck against the wall.

"Get out you four, get downstairs now. Time's up. Can't be allowing this Thomas 'ere any privileges—he's a prisoner of the court, he is. Get down 'em stairs quick before I have to push 'ee."

Thomas winked at his youngest daughter as she stubbornly stood beside the chest protecting her wall drawings. He moved over to her with the chair and placed it in front of the drawings. He ushered her gently towards the door. Standing still he hid them from Ben's uninterested eye. Thomas winked again. Old Ben was too busy eyeing Hannah up and down with his lascivious eye to notice any change in the wall behind Delia. Thomas quickly gave Harriet and Mary a pat on the shoulder and a fleeting kiss. They turned and slid out of the room. Delia meanwhile was caught behind Old Ben, between him and her drawings. Fortunately, he continued eyeing Hannah as she shepherded the other two down the stairs. Her father moved towards Delia, shielding her from the louche man and nudged her to the landing after her sisters. Seeing an ally against Ben, Delia turned to her father and, reaching up on tip toe, gave him a quick peck on the cheek. That wink had turned him from the side of the 'rough men' over to 'the family' side. Happy that her drawings were safe she turned and ran down the stairs. Thomas stayed in the corner, protecting them, until Old Ben grumpily moved out of the room, heaved the padlock back over the hasp and left him to his supperless evening—and to moving the chest in front of the drawings to hide them from his unfriendly gaze.

The girls waited at the bottom for Old Ben to waddle down the uneven stairs, laboriously pull out his huge ring of keys, choose one and insert it in its keyhole. He turned it and pulled the door ajar. The girls squeezed past him and fell out into the cobbled Gaol Street, into the noise and bustle of familiar Halifax. No-one spoke but walked swiftly back down the hill, through Skircoat where Thomas' workshop still stood with Job Turner its solitary worker. They walked on, across the river Calder at Copley Bridge and back up to their Greetland home through the bluebell filled North Dean Woods.

When they arrived home, they were subdued. Peggy watched them and without saying anything resolved not to send the younger ones again. It was only another eight weeks until the hearing in Wakefield on 28th July and it was better, she deemed, not to scare the girls.

Peggy herself continued to go, twice a week, as did Joe and Hannah. They took parcels for Old Ben—and the women kept parcels for Thomas hidden under their clothing. They kept Thomas abreast of what was happening, as best they could, telling him of the antics of the churchwardens clearing out the pubs when the vicar was preaching his sermon to increase the count of those in Sunday morning service. Formerly he would have inveighed loudly against the horror of forcing people into church. The new, chastened Thomas quietly heard the story and muttered—"Bad Business, bad business" and his two eldest children had to move on to other stories to keep engaging their now rather silent father.

Thomas never moved his chest back to the old place. He never again saw the pictures his youngest daughter had uncovered but he did try drawing to occupy his time. Old Ben saw no use for paper nor quills, not even as objects to sell. As long as no paper left his gaol he had no objection to unused paper entering it under his derisory glare. Thomas drew to pass the time, and dined on Peggy's food parcels brought in under her skirts to evade old Ben's grasping hands—while open baskets were handed over to meet his 'deserving needs'. Thomas' release from Halifax Gaol could not come quick enough for the Mellor family.

80. The Courthouse in Wakefield, no longer in use.
In 1828 Thomas appeared before the Quarter Sessions Court of Insolvency
And was released on July 28th.

The weeks passed. Mr. Cadney lodged Thomas' plea to the court of insolvent debtors in Wakefield in July. Thomas was taken from his prison to the court at Wakefield on 28th July. It was hot and sunny and Joe, who had been allowed a day away by his uncle Joseph Fox, was sweating copiously in his Sunday best. He wanted to impress the magistrate as to his family's substance and worthiness. His Sunday best would tell the lofty judge that the Mellors came of good stock, were respectable and were one of the good families of the area. So, no workaday smock shirt today—instead a white cloth around his neck, a waistcoat over his shirt and a coat to cover it all. He was hot—and he needed to mop his forehead with a large spotted handkerchief kept in the pocket of his short coat. Merchants wore long coats and tall hats—Joe had no long coat and even if he had he would not wear it as such pretensions to grandeur would be unwelcome from a stripling of his age. One day, he thought to himself, I will add a gold fob watch to hang from my coat—just like the grocer standing, watch in hand at the front of his grocery store, welcoming his customers. But he was smart enough for today—and glad to catch his father's eye as he came into the dock in front of Sir Joseph Armitage, magistrate—one of the men who had pursued George Mellor with such ferocity sixteen years before.

Thomas saw his son Joe from the dock. He saw him sweltering in his Sunday best and appreciated the thought that had gone into the tight clothes that his muscular son never enjoyed wearing. Like his son, he too had put on his best clothes bought in London town, persuaded by his father-in-law. Mr. Thornton had more notion of impressing the gentry than Thomas had ever had—he had made more money than Thomas and he did more business with merchants from London and across in Liverpool and Manchester. Thomas listened to his advice— and felt easier when he saw his son following the same behaviour. He gave him a half smile across the courtroom. Then someone less kindly sneered at the man in the dock. His creditors glowered in the crowded court and jeered at the son looking down from the public gallery.

The court servants prayed that all rise and as they did, the magistrate entered and took his place. Mr. Cadney, in his place beside Thomas, with his sombre black dress and white bands around his neck, told the magistrate that his client was of good family, was well supported and that he had made arrangements with his creditors which had been agreeable to them. He told the court his client had fallen into unavoidable difficulties due to the dreadful trading conditions in the wool market four years earlier. He swore he would not be a burden on the parish if he were to be released. The magistrate nodded making no mention of any previous Mellors up before his court and gave permission for the release of the prisoner. Mr. Cadney looked up at Joe and nodded towards the door.

As agreed beforehand, Joe quickly left the court and went round the building to the warder's door. Mr. Cadney was waiting.

"We must move as soon as your father comes out." Mr. Cadney said quietly. "I've got a horse and carriage waiting in the High street just around the corner. I'll hurry your father to the carriage—and if any trouble looms you'll be around to deflect it with pleasant chat and a leisurely attitude. After we've been gone ten minutes or so, make your own escape quietly. The creditors might go back to Skircoat Green but we want to take your father to Greetland before any hear of him being there. He needs a bit of time to get used to being back—you all do."

He spoke quietly and carefully so no bystanders could hear. Dressed soberly, he was an old-fashioned lawyer with nothing out of place. Joe wondered whether his clothes were the same as they had been that day back in 1817 when he had attended the Savile Arms with his father. Clothiers had been in a bad way for years—Joe was relieved that he was not a woolman—whatever else happened people would need his machines and carts. He nodded to Mr. Cadney to show he had understood his role and together they stood waiting for the door to open and release Thomas.

Suddenly, Thomas was there, looking bewildered. Pushed out of the doorway he stumbled over the step onto the pavement. Mr. Cadney held out his arm to steady him and together they moved slowly down the street towards the waiting carriage. Joe watched whilst his father, slowly and gingerly at first, and then increasingly purposefully, moved towards his freedom. As he gazed he saw the coachman get down to open the door. He saw his father put a leg on the step up to the coach and Mr. Cadney whisk behind the carriage to the other side. At that point he was shaken roughly from behind by an angry, unkempt, ill-dressed man.

"Where is he, young man? Where is he? I'll give him a piece of my mind, I will—dirty thieving horror that he is. He's got off scot free—and hidden my money I've no doubt."

Joe turned and looked into the belligerent, square, hatchet-faced man who had frightened him as a boy in the Savile Arms. His eyes searched the crowd for a friendly face: there were none. He planted his legs wide on the paving and smiled.

"Who be ye wanting, good sir?

"You know perfectly well, you stupid boy. Where's your thieving scoundrel father? Where's the man that owes me? That's who I want, as well you know. Show him to me—and I'll settle with you both, you varmint."

Joe didn't change his stance, nor his smile. He kept his eye alert for movement from the carriage. He put his head on one side and, with a level voice, he said

"Well good sir, I don't rightly know. I'm looking for him myself but mebbe the court hasn't yet released him. I don't know where to look but mebbe you know another way he could have gone."

"The cheek, young snipper snapper, the cheek. I'll get you for your silly answers," and he tried to throw a punch at Joe. He was already stumbling as he had spent too long in the inn opposite the courthouse. Joe was waiting for that lunge and he quickly stepped aside as the man lurched forward. The man fell awkwardly on to the paving stones and Joe darted off down an alley.

81. View from Greetland towards Elland (Author 2019)

The man looked up and saw his running feet.

"I'll get 'ee. I'll get 'ee and 'im too. Just you wait. You'se a pair of rascally stealing thieves."

Joe wanted to stay and thump him but he had seen Mr. Cadney climb in the carriage. It drove off. It was time to skip out of it, to find the back alleys like his father had done after the Press Gang visit to Halifax. Joe wished he had better clothes for running. The sun was hot, and his clothes tight and heavy. He ran to the Inn to pick up a coach back to Elland.

Later that afternoon, as he was climbing the hill back up to his mother's home in Greetland he paused for breath, took off his neck band and waist coat and decided that he was far enough from Wakefield to be safe from the angry man. After a few moments, he moved under the trees and picking his way through the woods he kept to the shade as he passed the Rose and Crown (where his father had stopped to look at William Horsfall's superb horse on his way to Uncle James Mellor at the start of his apprenticeship in the wool business). Joe smiled as the view across the valley broadened out to his left.

PART III
THE BIBLE PLAYS ITS PART
1829-1840

82. Family Bible on a mid-nineteenth century table cloth
Note the cover for the sugar dish to keep off flies
Taken at Colne Valley Museum, Golcar. (Author 2019)
The Turner family used a Bible like this to record family details.

PART III—Chapter 24

Hannah attends Chapel
1829-1830

83. Square Chapel, Halifax—built in 1772 and visited in July 1772 by John Wesley whose followers later called themselves Methodists subdivided further in the nineteenth century. The Square Chapel was an imposing building just behind the Piece Hall attracting affluent business people. (Author in 2019)

With Thomas home, life changed less than the family had expected. Routines built without him continued unchanged; Thomas trudged alone to his workshop in Skircoat. He and Job Turner bought spun woollen thread to weave; the fulling, dyeing and tentering they outsourced. Cloth-dressing work they passed up to Joseph Baines in Paradise Row; the finished pieces they took to the Cloth Hall every Saturday morning despite its fast falling number of regular merchants and traders. Indeed it was busier with children from the local Sunday schools at the first Halifax Big Sing in 1831 than it was with regular Saturday traders. Thomas spluttered furiously when he heard Hannah had taken her tribe of Sunday school children from the Salem New Connexion chapel to his hallowed Piece Hall.

"That place be made for business, for serious stuff, for men—not for flimsy stuff like singing with children."

He grumbled furiously to anyone who would listen.

Of an evening, he turned to the Halifax inns and clubs, avoiding Gaol Street with its dark memories and berating the 'hotheads' drinking at the Waggoners in Skircoat Green. Their cry for 'Reform' did not bring back his young dreams. He was tired, with no energy to change hostile trade practices, nor to fight for Reform of Parliament, despite the furious arguments he heard reverberating all around. He told himself he had failed, that nothing could improve his situation. After a short drink, he trod home, surly and withdrawn, avoiding the family table full of chatter. They fell silent at his entry but, once he had withdrawn to his office, stories, laughter and gentle teasing filled the house. Thomas heard it in his lonely room and felt more alone than ever.

Times were hard; Thomas saw no improvement available. Indeed, he feared change as it meant losing more of his past. He joined the merchants' talk at evening societies, always on the fringe, never included in invitations to homes, but respected for his knowledge and ways with wool. He was still old Joseph Mellor's son and his uncle, James Mellor, had taught him well. Nor did anyone want to be on the wrong side of the men from Huddersfield; his father-in-law, Joseph Thornton of Lockwood, was big in that market, and inspired respect. They were cordial to Thomas and counted him as one of theirs, but not too closely.

Peggy, surrounded by her daughters, continued to work cloth from their Greetland home. Thomas would not do business with his wife. Diminished by her competence, he felt his father-in-law's greater strength. Despite his near eighty years, Joseph was still a significant force. Nevertheless, those long years of riding through the Yorkshire countryside were passing away. Thomas watched his father-in-law retreat to Lockwood and thought him too reticent, too solitary; he could not see the mirror held up in his own retreat to the Skircoat workshop. He could not see Joseph reflecting on past companionship with Abigail in the woods of their youth, nor that his older daughter Hannah Fox brought him closer to the memory of his wife.

Peggy, who ran her home and business as she had while Thomas had been away, became preoccupied with the futures of her girls: six of them to place, to find good husbands, to settle in good families with decent roofs over their heads, and to be treated with kindness. The time had passed when she could chat things over with Thomas—he was morose and lost in his own world, unable to bear the fear of being worthless. Peggy pulled her shoulders back and focused on what she could do best—feed, clothe and support her tribe of young—teaching them to support others as best they could.

The girls lived as they had when Thomas was imprisoned. Hannah taught the younger ones while Lizzie and Nancy helped in the closes and barns. Harriet spent as much time as possible reading but, during the day, she and Mary learned how to sew and mend. The older girls began to think of husband hunting—especially Hannah. She worried she would be trapped at home, anxious about feeding everyone. She knew she had to marry well so her sisters would not be trapped in drudgery. She vowed that none need work in Elland mills. Thomas knew nothing of these female preoccupations.

Day after day his eldest daughter urged her mother: "Nancy and Lizzie must learn a trade—dressmaking perhaps, or millinery, not wool like you and Papa. Then they can work at home, not in factories with long hours going late into the night. Their earnings will help and, it'll be good to have them busy at home. I'll teach the little ones to read and write so they can find something later when they're grown."

Peggy heard, and knew she should talk it out with Thomas—yet never found the right moment. Hannah felt unheard by either parent.

Hannah and Peggy often seemed to miss each other's virtues. Peggy found little time to lift her head from the daily rush of business around the house and in the barns. Hannah was irked by her mother's blindness to what was happening in the townships around them. She missed her Grandmother.

Grandmama Abigail Hirst from a straight-laced family of Independent Dissenters in Huddersfield, had attended chapel regularly; she read chapters of the Bible to her grand-daughters and reflected with them on the right way to treat both customers and workers. From the Old Testament she told stories of the difficulties of life, of the arguments among families and communities. She drew strength from her own reading and passed that on to her granddaughters.

Hannah remembered her reading aloud the psalms—all 150 of them—finding those that helped in difficult times. When Hannah was taunted in the town about her 'skivving' father Abigail read psalms of the psalmist needing God's help to live with scandalmongers and liars spreading falsehood. At her grandmother's death Hannah sang again the psalm of the Good Shepherd with which Abigail had eased their aching hearts in the anxious days of George Mellor's trial. On Good Friday she reread Psalm 22 speaking of despair and abandonment and calling for God's help out of the depths of loss and loneliness.

"My dears, you too will face times like this," Hannah remembered her saying. "Then read these psalms and you will find ways to meet the challenge."

Her grandmother had not been down-hearted, nor pessimistic. She had drawn pleasure from the changing seasons, welcoming each year's first snowdrop with excitement. She stopped to hear the blackbird singing from the top of his branch. She'd chatted with the robin cocking his head as he hopped down to pick out the glistening worm helpfully turned over as she prepared the soil for planting. She'd searched under the bigger leaves for shy violets and revelled in the mist of bluebells covering the wooded floor on the old road down to Huddersfield. Hannah drew on her grandmother's joy in the tiny detail of the great outdoors.

The horror of April 1812 still lingered in Hannah's mind; seared into her dreams was the image of George and his three friends riding, great coated and masked, into Dungeon Wood to shoot William Horsfall. She knew those events had scarred her grandmother—that she had been glad to move up to Greetland with Peggy and her girls. Free from those ghosts of violence, she walked in the woods and sang her favourite psalm, the last one, Psalm 150– Let everything that hath breath praise the Lord. She had passed on this love of singing to her granddaughters, particularly Hannah and Lizzie. She helped them face the darkness of life. Hannah missed her comfort and quiet strength, drawing none from her mother's bustle and work.

84. Interior of an early nineteenth century Non-Conformist Chapel with galleries and a preaching box at the East end where today the altar alone is usually seen. Hannah sat upstairs with Sunday school children. Notice the new use of iron pillars to support the gallery and pews with high sides. Members paid for their own particular pew—and rents were collected by church wardens in both established and non-conformist churches. The better the pew the higher the rent.

After Grandmama's death, Hannah listened more closely to the preachers who came to Greetland Methodist chapel. She was told what to think by the ministers. She sang Wesley's hymns, she studied the Bible as interpreted by the elders, and she muttered about those elders, asking her friends why they had to follow their lead so closely. One Sunday she and her friends ventured further, went to the Methodist Salem New Connexion Chapel in Halifax. Hannah came home buzzing with excitement.

"At the Salem chapel they believe that all the saints should investigate and interpret the Bible. They believe that lay people should help organise the worship, order the charitable work, should lead as well as follow. Together we change the world, make conditions better in the mills, ensure working people earn a decent wage, and are not turned off unjustly. They believe we should halt the injustice that is slavery. In the might of Jesus, we can change the world."

Hannah was energetically declaiming to her mother and younger sisters how thoughtful it was at the Salem New Connexion chapel when they heard the front door pushed open and their father's heavy boots scrape on the mat inside the hall.

85. St. Mary's, Elland drawn by Lucy Hammerton in Olde Elland, published in 1895 with copies held in Elland Library.

"Hansie, hush your chatter in front of Papa. You know how angry he gets with 'missions'. Hush Hansie, Hush!" Peggy was anxious to avoid an explosion from her angry husband—and Hansie often provoked him to fury with her enthusiastic talk of changing the world.

Hesitant Lizzie felt great distress at strong arguments. Anxiety flooded through her and she quickly intervened with a call through the hall, "Papa come, come in. I've made broth tonight, and some parkin." Hannah's flow of chat was stopped in its tracks, and the girls moved to prepare the table for tea.

Walking to chapel each Sabbath, Hannah discussed with her friends how people could change God's world, how they could ensure God's justice for the poor as well as the landed. She wanted no part of bishops or clergy telling her what to think. With as good a mind as any, she wanted to work out what the Greek Testament was telling her about her Saviour's life and commandments. She knew God's grace was afforded to her however low she fell, that He loved her and granted her salvation. She felt her grandmother's deep convictions, and strength flowed into her—along with Abigail's contented joy in the natural world.

Thomas felt safer in the hands of St. Mary's, the Anglican church in Elland. There he was surrounded by fellow clothiers, and in the church-yard by long dead family. But to keep Peggy happy, with her strong Non-conformist views, he varied his church attendance. Sometimes he went with her and her father to the Baptist chapel above Elland Upper Edge. Occasionally he visited the Greetland Wesleyan Methodists with his younger girls and made infrequent trips to his cousin Tom at the Particular Baptist Roadside Chapel in Rishworth. But now, with bit-terness towards the merchants who had demanded their pound of his flesh, he refused to attend the Square Chapel in Halifax where success-ful business families gathered each Sunday. Peggy went weekly, for the whole day, to the chapel above Elland; she was one of the elder women, in a group with her sister Hannah Fox. She never discussed the ser-mons, nor took part in the great arguments about salvation, nor about lay control of the chapels. She kept her hands folded in her lap, her mouth closed and minded the young girls as they danced about in the surrounding churchyard. Mostly her thoughts were dominated by the chores she knew she had to return to the following day. Neither parent seemed engaged with their daughter's passion for justice.

Hannah, with her ambition to change the world, would not let things lie. She read and re-read the Bible at home and at chapel in study groups. She struggled to understand its contradictory statements, but she remained convinced of God's great goodness—as had her grandmother—and worked zealously to make the world a better place. Eager to pass on her learning and love of books she spent most Sundays teaching in the Sunday school, and with her clear tuneful voice enjoyed the hymns of the Wesley brothers who her father and uncle had heard preaching in the open air on the hillsides around Halifax some thirty years earlier.

Sundays found her practising good 'Sabbath' behaviour. She taught young scamps from workshops and homes in Greetland, Elland and Skircoat Green. Some learnt their letters well, but many more fidgeted and longed to be out, chasing each other around the churchyard surrounding the newly built chapel. They were cuffed round the ears by the lay elders for this disrespect. Singing enthusiastically in the gallery lifted Hannah's heart and made her smile.

From her perch with the children, on the long benches, leaning on the railing that kept them all from falling into the mass of bodies in the nave of the chapel, she looked down and, one Sunday, she noticed a tousled-haired young man who sat on his own at the front. She recognised him as the son of Father's grocer acquaintance in Halifax High street, John Fisher, the man who brought boxes of tea to the polite of the area. He was a Quaker, a Friend, and had family down in London town. The Fishers lived at Springvale near Grandfather Thornton in the Lockwood area just outside Huddersfield. After the executions of 1813 John Fisher had visited the bereaved families to support them. He had written an account of these visits and showed great concern, but no help had been forthcoming from the local gentry or magistrates. Hannah wondered what brought his son to the Salem New Connection Wesleyans.

After the service ended, Hannah took the restless children outside for their picnic lunch in the graveyard around the chapel. She was watching them play when she looked up and saw the young man standing awkwardly beside the tombstone on which she had spread her food. He was holding his cap in his hand and shifting uncertainly from foot to foot. Hannah blushed as she held out a sandwich.

"It looks like you have nothing to eat. Have this. I've plenty, and to spare. Mother always makes us take more food than we ever need. She thinks we will exhaust ourselves and become famished if we do not carry a bagful of provisions."

The young man was unable to resist the proffered pie. He was hungry and the sight of the chunk of pastry encasing the ham and eggs was too tempting.

"I shouldn't really," he said. "But it's too delicious to refuse. Thank you, thank you."

"You're new to this chapel, aren't you. I haven't seen you here before," Hannah queried.

"Yes, it's my first time with these brethren. My parents go to Friends Meetings. They were married by the Friends on the Northampton circuit

but I want a little more liveliness and I'd heard that it's good here. So here I am. My name's Joshua Fisher, son of John Fisher of Springvale. I live over Lockwood way. My father trades in Huddersfield Cloth Hall as well as dealing with his grocery business in Halifax." Joshua looked directly at Hannah and held out his hand in greeting.

86. Thomas and Peggy in 1805, Hannah and Joshua Fisher in 1830 and Harriet and John Baines 1838 were all married here (Author 2019)

"Welcome," she said. "I've not been long coming here myself. I like the discussions, the sense that we can make God's world better. I hate it when church people tell us that we can do nothing to make things easier for the poor. That isn't what our Saviour meant when he told us to 'Love our neighbours as ourselves'. We must serve them and so serve Him. So yes welcome, most welcome."

She spoke with a passionate conviction and as she did her eyes lit up, her face moved vividly, and her breath came more rapidly. Joshua was captivated. He spent the rest of the lunch break outside with Hannah while she kept an eye on the children and talked fast and furiously about the changes she wanted to see in God's world, for the sake of all God's children. After that Sabbath morning, the two were often to be seen together, week by week, discussing texts and commandments, and contributing to discussions about lay leadership in chapel, and about Reform in Parliament.

Joshua walked Hannah home from chapel in Halifax, across the River by Elland Bridge, and slowly up the hill. They took the long way round. He became a regular at the table for the evening tea and worked a calm reassuring kindness with Thomas himself. He brought news from Huddersfield and from London. He never presumed any knowledge of the wool world but quietly spoke of the grocery business he would be opening in Brighouse, a growing centre of trade despite keeping its air of country calm. Soon afterwards Thomas went up the hill to the Halifax grocery shop to pass the time with John Fisher, his father.

So it was, on Christmas Day in 1830, in Halifax parish church, that Hannah was wed to Joshua Fisher, a grocer supplying tea to the inhabitants of Brighouse. Her parents were content that their eldest daughter was marrying in the same church that had seen them married a quarter of a century earlier. His parents knew that although Hannah would never understand their commitment to silence at their weekly worship, she was nevertheless an upright Christian and would raise a godly family. Hannah and her new husband both signed the register in their own hand. They moved to Brighouse where Joshua worked long hours in his shop—and they attended the Brighouse Salem Chapel. Hannah took her carefully worked stitchery from her bottom drawer to her new home. Her quilt had pride of place on her new double bed.

At home, her older sisters had more space in their rooms but their lives continued much the same. Little Delia though felt lost, bereft of the big sister who mothered her.

PART III—Chapter 25

Hardship Returns
1830-1835

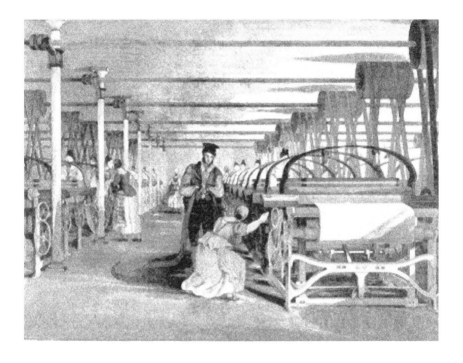

*87. Large mill staffed by women—female wages were lower
than men's—so attractive to employers.*

In the dark and cold of January 1831, ten-year-old Delia mourned the loss of her big sister. She cried herself to sleep; she picked at her food; she became sullen and refused to play out with her friends. When Hannah and Joshua came over for Sunday tea, Delia turned away from her big sister and crept upstairs to her bedroom. She refused to speak to Joshua and roughly threw down his eating platter when told to set the table. Even her father noticed the change and told her roundly to stop being rude, to mind her manners. Hannah was distressed by the pale face and dark rings under her little sister's eyes. Afterwards in the parlour she asked her mother what was happening to her baby sister.

"She's growing, she's tired and she misses thee, my dear," Peggy replied to her eldest daughter, who'd barely drawn breath recounting all the good things happening to her in the exciting new grocer's shop in Brighouse.

"But that shouldn't be, should it, Mother? She's got all the girls, and you, and Papa—she shouldn't miss one of us with everyone else safe around her."

"Mebbe not, but mebbe she does. Only time will tell, Daughter, and only time will heal her. Let's wait and see. Mebbe she'll find her way through it all. She's not a baby anymore and has to learn to deal with life's changes."

Peggy was troubled by Delia's mourning but saw it as strengthening her. Peggy sighed; she felt her girls didn't fear circumstances enough. They'd been calm during Thomas' time in London but their grandfather's money and her own hard work had shielded them from the disastrous loss of home and income that debt usually inflicted on a bankrupt family. Her girls did not push her for fancy clothes and bits of jewellery; they minded their work around the house and in the farm closes. They helped each other (in between their arguments) and now, thanks to Hannah's advice, Lizzie and Nancy were dressmaking together and bringing in small amounts of money to help with household bills so that fires were lit in the cold, dark winter. But was their fear enough to keep them safe? Peggy worried every day about their futures.

The younger ones were growing pretty; Harriet and Mary attended a millinery workshop in Elland Town where they learned the rudiments of straw plaiting and hat making. Without her sisters at home Delia needed occupation; she had too much empty time and space for her own good. Peggy pursed her lips, turning her attention back to Hannah's stories of her grocery customers. Hannah rushed on scarcely pausing for breath, let alone understanding how lost and lonely Delia felt.

In February, Thomas' cousin, the Reverend Tom Mellor, dropped by while riding from Rishworth to old friends in the Steep Chapel at Salendine Nook above Longroyd Bridge, that same congregation who had sent him forth to plant a new Roadside church up the Calder valley nearly twenty years earlier. Once he had settled in the back parlour with a cup of tea and a scone baked freshly that afternoon, he sighed and told Peggy,

"My Mary's in trouble, her health is fragile and our Benjamin's little ones are too much trouble for her. I don't know what to do, how to help. I have to ask the ladies from chapel to help—they already do so much for the Lord—I don't want to lay a greater burden on them."

Peggy nodded her head as she pushed her needle through the nightwear she was making for Delia.

"This child'll be the death of me," she told her cousin. "She's grown three inches in the last year and nothing is long enough for her. The other girls are still wearing theirs so there's nothing for hand-me-downs anymore! What sort of trouble is afflicting your Mary?" Peggy stilled her needle and looked at Cousin Tom. His eyes were harsh and his mouth tightened, straight across his face. Peggy was startled at the change. What was making him so tense and unyielding?

"Times be hard," he said. "No peace came to working families at the war's end. Instead harvests failed, prices went up, jobs got scarce—unless you wanted work in the mills living in tiny cottages built with no space to grow food. Our fellowship has more than its fair share of families who know what troubles mean. But Mary's troubles are different. Unlike our flock we have a little to spare: my school teaching brings in extra, our close keeps us in food and milk. We're well enough. Our children are well enough, especially Joseph with his paper-making business,

Benjamin with his cotton work—so much machinery. The little bairns are well. But now it's as if the sun has left my Mary's sight, as if she finds no pleasure anywhere, she's a-sighing all morning, weeping into the wash tub, and when I ask her what ails her, she says 'Nothing.'—I don't know how to make it better." He sipped his tea, put it back on the table and carelessly slopped it over the cloth.

"I'm sorry. What a mess, I'm so sorry, Peggy dear."

Peggy stood up and telling him it was of no importance, she went for a cloth. She knew women who lost their energy after their children left home—some passed safely through it—others never recovered their spirits; their families languished with neglect, losing the smiles from their faces. She thought their cousin must have seen such women wilting as he shepherded his congregation over the last twenty years. Yet he had no idea how to manage his own wife's sadness. She was perplexed as to how to advise this cousin—who had given sound advice so much and so often to her and Thomas—but could not extend that advice to his own family or to himself.

Tom leant back in the wooden armchair beside the fire. His eyes closed. Peggy came back and, seeing his tiredness, crept back out, pulling the door gently behind her. Back in the kitchen, she continued crushing currants for her winter preserves. Delia came in and stuck her finger in the wine-coloured paste now piling up in the bowl beneath the sieve.

"Stop that, little wretch!" her mother told her. "There'll be nothing for our winter fare if thee takest it now. Go and sit quietly in the front parlour with Cousin Tom. He's sleeping just now so take thy sewing. When he wakes, thou canst give him whate'er he needs."

Obediently Delia crossed the hall, silently opening the parlour door and tiptoeing to her chair. She sat for some while with her sewing, and when her reverend cousin began to wake, gave him a big smile. He was annoyed with himself to discover he had drifted off but delighted that sunny Delia was there to welcome him back to wakefulness. As a babe, with her giggles of pleasure at his tickling of her belly, with the claps she gave herself at each of her early steps, she had made him laugh. Delia was a-tuned to the needs of others: when they smiled, she smiled with them; when they cried, she allowed herself to be cuddled and gave them healing. Delia read the needs of others without knowing why or how she did so. Her response was natural and measured; others left her more cheerful than they had been before their paths had crossed hers. Even in his current low mood, Cousin Tom felt her sympathy, and her delight at being alive, catching it for his own pleasure.

Restored by his tea and scone from Peggy, and lightened by his encounter with Delia, Cousin Tom collected his whip, riding coat, and gloves from the hall stand and made his way out by the back door, to the mounting steps and his tethered horse. The sleek and glossy-coated animal was contentedly eating his fill of sweet hay placed in the manger beside the steps.

"Goodbye, Peggy," he called down to her from his height on the horse. "You have eased my day. Give my love to Cousin Thomas—and keep your spirits up—you have a lovely, if lively, family of girls."

"Don't I know it, Cousin Tom," said Peggy as she stood by the door. "But they be good girls. And at least one of them is now safely in her new family—only five more to go. Fare thee well, Cousin, and take my love to Mary. Keep her in good food and she'll soon recover her want of spirits." Peggy and Delia stood by the back door as Cousin Tom rode out of the yard, his mount's hooves clattering across the cobbles.

"C'mon, my girl, to the kitchen. Let's get that preserve finished and bottled before tea tonight." So saying, Peggy chivvied Delia back inside the kitchen and the two of them worked companionably together till tea.

That night though, Peggy tossed and turned in bed, as she considered how her little Delia could learn to flourish without her big sister. Her son Joseph's absence in Rastrick with Uncle Joseph Fox had left the house quieter but not emptier. Today, Peggy thought, Hannah had left, and the four older girls were often out and busy about their chores. Delia found her home empty. She no longer had to fight for a space at the table, nor in the parlour; no longer had to rush to eat her food before anyone else did. She found enough to do around the house to keep busy—but listened for the voices that were absent. Her world was getting smaller just as the rest of the family's horizons were expanding, taking them away from the childhood world of their baby sister. Peggy worried for her.

The next day Peggy suggested that Delia who loved singing, serve in the Greetland Wesleyan chapel choir. She took her for choir practice on weekday evenings. At chapel Delia improved her own reading by helping the children in Sunday school to learn their hymns. She followed all her sisters in Greetland but Peggy went with her own sister to Upper Elland. Every Sunday, early in the day, Delia would stand with her sisters by the barn on the track outside their home and wait for their friends to come chattering along. Every week they would bring their little packages of bread, cheese and apples to eat in the churchyard while their elders sat and talked inside.

The children ran around the tombstones beginning to fill the churchyard, avoiding the small ones that reminded them of their friends taken to their paradise by the good Lord. Delia knew that the Lord was good, that He gave and that He took away but she struggled with the idea that God needed her friends more than she did. She was told they were at rest and in great happiness but still she rebuked God for taking them from the fun in this world, for taking them before they could finish their play, for stopping them running in the fields together. She thought it unfair that God should put his need for them before her need, before the village's need. She knew parents grieved hideously for their little ones, and that mothers shouted at the children left behind when they missed the ones who had gone.

Her family were often too busy to notice Delia. Father was morose, preferring his shop in Skircoat to being at home. When his bad moods took grip she kept herself safe by being quiet and keeping out of his way. Mother kept her busy, running to and fro on errands but rarely sang at her work. Lizzie, always quiet and distant, never recalled what it was like to be little. Nancy and Mary were in Elland town, learning to cut, sew and design dresses and hats, while Harriet had her nose in as many books as she could find. Delia felt lost and alone.

With fewer people to observe, with less gossip to hear once she'd finished her work Delia ran out up the hillside. There she watched the streams babbling through the moors, listened to the birds singing out their little lives from the trees of the valleys. She sat, still as a mouse, waiting for the hedgehogs to pass, for the foxes to prick their ears as they scented a rabbit or vole. She learned to read the clouds and to know when the weather would change and when she had to hasten home to escape her mother's chiding for the wet clothes clinging round her legs. Drawing her knees up under her chin she sat, sheltered by the foxgloves growing under the stone walls, looking out over her valley. She watched smoke puffing from mill chimneys; she heard the clatter of harness and of hooves on cobbles down in the valleys; she saw men in the closes swinging their scythes at the summer's hay; she listened while the boys called their sheep across the moors clicking their tongues at the dogs rounding them up; she heard the cattle lowing when it came to milking time and knew then that she had to run home to do her own milking. Delia loved her time alone on the moors above their house and barns. She might be disorientated and alone, but above their home, with the wind in her face, she found a world she loved, a place where she belonged.

One day, she was milking the cows when she heard her mother calling.

"I'm coming, Mother. Just let me finish with Daisy. She has lots of milk today and needs longer in milking," Delia shouted across the yard.

Ten minutes later she walked into the kitchen and found Hansie and her mother sitting at the kitchen table. Hansie got up and went to pour the kettle with its steam still rising as it stood on the trivet beside the fire. Her clothes seemed uncomfortable. Delia was surprised at her neat sister losing interest in her appearance. Nancy came in and stood with her hands on her hips. She stopped in the doorway and pointed at her sister.

"Well, well, Hansie. You think you can fool us, Big Sis! You're expecting, aren't you? When, when? I'm so pleased, so happy for you. Why have you hidden it from us? No wonder we haven't seen you this last three months? Too busy working, your messages said. What nonsense. Too busy being nauseous, I reckon."

Delia's face dropped. She did not want to imagine her sister with her own baby. Aghast, she turned and ran out of the kitchen, up the stairs to her room. She threw herself onto her bed and buried her head in the pillow.

Downstairs all was bustle and chatter. Nancy loudly explaining to each sister as she arrived home how she had discovered Hannah was expecting. Their mother, anxious as all older women are about the dangers of forthcoming births, kept kneading her dough and filling her pies so that all could eat. Even their father showed a smile when he was told the news but he glanced across at his wife and saw her shoulders shrug with a tiny movement of anxiety. Hannah herself sat at the table and told them how she was preparing for this new little one coming into the family.

"Joe's known for some time. We asked him to make a crib for us—a crib which can sit beside our bed. Joe's in and out of our shop all the time, him and the Fox brothers up in Rastrick, and the Thornton boys. They never stop chatting about the stone they get from the closes below old man Fox's farmhouse. Joe himself talks endlessly about wheels, machines and axles. There's a new cousin come over from Castleford, a Richard Walker. He's another joiner and they all take commissions together. Sometimes I wonder whether we're a grocer's shop or a manufacturing market. Still, once Joe started making the crib the truth was out. They've all been taking good care of me, Mother. Now I feel fine, not tired anymore, and no longer sick to the bottom of my belly from strange smells and most food."

"That's all very well Hannah. But it's time you took good care of yourself. Who's going to help when the baby comes?"

Peggy Thornton was brisk and business-like to cover her fear for her eldest daughter. She herself had always carried and borne babies easily with no mishaps but although she prided herself on her own healthy births, no woman with much knowledge of living in 1830s England could approach childbirth with anything but trepidation. If the birth itself was fine, then the fever afterwards could easily carry off the healthiest mother. Babies too were liable to death by fevers carried in the air around them. Peggy knew now that it was her time to carry those anxieties quietly within herself, to offer help with the laundry, with the feeding of the nursing mother, and to keep the new mother calm and relaxed. It was not an easy thing to do when her innermost being was shrieking out about the care and anxiety that babies gave their mothers. Still, that was no way to carry on and she abruptly introduced the subject which was worrying her most every day: Delia.

"I will send Delia over when thy time comes. She's a neat little worker and knows how to prepare food and keep the household clean. She'll be a great help, and it'll be good for her. The rest of the family know what it is to have a babe in the house. But she's our own babe and has seen no little ones come into this world. It'll be good for her."

"Mother, can't you come? Delia and I will not know what to do. You do. Can't you come?"

"That's ridiculous, Hannah. I've a workshop to run here, and besides Joshua will find me too much in thy little house. I'm no good off my hillside. Just remember how much help thou gavest when Delia herself was born. Thou were't the same age she is now—I couldna' have managed without thee. She will be perfectly capable and a great help, and it will comfort her. She misses thee."

As far as Peggy was concerned that was the business settled. Hannah was less sure. She'd seen the look of horror cross Delia's face when she learnt the truth about the baby's arrival, and she knew how long she had been upstairs, silent and hurt. She went upstairs cautiously as Delia, like her father, could explode in anger when badly hurt.

"Can I come in?" she whispered as she pushed open the door and saw her crumpled little sister crushed onto her bed. She slid across the room and sat down beside her, gently smoothing the curls from Delia's flushed and damp face.

"Are you really having a baby, Hansie? Can't you stop it? Change it so everything can go back to how it used to be?" Delia sat herself up on the bed and looked hopefully at her sister.

"No, my poppet. No. I can't change it, can't make it all go back to how it was. And, dear little Lucy Locket I don't want to. I want to have this baby—whether it's a boy or a girl—and with our family it's likely to be a girl even though Josh wants a boy to help him in the shop. We go in for girls, we Mellors. Look at us. Six of us girls and only one boy for Papa! Josh and I both want this baby. I'm strong and healthy and I feel it kicking hard inside me and know it's a strong little 'un. Look put your hand on my belly—it's kicking now—you can feel it."

Hannah guided Delia's hand over her belly to where her restless infant was arching its back and kicking its little heel against its mother's stomach.

Delia felt the little push and shove and gasped with delight.

"Is that the baby? Is that what it does? Is it alright? Will it do it again?"

"Indeed, Delia. I want it to. The more it kicks the stronger I know it to be, though I'd prefer it to kick in the daytime rather than when I've just sat down to have a rest in the evening." Hannah grinned at her little sister.

"I used to feel you kicking against Mother's stomach when you were a tiny one inside her belly. Sometimes you would kick me as I snuggled up close to her as though you wanted me out of your way!"

"Did I? What did I look like when I came out?"

"To tell the truth, your face was a bit scrumpled when I first saw you. That nurse who helped Mother had wrapped you up so tight we could barely see your little face—and she was so cross that Mother had let us all in her room to see you. And then you started rooting for food and the nurse quickly shooed us out so Mother could feed quietly. But Mother knew what she was doing and she sent Nurse off very soon. She wanted us to see you and to take turns in holding you—and that, Nurse would never allow. She was bossy and thought only of Mother and the baby; she just thought of us as nuisances!" Hannah laughed as she saw in her mind's eye, the look of horror on Nurse's face when she had entered the room with a bawling Momo in her arms.

"I was bringing up some water and towels when Momo climbed the stairs calling for Mother. She was two and only just safe on the stairs. A few steps up she decided to sit down—disaster—she sat and bang, she fell backwards and rolled down the stairs. There was no damage, so I picked her up and took her to Mother. Nurse was horrified and wanted to send us away but Mother would have none of it. We all came in and peeped at you in the cradle. I persuaded Momo to come downstairs to eat the cookie I had made for her, and we left Mother and you in peace!"

As Hannah was talking, Delia saw her face light up, saw her eyes crinkle at the corners and heard the laugh in her voice as she remembered coaxing the recalcitrant Momo out of their mother's room. She felt the love and affection that had been given to her as a tiny unsuspecting babe; she began to feel that same love for the insistent little foot pushing under her hand.

"Can I come and help you Hansie? Can I come and help you like you helped Mother when I was born?"

Hannah was relieved that her little sister was relaxing, that she was letting go her fear and anxiety and feelings of rejection. She would have felt safer with her mother's attendance but she remembered her own pride in helping at Delia's birth and was glad that she could give that pride back to Delia herself.

"It will be lovely to have you helping, little Sis. There's just the right space for you in our tiny little box room. And when the time comes I'll get a Nurse as Mother did and you can keep everything else in apple-pie order."

"Hansie, that's so exciting. Let's go and tell Mother that I'll be helping."

Together they went back downstairs, back to the family, Delia happy that she had a role and a place with her sister, Hannah contented that she could comfort her anxious little sister and give her a place in life.

Hannah was as good as her word. Not only did Delia help with her first baby, Elizabeth, who arrived in October 1832. Two years later Hannah called for help with the next baby, their only son, Joseph. Delia was the one who cared for children while her sisters learnt trades. Their father continued working, without enthusiasm, with old Job Turner in the shop in Skircoat while their mother kept her little wool business ticking along in Greetland. Harvests failed. Food prices rose. Discontent was rising in the valleys of the West Riding.

In Rastrick, Joe Mellor was expanding his horizons. With Uncle Joseph Fox he was selling York stone to the merchants paving the growing streets of London, Bath, Bristol and York. At the same time, he was building coaches and farm machines. He worked with a cousin of Joshua Fisher's, Richard Walker, the carpenter from Castleford whom he'd met on the canal one day as they were unloading goods for his grocer brother-in-law. The young men often met with each other discussing business in the Brighouse local, just as Thomas did with the older wool men of Halifax. The young men laughed together and respected each other's work.

At the Fox farmhouse Joe looked sideways at Mary, Uncle Joe Fox's striking daughter with her high cheek bones and flashing eyes. At new year 1835, as Nancy and Lizzie had predicted, the morning of Thomas Mellor's arrest nine years earlier, Joe Mellor asked Uncle Joseph Fox whether he could address his daughter, Mary.

"Young man, I thought you'd never ask. It's bin moonshine and roses with my girl for months now—and I've bin watching you—not above blushing yourself when she comes in the room. You're a good lad now, you're making your business and are good with the customers even if you don't agree with them all the time—you need to bide your tongue sometimes for your own good. But you and your cousins are working well together and if business in this country goes on well so should you. Mind you, that's a big if. Business goes very shakily these days, what with all the argey bargle about Reform in parliament and that business of religious conformity. People worry about the slaves abroad; they should be looking at the slaves in the mills at home here."

Joseph Fox halted. He worried about the world, he worried about his family but he never worried about his business. He had his land, he had his stone and he had his timber. He reckoned people would always need housing and machines and he stood ready to keep them supplied.

It was other businesses which needed to consider the 'hard times'.

This nephew of his, who had been working with him since he was a boy, would continue making good work for himself. He would take care of his girl and make a good life for her. Joseph Fox worried more about the unfairness within the country. He disliked the mills down in the valley. He saw people becoming pale and bent as they worked long hours, living in long terraces of tiny houses with no land to grow vegetables or keep animals. Children, taken to the mill to earn dangerous extra pennies gathering fluff from under the machines, had nowhere to run. His nephew Joe and daughter Mary, he hoped, would make a better life. They would be respected in Rastrick and Brighouse—his name would see to that—and they would find new ways if the old turned sour.

Joseph Fox and his wife, Hannah, Peggy's sister, wanted their daughter married in style. Joe's parents, Thomas and Peggy, had married in Halifax back before the glorious battle of Trafalgar, and wanted Joe and Mary to be married in the same wide stone church. There weren't many plans to be laid: Joe wanted his sisters there and the Foxes themselves had many family around Rastrick. They were to marry by licence thereby avoiding the calling of the banns three times in the weeks before the wedding. The young men who worked together with Joe and his uncle took the day off work. On 4th April 1835 in St. John's, the parish church for Halifax, the Rev'd Coulthurst married Joe Mellor and Mary Fox; afterwards there was a big party at the Inn down the hill in Skircoat.

The wedding was a happy event. The families feasted and danced for many an hour. Sharp-eyed Peggy Mellor watched her girls as they danced. With five more to marry safely she worried that Nancy was becoming too familiar with Joshua Turner, son of old man Job, Thomas' sole companion in his Skircoat workshop. Job was loyal, there could be nothing said against him, but he was rough and his appearance made him look bucolic and slow. He had no aspirations to better himself and his attendance at chapel was irregular. Thomas might inveigh against the hypocrisy of chapel folk, but the Thornton side of the family were faithful and observant chapel people. Among their own children, Hannah was building a busy life at the Salem New Methodist chapel. She and Joshua Fisher had donated to build the new chapel in Halifax and, until her own little ones kept her busy, had been a Sunday school worker. Peggy was quiet about chapel when Thomas spoke out against the hypocrites but in her heart of hearts, she was anxious that her girls should marry good chapel folk. And Joshua Turner could not be called that.

While she was watching she noticed Nancy had put on weight. She was looking tired and had no enthusiasm for dancing. Peggy, alert to any sign of trouble in her family, began to watch more closely and when Nancy went outside for a breath of air, she followed close behind. Nancy was flustered. She motioned her hand to her mother to say she did not need help. Peggy was not to be put off.

"Young lady, tell me thou art not expecting," she demanded in a low whisper when they were out of earshot of Halifax gossips.

"Mother, how could you think that?"

"I'm not blind, my girl, nor stupid. I've seen many women in my time and most start like thee: lacking energy, picky over their food, and then thickening at the waist. Don't try to bamboozle me, girl. Just tell me when and we'll work out what to do."

"October." Nancy kept her eyes on the ground and her voice low. She'd been dreading this conversation with her mother. Peggy's brisk-ness reasserted itself. When her family saw trouble, she saw a way to help them, a way to get through. She was quick and abrupt with this decision.

"At least we know his family. 'Tis Joshua Turner, isn't it?" Nancy nodded her head miserably.

"Well, Job won't want a fuss either so here's what we'll do: thee and Joshua had better go off to Elland Church, get thy banns called and be married quietly within three weeks. Thee canst stay in Sowerby to have the babe. I'll send Delia to help, she's become very useful at these times. People will wag their tongues. That can't be helped but 'twill be yesterday's story and thou wilt be respectable again once they know 'tis legal. I'll tell Papa. Now get back inside and no word of this to Joe and Mary or anyone else. I don't want to spoil anyone's day."

"I am so sorry, Mother. We never thought it would come to this."

"That's the trouble with being young—no thinking—not about this, nor about much else besides. Awwh, get along with thee, Nance. Don't cry. It'll be a bonny babe and Joshua will make a good husband, even if he never sets the Thames on fire. His family are loyal—we know that for sure—and thee hast nimble fingers so can make money with thy dressmaking skills. Thee be clever. Look how many of the Halifax fine ladies come with commissions for special gowns. Once we're through this awkward stage it'll be lovely to have another infant in the family. Go along now, go back inside and dance. And keep quiet to thy sisters."

Peggy led the way back inside. Nancy followed wondering how she and Joshua would pass these next few months in Sowerby. Three

weeks later they were indeed married with sister Harriet as a witness. Delia went to see them and reported that Nancy was doing well. Peggy too went over to see her daughter and when her time came Delia was with them. Later everyone came to see the newly born Margaret Turner. Even Thomas was impressed by the new one's name, telling Nancy that if she had borne a babe as strong as her mother after whom she was named, he was content.

88. The east end of St. Mary's Elland where Nancy and Joshua Turner were married in April 1835 and where Thomas Mellor registered the birth of his three youngest daughters. (Author 2019)

In the meanwhile, Lizzie took marriage into her own hands. Richard Fisher Walker, the carpenter cousin from Castleford, had joined forces with the Foxes, the Mellors and Thorntons of Rastrick. The young men designed and built together in the Fox workshop in Rastrick and came down to see the young married Fishers in Brighouse. There was good stone quarrying, and more than enough work with carriages, wheels, farm machinery to fill their young heads with ambitious dreams of wealth and good standing. Quiet Lizzie used to stop by Uncle Fox's shop to watch the work, and more particularly Richard Walker. Theirs was an affair conducted away from Peggy's anxious eyes, and very discretely in front of her sisters who were always on the lookout for tales to tell at home. No news travelled back to Peggy. In November 1835 she and Richard married, on their own, in Castleford church.

The young men, bound by chapel loyalties, family ties, their own strength and good natures, collaborated well. Despite their dreams though, society kept them in their place. As Non-Conformists they had lower standing. Even in independent Yorkshire, life was mostly controlled by the landed gentry and the Anglican church. Rents rose and leases terminated at the will of the landed; if landlords heard arguments about parliamentary representation or demands to reduce rents they became hostile. In chapel and on the hills, the young men listened to lectures about freedom of slaves; they rallied to self-education initiatives; they debated the freedom of Man; they discussed the issues of taxation without representation raised by the Americans; they heard stories from a new land on the other side of the world. They heard tales from Van Diemen's land from prisoners transported to a new life, some of whom were Mellors who had fallen foul of the authorities for being too outspoken or for poaching to fill their families' bellies.

Meanwhile, back in Greetland Peggy had her own preoccupations. Hannah, Joe, Nancy and then in November Lizzie, she counted four of her children, to be settled. Only three, Harriet, Mary and Delia, to be married. But Peggy worried: where were the young men of good family to marry and keep a good home for their wives and children. Better than most, Peggy knew how important the right choice was. Young

Delia and Mary, careless of their mother's concern about their futures, loved social events following this year of weddings and reckoned that one day they too would be wed—just not yet.

As suitors, Peggy dismissed Thomas' old friends and business associates—they were woolmen. Peggy could see that wool needed capital, the sort of capital the Mellors lacked. Without capital, men could not buy new machinery, construct new mills or even invest in bales of wool being shipped into the ports of Liverpool. Thomas today spent more time on his closes and less in his workshops—more a farmer than a wool manufacturer, thought Peggy. In her Greetland barns she too was doing less; she worried about their old age. The old world was changing.

Delia danced along the byways and highways of the Calder Valley. She'd been frightened of the 'rough men' who'd broken her father, but she had grown up safe from the poorhouse, that terror for families struggling to make ends meet. Grandfather Thornton, brother Joe and her mother worked on throughout the years of her father's exile. Their work had kept her safe. She knew she had to help somehow but thought her older sisters would continue to produce babies and that she would continue to help with them. Not for her going out to learn a trade. She helped at home and visited family to help out. In October 1835 she went to Nancy to help with baby Margaret but Peggy had decided family babies were not enough to keep Delia occupied at home. It was time she learnt more.

PART III—Chapter 26

Rishworth Roadside Chapel
1835-1837

89. Rishworth Mill from Roadside Chapel (Author 2019)

In Rishworth, age brought no let up for Cousin Tom; his chapel membership increased. He rode his big roan mare round Stainland, Rastrick and Skircoat, and to his friends in Salendine Nook's Steep Chapel, as he always had. He thundered sermons from the pulpit to his devoted members at the Roadside chapel. He urged the elect to show the love of God in their lives, to follow the path laid out by their Lord, Jesus Christ. God was gracious and merciful. Man was in sin and strayed from the truth and light every day. His Sunday school flourished—bairns came without paying the small amount he said he charged but others from the congregation made sure the Sunday school was regularly financed. His kinsman, Benjamin Mellor from the Stainland mills, was a good friend to all Sunday school mission, and his own son, Joseph, took time from his paper manufacturing business to help in the school every Lord's Day. His wife, Mary, continued frail; she sighed with fatigue at the end of every day.

In neat copperplate handwriting Reverend Tom kept meticulous records, required by law: records of babes being born, of weddings being made and of the deaths of those buried in their plots beside the chapel. 1835 burial records had increased with infants dying in greater numbers than the old. Sorrow hung heavy in the air when his gathered people brought to him their little ones in their tiny coffins. Last year he had buried three infants and three young children, all called to rest before their time. Harvests were failing again, prices rising. Food was dear, cholera spreading.

His sons: neither Benjamin, driving hard with his cotton-spinning business, nor Joseph with his printing had time for the Lord's daily work in the community. His wife, Mary, was worn down by the stream of people coursing through their home. The minister had seen families with little time for care, falling apart and falling away from the Lord's path. He did not want this to happen in his home. His people might be the 'Elect', called by the Lord, coming in glory at the day of Judgement, but in the meanwhile on this dark earth, God needed humans to help in guiding them through challenges. Minister Tom needed help. He remembered his cousin Peggy's deft way of handling the troubles heaped on her shoulders and he recalled the laughing eyes of her youngest daughter. Now was the time, he decided, to ask for help from that quarter.

In the November 1835, he put pen to paper to Cousin Thomas. He begged his pardon for intruding in his family affairs, which he knew were difficult with so many daughters to be married off, but he wondered whether his youngest girl, Delia, would find it amenable to her health and enjoyment to lodge with him and his wife while helping them with their grandchildren. He dropped sealing wax across the back of the envelope and then took it down to the post mistress in Ripponden for delivery in Skircoat the next morning. Thomas received the idea well; not so his daughter, Delia.

Delia was enjoying stepping out in Brighouse with her new sister-in-law, Mary Fox Mellor. Mary knew everybody. Her father's business was extensive and she had the pleasing knack of enjoying the company of all. Tilting her head encouragingly on one side as she listened, her companions responded warmly by telling her everything that was going on. Delia loved accompanying her on walks through Brighouse. Her social network expanded rapidly while Hansie and her husband gathered many new customers from Mary's wide standing. Business in the quiet town was a struggle but the young Mellors and Fishers were doing their best to take every advantage.

Since Delia's introduction to maternity-care in 1832 she had helped with two more Mellor babies, Joseph Fisher and Margaret Turner, and she was waiting her next call to help Nancy this autumn. Delia knew Nancy's Margaret had come sooner than she had business to be doing—Father was displeased with the indecent way the young couple had behaved—unlike Joe and Mary who waited until their wedding had passed. Delia's enthusiasm for visiting Halifax, which she did while awaiting the next babe, continued unabated.

Her mother was less pleased, however. So when Cousin Tom wrote his letter it met a kind reception.

Delia was to go to the manse at Rishworth. Remote, near the high moors and busy. There Delia feared a prim approach to life. At fifteen, she wanted to spread her wings. Helping out in a quiet Baptist manse was not exciting. But she was a dutiful daughter; she obeyed her parents to lessen their financial burden and, like her sisters, knew she must find a husband.

Previously Peggy had already told her youngest daughter it was time to learn a trade. Delia, reluctantly hearing the tone in her mother's voice, realised it was impossible to argue. She thought she would be apprenticed to the local milliner in Elland. Then her father brought home Cousin Tom's letter and Peggy's plans changed.

"I don't like the way Cousin Tom has couched this. I don't need his help or his condescension. He may have a path to glory in the after life, but us lesser mortals have to work to find glory in the here and now, not in the claptrap they spout on the Lord's Day." Thomas could not resist a dig at his clerical cousin, even while supporting his proposal.

"Thomas, he's not being condescending. He needs help for his own family for the next year, and it might help us as well. Delia would benefit from his guidance. Cousin Mary is a good housekeeper for all she has lost her energy in recent years, and it's a good congregation he keeps at Roadside Baptist Chapel. There's plenty of family there and most are doing well, though not all as flashy as Benjamin at Stainland Mill."

"He's less flashy since the fire burnt him out in 1832. I hear he's trying to recuperate some of his losses by setting up a new insurance operation. That'll do him no good. Fires happen and fires destroy, whatever we do," Thomas grumbled; he was touchy on the subject of successful relatives.

"Thomas, enough of that. Benjamin is working and finding a way to get himself and all his workers back into business and, by what I hear, rather successfully. I reckon Minister Tom might help our Delia with her books."

Peggy knew that, despite his troubles, her husband wanted his children educated and if he saw a way of educating them without paying out money, he would think it a good thing. But, at these words, Delia's heart sank. Her father, she knew, thought she was spoiled and out of hand. He told her that the Reverend Tom would lead her into stricter ways and give her some of the learning she had missed through the debt crisis of ten years earlier. Thomas accepted the idea of his baby leaving home. When their father and mother agreed on a plan, the girls had to accept it. This plan was no exception.

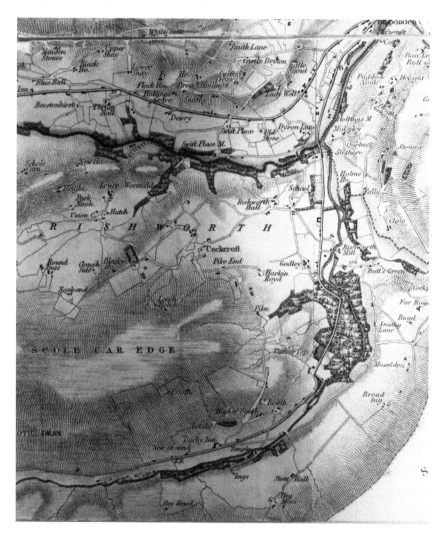

90. 1834/5 Map of Ryburn Valley. Showing Rishworth Moor above Rishworth Hall—the Roadside Chapel, south of Rishworth School, north of Godley hamlet, and opposite Rishworth Mill, lying beside the Oldham Road and above the River Ryburn flowing beneath Scole Car Edge." (Calderdale Archives, WYAS)

Minister Tom was fit and energetic; his wife Mary less so. Their children were producing children of their own, and the Roadside Chapel membership was swelling with cotton twisters and cotton spinners newly recruited from Rishworth Mill. Tom was a kind and learned man, and diligent in serving his congregation; Mary a capable housewife used to feeding many mouths. Both parents thought Delia would learn. Minister Tom's invitation was accepted.

So on a raw November day in 1835, immediately after Lizzie and Richard's wedding in Castleford, Delia found herself well wrapped in coat and shawl, a blanket across her knees, perched on her trunk in the back of John Whiteley's cart. They crossed the moors beyond Stainland, down to Billy Mellor's bridge at Ripponden, and along the Ryburn valley to the Roadside Baptist Chapel. She was leaving home.

It was only six miles but with a heavy bag, she needed a carrier. The cart pulled up at the end of the track and Delia climbed in. Peggy waved her hand vigorously and forced a bright, fixed smile across her face. She knew it was good for Delia to find the world for herself. It was good to get more learning and who knew, with the educated congregation she might find herself a good husband, although she was young to be settling down. Sensible though she was, Peggy hated her young going off on their adventures. She hid her fears behind a brisk manner and organised their belongings into bags, overriding any objections. Once they had gone, she turned back into the house and began a frenzy of cleaning and brushing and shaking of curtains and covers. After that she shifted into the quieter world of her now emptier house without ever betraying how lonely she felt.

Once Delia accepted this stay with Minister Tom of the Particular Baptists she turned her mind to the new life with zeal. Like both her grandmothers she loved the moors and enjoyed escaping into the wild hills. She enjoyed the animals she tended and even more, her play with young children. She wondered whether she might meet a good-looking young man, like Hannah had done at the chapel in Halifax. She knew she had to listen with care to Cousin Thomas—church people were particular about what they believed. Hoping her days would not be heavy with long prayers and daily Bible readings Delia expected people to like her and enjoy her company; she had no reason to think this company would be any different. Despite her frozen nose and fingers, she sat with a smile on her face, in the bottom of the rocking cart.

An hour later she was dropped outside the well-built little chapel with its school buildings on one side and the manse on the other. Cousin Mary heard the cart draw up and moved slowly through from her kitchen. Delia stood uncertainly in the road beside the pretty iron gate while her trunk was unloaded.

Cousin Mary called to her from the door. "Pet, how lovely it be to welcome thee. The Lord brings thee on this windblown day and we welcome thee in His name. Come, Pet, let me see thee better, come closer."

Mary stood, more bent than Delia had remembered, and peering as do short-sighted people. She was motionless but smiling. Delia no longer hesitated in walking up the short path to the manse door.

"May the Lord bless you, Cousin Mary. I am glad to stand still without being jostled and jolted in that lumbering cart. But John, the carter, is a kind soul and he brings my trunk up now."

91. Milestone on Oldham Road near Roadside Chapel, Rishworth (Author 2019)

"Bless thee, John. 'Tis good to see thee. Is thy poor mother any better?"

With that invitation to talk, John dumped the trunk at the door and pulled out his kerchief to mop his forehead. He gave Mary Mellor, the well-respected minister's wife, a full account of all the ailments his mother was suffering: her pains, her hands crippled with arthritis, her tight breathing, wheezing chest, her uncertain temper. Mary listened patiently knowing how unkind his mother could be in her pain and how John suffered from her blistering tongue when he touched her in the wrong way. Delia was bemused. She shifted from foot to foot wondering when she could move inside the house and when her trunk would reach its final destination. Eventually Mary turned to the trunk stuck in the middle of the path and said,

"Goodness gracious, my oh my, all this talk won't move this trunk one little jot. And I daresay, Delia, and thee, John, could do with a little drink, wouldn't thee now? If thou couldst take trunk upstairs to the back room John and then come and join us in kitchen. I take it tha'd like a little cup of tea with us?"

92. Iron gate into Roadside Chapel churchyard (Author 2019)

"No, Ma'am, no, but thank 'ee, thank 'ee. I must be getting on. I've another load to take up to farmer Gledhill, up top and day's getting no longer while I chat here!"

Cousin Mary turned and shuffled through the passage to the back of the house. Following her, Delia saw through the open kitchen door, three children poking their fingers under the cloth covering the dough rising in its bowl on the dresser.

"Amos Mellor, I see thee. I see thee leading the bairns astray. That dough's for rising not for poking. We need bread tomorrow. Leave it be, all of you."

Mary sounded fierce. Delia was unsurprised that all three children dropped their fingers and stood shamefaced beside the dresser with hands tucked inside their clothes. The taller boy seemed to be near her in age while the other two were only five or six in years.

"Now come and meet thy cousin Delia who is here to help with some of the work children make for us all. Delia, this great lump here is Amos, our first grandson, Joseph's first born. This boy here is our Tommie's boy, Joe and the little 'un is Sarah, his sister—Amos is their star—where he leads they go. Ben's baby, Tommie Babe, is down the road with his mother just now! But Amos is more often away these days, he's learning to be a printer from his father, Joseph. But where's my manners? Delia, sit thee in that chair while I make a pot of tea. Even out here near the moors, we have modern refinements: I bought this pot on a visit last month to thy giddy Halifax town – 'tis beautiful, an't it—and just the thing to welcome thee into our household."

Delia, more than a little confused by all these introductions and names, sat down smiling shyly at Sarah. Amos and Joe ran out the back door. Sarah sidled towards Delia's chair and looked her up and down.

"Be 'ee her that's staying here, now there's so many childer?"

"I believe I am," said Delia, unused to such a direct question from a five-year old and even more unused to the frank stare with which she was being appraised.

"Sarah, cease your questions. Take Delia up to her room while I make tea. She's sleeping in the small box room where you children sleep if you're here overnight."

"Where'll we sleep then, Grandma? We need sleep, just like this Delia."

"Husssht, Sarah. Tha'll sleep where the Good Lord gives you a pillow. Remember our Lord Jesus told us not to worry about sleep nor food; the birds of the air are given their shelter and so are we—so haste thee upstairs and help thy cousin with her things."

"She's not my cousin. Amos is my cousin—not her."

"Sarah, thou hast more cousins than thou knowest. Mellors are scattered all over the Colne and Calder, and most of them are relatives. So haste thee, be kind and show Delia her room and if thee be not quick then mebbe the scones will all be gone when thou comest back down."

With this she gave the sulky child a little push and nodded her head at Delia to go with her. Delia stepped up the stairs behind Sarah, who opened a door off the landing and then turned and fled back outside to find Amos and Joe. Delia found herself looking into a small room with a window on the wall in front of her. Dust lay on the windowsill, and on the bare, creaking floorboards, a small rag rug. Under the window was a stone-topped stand with a wide bowl and jug of water; beside the stand stood a wooden chair, a clothes horse and, along the side wall, a narrow iron bedstead with a patchwork coverlet spread over the lumpy mattress. Behind the door was a small chest for her clothes. For the first time in her life Delia would be sleeping in a room on her own—it gave her a thrill of excitement. The trunk lay bound on the floor at her feet. She set about putting her things in their place. For the next quarter of an hour she was content. Then her cousin called and she had to face her new family. She went downstairs with some fear.

While she was attending to her trunk Minister Tom, still in his riding boots, came into the kitchen. It was his habit to read his Bible and craft his sermons most mornings and after noon, to ride down the valley to Ripponden. He called in at cottages to find out how his flock were doing. The township was growing and his record of births gave him great joy. He watched the bellies of the young women get bigger and welcomed them and their babes into the chapel. But this year, deaths were increasing—many struggled with hunger—and sickness stalked the land. Minister Tom was troubled.

Those Non-Conformists who were better off, manufacturers like Thomas' kinsmen, Benjamin Mellor of Stainland, and Samuel Mellor of Soyland, were often friends to Sunday schools, and friends to ministers of small chapels in outlying places. The Reverend Tom and his wife Mary had a small house and a small but steady income from his church people, and their manufacturing friends. In addition he received some income from his teaching work. The desire for education among the dalesmen was spreading. The word of the Lord was heard over the moorland. Minister Tom and his good wife Mary were well and widely respected and comfortable, but not luxurious, in their manse beside the chapel.

"So young Delia has arrived has she Mother? I will be pleased to see her. She has such smiling eyes as I remember."

"Tush Man, she's unpacking her trunk. She looked glad enough for the cold journey to end, but our little Sarah wasn't over-welcoming and I think we're going to have to improve her manners to her new cousin. Amos and Joe scarpered back outside pretty quick too so take care of Delia, she'll be anxious about being away from her family for the first time."

"That may be so, my dearest. The good Lord will take care of Delia and show her the way into all our hearts. Are we dining soon? Is she dining with us?"

"Aye, Tom we are. And will thee be saying Grace over our meal as ever, but not too long, my dear. We don't want to fidget the children."

"Oh ye of little faith, wife. The good Lord will lead the children where He will and there's nowt we can do to gainsay him. But yes Mother, I will watch my length just this time!"

Turning back to her fire Mary heaved a sigh of relief. Her husband was full of the love of the Lord, and when the children could least bear it, he seemed called to wax at length about the gifts the good Lord showered on them and their family. She had to keep them quiet, stop them smirking through their fingers at each other as they pretended to be deep in prayer and then prevent arguments over who should be first to feed once the Grace had been completed.

Amos brought in both Joe and Sarah; all three sidled into their places at the farmhouse table. Only Delia's place stayed empty.

"Shall I go and call her?" said Amos

"If tha' wouldst, dear."

Two minutes later Delia came in, flushing red with embarrassment that they had had to wait. Minister Tom wasted no time in asking for the Lord's gracious mercy on this, His food, laid out for His chosen people. He included Delia and her family in his blessing and so, even before she sat down, she felt welcomed. Within moments of sitting down, Tom was asking about the folk back in Greetland. Delia chattered happily about them and shared little jokes with the minister about the long nights he and her father had spent sat outside on their bench underneath the girls' window, drinking small beer in the quiet of the evening. Amos and the children sat silent, resenting the attention she was being paid.

As the family rose from their meal a timid knock was heard at the door. A man stood twisting his cap in his hands, shifting from foot to foot.

"Reverend Minister, could I be having a word with thee?"

"Ye be welcome, my good man. Dost thou have news of thy good woman, William?"

"Aye I do, I do."

"Come to my study then"

With a quick rush, Mary intervened before both men left the room. "But first William, how is Elizabeth? Is the babe well?"

"Oh aye, Ma'am. Both Elizabeth and her babe are well. She has the lungs of a two year old with the roar of her cry. And we've named her Hannah after the story of Samuel's mother who gave up her son to the service of the Lord in the temple of the Lord. We've waited for this little 'un and the Lord has given us blessing."

"Well, young William, it seems that I had better bring my ink and quill to fill in the record and then we can fix a day and time for you to bring the babe to chapel for dedication. Shall we suggest next week, the 5th of December 1835? I'm sure my cousin Delia here will be delighted to help you with the babe and leading her in."

Delia nodded her head enthusiastically. She knew how precious it was when all the world gave thanks for a child's safe delivery. She had already done this with Hannah's and Nancy's little ones. She was hoping for more thanksgivings.

This was life at the Manse beside its Roadside Chapel. Lengthy grace over the meals, calm and lengthy household prayers in the morning, and shorter, more reflective prayers in the evening. Always the Bible was used: always the stories and examples pulled from the Old or New Testaments. Each prayer time, Minister Tom would take down the big family Bible from its shelf above the chest. He would turn over the thin, fine leaves with their gold edges. He would take up the reading from the ribbon he had left tucked within the crinkled pages from the previous prayers and he would read slowly and melodiously the old, old stories. Delia was entranced. Of course she knew many of the stories, but she had never heard them read like home stories. She'd never heard them read as though she knew all the people within them. No one had explained why this king or that king was avoiding the will of God. Minister Tom did all this. He made the stories come alive and he used them to illustrate how the world around them was making the same errors and still transgressing the ways of the Lord.

Amos, Sarah and Joe grudgingly accepted Delia's presence at their grandparents' home when they came over. Delia taught Sarah how to decorate a bonnet for Easter and Sarah became more friendly. Five-year-old Ben often came to bake with his big cousins and the children had fun dipping their fingers into the cake mix before the bowl was washed away.

One morning Cousin Tom called her and asked her to join him in his study.

"I can see you are interested in the stories we tell from the Holy Book, my dear. I would love for you to help the little ones in the Sunday school. Do you think you could look after them in the gallery until it is time to take them outside so they can run and play? Later you might be able to help the teachers in the school, it is so rewarding to see a child grasp the way to do something, and to see, in their eyes, the light when they understand a story."

Shyly but with pleasure, Delia nodded. "I don't know much but I can look after them in the gallery if that is helpful. But you should have my sister Hansie here. She's our Sunday school teacher; I'm just a learner."

"We're all learners, Delia. We must stay learning throughout life, discerning the Lord's way for each one of us." Minister Tom was impressed by Delia's humility and thought she would, in time, become a very good teacher. He did not want to overwhelm her hence this gentle start with play supervision.

At the manse Delia looked forward to prayers and, as she began to know the people for whom the minister prayed, she welcomed the chance to name the troubles that beset them, and to reflect on how she could help others.

When Minister Tom asked her to teach the little ones, Delia was taken aback. She did not see herself as a teacher. She was the baby who had to be taught. It was true that she enjoyed being with the children. She loved running with them, hiding behind trees so they laughed, jumping high over imaginary rocks—and then falling down ditches— and ducking as the children pelted her with leaves. She had a knack of calming little ones who had fallen and bruised their knees or scratched their elbows on the brambles besides the road. But a teacher…

Cousin Tom continued kindly.

"I can see you have not thought this possible. But you are so kindly with the little ones, you laugh and smile with them, you take seriously what they tell you. If you treat children well, then you can teach them and show them a path through the challenges we all face. Go off to Cousin Mary now and think it over—don't rush. Remember I will give you all the help I can. I can go over the readings for the lessons, I can explain the difficult words—and you can pass it all on."

So it was that once a week, Delia went into Cousin Tom's study and sat herself beside him at his great desk so she could teach others at Sunday School. He explained the meanings behind the parables, he explained the links between the Old Testament and the New. He unravelled some of the contradictions and he teased out the meaning for living today. He talked too about helping with reading and writing and numbers. It was important, he said, to get children to write with meaning and clarity. Nowadays, he said, it was not enough to make your mark in front of a witness. It was crucial to read so you could understand what was happening in the greater world. He expected her to improve her own reading and writing, and helped her to construct letters to her father back home. Delia, in learning to teach others, learned herself, as her father had hoped.

The times Delia loved best were when she led the children out of the gallery, down the small spiral stairs at the back of the chapel and out into the graveyard surrounding the buildings. Her favourite child, Alan Howe from Sowerby Bridge, held her hand tightly as he stepped down the twisting stairs. In the gallery he sat close to her, whispering to ask what was happening down below. Outside, as she sat on a tomb-stone, he would bring her small nuts and interesting stones that he found beside the wall running around the grassy graveyard. Together they scratched pictures in the open earth beside the chapel building and progressed towards mapping out a little settlement. Alan cupped his hands in a little beck running beside the road and dammed up a tiny lake beside their settlement. If a bigger child rushed up Alan shrank back towards Delia and climbed onto her lap for comfort. When Delia stood to play 'In and Out the dusty bluebells' Alan stood with her. At the beginning he shrank from joining with the older children but with Delia holding his hand, he learnt to join in enthusiastically. When they sang nursery rhymes, he loved shrieking as they moved faster and faster. At the end he would collapse in laughing exhaustion on the grass. He rushed to Delia as soon as he saw her, demanding a big cuddle. Delia felt warm, proud and excited as she affectionately swept him in a big hug at the start of every service and felt his eager little body in her arms.

And then one Sunday in February 1836, there was no Alan. He was ill, someone whispered. The next Sunday he was no more. He had died within three days. Vivid, giggling, loving Alan was gone, gone in a little box under the earth that they had scratched and played in. Delia was distraught. But for all the other children she had to keep herself calm, to smile and play, to dance and sing. All the while her arms ached to hold the wriggling child she had come to love.

A baby was born once or twice a month; everyone rejoiced. The other visits were much harder to bear: the visits when faces were strained, when tears flowed and it was very, very hard to bless the Lord. All that could be said, often in stony, unflinching stoicism, was that the Lord gives and the Lord takes away. During her year at the manse Delia saw twenty-three burials.

Minister Tom and his loving wife Mary found it hard to bear the deaths of so many. Five of the elderly were called to the Lord. That was bearable but when eight infants were called to rest, people wept silently. But more heartrending still were the children and young adults whose lives had shown so much promise and yet who could not stand the pressure of the cholera around them: seven young people—some Delia knew—Hannah Berry from Greetland, Hannah Riley four years older than herself from Stones mill. Nine-month-old Abraham in October, following a father who'd died in July, leaving a bewildered and desperate widow. How could one family bear so much loss, one woman such pain?

And then there was Alan; nearly four and twisted round her heart. He had climbed on her lap to hear her stories, run away from her when she wanted him to line up to go back into chapel. He had brought her snails when she was sitting with the children outside, sharing her lunch while the elders debated inside. One Sunday he was whispering in her ear and pulling her skirts, the next he was gone. Cholera did its work quickly and painfully, and it went for the strong as well as the weak. Delia was angry with God, and with the world for allowing such a dreadful disease to flourish. At night she woke thumping her pillow, tears of rage coursing down her cheeks.

Minister Tom could see Delia's distress and used the morning prayers to soothe her loss and loneliness. He listened to her angry shouts against God's will. She could not see the sense in God's good world when Alan's father came shambling to the Minister's manse. She raged, vowing never to have children, so none could be taken from her. She prayed for Alan's mother and father. She prayed for his friends. She prayed for herself and over the months slowly and gradually she found something she might call peace. Cousin Mary, who had mourned many a child, told her this fierce pain would pass, that children taken thus were spared the harshness of life. But still Delia wept. She wept by herself under the coverlet of her bed at night as she thought the minister would think she did not trust God to take care of his chosen people if he saw her weeping.

Her letters told that her own family were safe, that in Greetland the cholera was not tearing the hearts out of people—although rife in Halifax. Eighteen months passed with no visits allowed for fear of transferring the pestilence. Cases declined. At last she was allowed home to help her beloved sister, Hannah.

93. Last look back at Ryburn Vale (Author's 2019)

She left Rishworth on a warm August day in 1837 with sadness, grateful for the lessons she had learned from Cousin Tom about a good religious life, a satisfying cycle of prayer and Bible Study—but with great joy that she could again be part of her own family, her own sisterhood. Since her departure Hannah, Lizzie, Nancy and Joe's Mary had all had a baby. Hannah's third baby was a second girl, called Sarah. Back home, when Delia saw this noisy, demanding baby, a hole was filled in her heart. As she lay the baby back in her crib with the child smiling up at her, she promised that she would do all she could to keep her alive. Delia was home and expecting life to go on as before. Little did she know what a storm was brewing.

PART III—Chapter 27

Family Strife
Winter 1837-1838

94. Preparing a festive meal in a weaver's home around 1850
Colne Valley Museum, Golcar, West Riding, Yorkshire (Author 2019)

Carter John Whiteley took up Delia's roped trunk in August 1837—as he had taken it up in November 1835. The cholera was easing; it was safe to travel without taking the dreaded disease home. As she jolted along the road, over the little packhorse bridge across the River Ryburn, and then up across the moor and onto her own home Delia was imagining their happy reunion. Her sisters, their children and husbands, herself and her father and mother would gather round their own table—she would sleep in the room she shared with Momo. She would hear the gossip from Harriet about what was going on in Halifax. She would visit her father's workshop in Skircoat and see the business he was taking up to Joseph Baines and his son, John, in Halifax's Kings Cross street. She would be called to Nancy's second confinement later in the year—and perhaps to Lizzie in Castleford. Life would go back to normal.

But at home, nothing was normal. Money was tight. No work came into the Greetland barns. Thomas and Job had no cloth to sell from their Skircoat workshop. Grandpa Thornton had died during the summer. Mass meetings erupted in Halifax and Papa inveighed mightily against the rabble-rousing rebels drinking at the Waggoners Inn. Crowds trekked out in their thousands to raise their voices at Chartist meetings. Young people worried about the slowness of trade, by the difficulties they met everywhere, and by the fury of the Radicals.

The only bright spot seemed to be Harriet's friendship with John Baines; John, the eldest son of Joseph Baines, a big man in Halifax King Cross area and he who'd helped Hannah and Nancy at the time of the Peterloo massacre. He and his son John ran a profitable business filling their barns along Paradise Street and Cross street with pieces of cloth, then selling them in Halifax Piece Hall. Thomas Mellor, standing with the successful Joseph Baines in Paradise Road, thought the old times had returned. His son and sons-in-law knew otherwise, but Thomas, at last, saw himself as the wool manufacturer he was reared to be.

By the year's end Joshua Fisher, despairing of making a decent profit, was talking with his father, John Fisher, the tea merchant with London connections. For generations the Fishers had been Quakers bound to their families and their religious beliefs trading the world over. With strong social consciences Friends strove for greater justice among the poor and dispossessed. John Fisher recalled the shocking interviews he had conducted with those bereaved by the Luddite hangings in 1813. Ruin and starvation again faced families whose menfolk tried to address inequality. Now his son was facing trading difficulties. Young Joshua Fisher, as ambitious as his father-in-law, Thomas, was searching for new ways forward. His wife Hannah shared her husband's desire for greater scope and greater standing. This common purpose confirmed their ambition to improve the world. That however did not mean they were clear about how to achieve that ambition.

In London, the government, worried about the riots and unrest across the entire country, talked about emigration as a way of solving both hunger and unemployment. The Fisher family saw this as a heaven-sent opportunity for Joshua to improve his lot. They wanted to invest in a shop and trading post set up in the new city of Adelaide, South Australia. Hannah saw her childhood dream of travelling. Joshua saw a future as a successful merchant. Their family would prosper. Joshua and Hannah's discussions became clearer, their plans to migrate solidified, but they talked to no one except Joshua's father.

95. Hobart, Tasmania, Island to the South of Adelaide
(archives of South Australia)

British traders re-purposed slave ships to transport convicts to New South Wales in Australia—an enforced migration. Abe Mellor had been one such unlucky convict in 1818. But in 1835 the government discovered emigration of free Britons to the new province of South Australia as a painless way to reduce economic distress and national discontent. Ships were commissioned and government plans made finance available. Thus began the migration of thousands of nineteenth-century Britons backed by their home government.

In contrast to the widely connected Fishers, the Baines of Halifax were against all talk of emigration. After the Luddite uprising in 1813, three Baines men were imprisoned, which although less harsh than execution, had dire results when men were incarcerated in the rotting hulks of old ships, off ports such as London and Portsmouth. The Baines family, seared by the deaths of two of their three young relatives while serving sentences in the hulks, imprisoned in dark damp hell-holes,

resisted all arguments to send young people into any ships.

Halifax raged with arguments about trouble-makers and imprisonment, about riots and poverty. Public concern rose about the injustice of transportation. It was likened to slavery, while Charles Dickens later famously raised its horror in his book, *Great Expectations*.

96. Early nineteenth-century Halifax was graced with public buildings like the Assembly Rooms and circulating libraries and mechanical institutes of education

One morning, soon after her return to Greetland, Delia took back a book of sermons to the library in Halifax. Her father accompanied her. In the front room, sitting forward in their leather armchairs, with newspapers spread across their knees, they saw two neighbours, John Fisher and Joseph Baines, arguing bitterly. The level of their voices and the angry stares warned Delia and Thomas to keep quiet and remain unseen beside the library desk.

Joseph Baines leant forward, knocking sheaves of paper onto the floor. While struggling to collect them he spluttered out his argument with John Fisher.

"Look here, John, if we transport any more of our men to far off parts we'll lose anyone capable of arguing against the government. We've got to be able to change people's minds here at home otherwise the landed classes will take all and the people will suffer. Take my cousin Edward Baines, the journalist. If he emigrated then there would be no one to put the case for reform in the newspapers. Without that voice justice will be lost. It's vital we keep fighting." Joseph Baines stabbed his finger wildly at his sparring partner, John Fisher the Quaker. Joseph, former innkeeper and now cloth-dresser, spoke harshly and bitterly. He had never forgiven the magistrates for condemning his relatives to their lingering death in Portsmouth's cruel shipping hulks. Despite never subscribing to political agitation himself he insisted that the landed interests needed challenging. His personal loss sharpened his arguments.

Although scarred by his visits to the bereaved after the 1813 hangings, John Fisher replied calmly drawing on his knowledge of his well-heeled customers and of his family's London contacts. He felt the bitterness and injustice of children and women struggling with starvation because their men had rebelled against injustice. But for him the way forward was taking their work elsewhere, not planning lengthy charters and protest meetings. He spoke with measured tones.

"Joseph, I understand the bitterness of the transportation system and I defy it to reform any convicts or any agitators. That doesn't mean that the land of Australia should be dammed because convicts are sent there. This country of England is too full—we know that—people can't get work, families have no food, workhouses overflow. If the young can take steps to improve people's lives back here by developing the space over there and improving their own chances, we must allow them to take those steps."

John Fisher, as a calm Quaker, argued quietly without the anvil of personal loss intensifying his voice. The angry Joseph Baines spat back, "So John, you'd see Halifax condemned to be run forever by the landed, to be run against our own interests as traders. You'd let the young run away from our problems, leave us to suffer imprisonment for having views. I'd never let my John run from his family. We need him here to keep fighting, to keep going. Leaving these shores is cowardice. I won't have no cowards in my family."

Joseph Baines, a forceful man at the best of times, shot these words at John Fisher, a man more used to the calm of Quaker silence and careful negotiations between merchants than the rough and ready dealings between clothiers and weavers. Joseph Baines spoke as he found, he called a spade a spade and was proud to be uncompromising and forthright.

Startled, John Fisher rose from his chair, folding his newspaper with care, and returning it to the rack, he spoke slowly, considering his words. "Joseph, my friend, that's no way to talk to people. I will support my son to do whatsoever he thinks best. It'll be better to let matters lie between us. Good day."

He moved unhurriedly across the floor, his footsteps sounding measured and steady. Joseph Baines stood up, glared at his departing back and, red-faced, retrieved his papers from the floor.

Delia, alarmed by the hostility the two were showing, turned back to the librarian, pushing her book across the table, silently pleading with the man to take it quickly so she could leave. The librarian glanced at the angry men, breathed in heavily and crossed Delia's name off his list of borrowers. Thomas Mellor listened and, silenced as always by the hostility of Halifax associates, said nothing. Delia knowing little of George Mellor and the shots fired in Dungeon Wood seven years before her birth, condemned her father for his silence. She wanted to challenge

Joseph Baines. And to ask what John Fisher meant about his son, her brother-in-law.

Frustrated by her father's silence in the face of conflict she stalked out of the library and turned down the hill towards Skircoat Green. The pair walked stiffly until Thomas announced he would stop at the workshop and asked Delia whether she was happy walking across Copley bridge on her own. Relieved, Delia nodded giving him a brief peck on the cheek and walking on. She did not understand the feelings revealed by the argument in the library.

97. Ancient Halifax Hotel used for the circulating library in early nineteenth century

Delia knew Non-conformist religious people wanted freedom to take part in universities, the military and Parliament. A few years earlier the Catholics had been granted emancipation after heated debates in Parliament. Dissenting Protestants remained outside; the Anglican establishment, despite being brother Protestants, feared them more than the less numerous Roman Catholics. Her Rishworth friends were refused parity with the Anglican clergy. These debates in pulpits up and down the country led to bitter divides in many regions of England, including the independently minded West Riding of Yorkshire.

Only twelve years old when the entire country was riven by fierce debates over Parliamentary reform Delia heard, without fully understanding, the huge frustrations of swathes of respectable maisters and artisans denied a vote despite the Great Reform Act of 1832. Her Minister Cousin Tom deepened her understanding while helping her with Sunday school teaching. Chapel people, constantly debating how to govern their own religious lives, spread their concern into debates about how to govern people who had no representation in Parliament. Delia knew these arguments but mostly in the abstract. Today they intruded into the personal. Men arguing, men she knew well, arguing heatedly, disturbed her. She did not know what to think.

Even without Hannah and Joseph's early experiences of riots and shootings during the Luddite troubles she was frightened by the ferocity of the Chartist movement and the shouting of large crowds. She longed to keep everyone happy, everyone in agreement, everyone calm. Back at home she chatted with her mother.

"Mother, do you know why there is so much argument?"

Peggy, straining her eyes to stitch the flounce back in Delia's dress torn on the climb up to Greetland, told her daughter to stand still and shook her head before she replied. "I've never been able to understand it, Delia. It's been going on forever. Papa and I were terrified by Cousin George Mellor flaunting his ferocious arguments back before your birth. We lost customers over all that; they didn't trust family tainted with the same name. That's why Papa has always kept his own counsel wherever he could. That's why he was sent to London when you were little: a creditor hounded him because George had been King Lud. He's always kept his silence to protect family and business."

Delia breathed a soft as she saw again her father stiffen in the face of the argument of his two friends. Perhaps she had been too judgmental. Perhaps his silence was courage, not cowardice. She returned to her questioning.

"But if we keep silence how can we make things better? How will people know it's wrong to keep working people hungry and powerless?"

Delia knew from her time at the manse that working people could easily slip into destitution and starvation because something outside their control went wrong. She thought this unfair. Peggy, whose philosophy when faced by difficulties was to put her head down and survive day by day until times became easier, sighed and said, "I never know. I never try to change the world. I just change how I deal with it. I know that I can only change myself. I know I have to do what has to be done; I have to go step by single step. There," she said patting her needlework, "That's the flounce safely sewn on. Off now, it's time to prepare our food for the family gathering this Sabbath."

Later that week, John Fisher told his son that he could release capital to set up a business in South Australia, in the new city of Adelaide. Hannah had read for months every titbit she could about South Australia. Joshua had examined every advertisement appearing in the Bradford, Leeds and Halifax papers. They heard that a leading soldier, Col. Gawler, battle hardened during the Peninsula war, was being dispatched with his family to become the new Governor of South Australia. Colonel Gawler's family would sail from Blackwall on the River Thames in May 1838 on the ship Peston Bomanjee. He himself would join the ship a month later, at Plymouth where many more emigrants would embark. After long nights of prayer, discussion and reflection, they made their decision. Joshua, Hannah and their three children would sail with Governor Gawler and his family. At last it was time to talk to the Mellors, to declare their intentions to leave. They planned this for the family gathering the following Sabbath.

At the same gathering, Harriet planned to declare her intention to marry John Baines in the autumn. Delia, back in the family and learning a trade as a milliner, felt as grown up as any of her sisters and wanted them to acknowledge her new maturity. Nancy and Joshua Turner were bringing the newest Turner babe, Hannah, now two months old. Hannah and Joshua Fisher would come with their two toddlers and the new baby Sarah. Even Lizzie and Richard Walker were coming with six-month-old Billy from Castleford. The whole family would be together again. Peggy was looking forward to a noisy tribal gathering. Even Thomas had shaken off his customary depression and silence. It was set to be a happy family occasion.

Two days before the gathering, Joshua Fisher told his brothers-in-law in Brighouse of his emigration plans. Joe Mellor, Richard Walker and Joshua Turner had seen for months that Joshua's business plans were not moving forward as he hoped. They saw the stalling of his hopes for a greater role in Halifax. All felt the weight of the old preventing forward movement. Emigration though was a huge step. They were lost for words; none could see how it might work. None knew how Thomas would react.

Delia watched the young men troop into the family kitchen. She felt a heaviness in the air and could not imagine what it might portend. She wondered whether all the babies were as well as they should be.

Mary, with her eyebrows raised, glanced at her as they gathered the new Fisher babe and her two siblings, and the toddler, Margaret Turner, keeping them safe from the fire hearth. Nancy, Lizzie and Mary Fox kept their babes close in their arms. The men sat down, bringing in benches from the workshops.

98. Lt. Colonel George Gawler—His appointment as Governor was widely talked of in early 1838. His exemplary military record in the Napoleonic wars reassured people that this emigration proposal was a 'safe' enterprise. (Wikipedia)

"We've got some news," Joshua Fisher muttered.

"Well, spit it out boy. It looks bad by your face. The sooner we know the better." In his anxiety Thomas spoke sharply.

"Hannah and I are sailing to South Australia in May," Joshua replied baldly with none of his usual lilting tones and joking eyes. "We're emigrating to Adelaide."

The room was stunned. None of the Mellors—apart from Hannah—had ever imagined anyone leaving Yorkshire, let alone England. It struck as would the news of a death. Few people ever returned from that wild place with savages and dragons lurking in the deepest oceans. Transported men sent back the odd letter—if they could find someone to write on their behalf—but their news was of hard labour, of chafing restrictions imposed by guarding soldiers. When released from bondage none returned to Yorkshire, none sent back money. It was widely assumed they were dead. Yorkshire folk, raised to live on the moors that gave them food in life and rest in its churchyards at death, could not see life beyond their county borders, let alone beyond their country. Families argued, families fought, families bore grudges against each other for years. But families stuck together, families helped each other—for if your family did not, then who else would. Emigration broke families, snapped the bonds between generations, between siblings, cousins and neighbours.

Unimaginably fearful, Thomas and Peggy sat silent. Harriet burst out fiercely, "That's wicked. You can't take the babes from their land. You can't leave your parents to their old age. There must be another way, another way of improving yourselves. What about London? That'd be safer—and less final."

In anguish, Delia was freed to speak. "What about us? We'll never see our sister again, never see the children grow up. And you might die on that dreadful sea voyage. Hansie, no, you can't go. I shan't let you. I can't."

She stood up and still shouting, turned to Joshua. "It's you that's made her do this. You never loved the family. You always wanted to be free of Yorkshire—like your grandfather. You despise our little ways, you want a bigger stage, a grander world, you should be ashamed of yourself, killing our family like this."

Peggy pulled at her skirts, urging her to hush and sit back down. Hannah spoke quietly through the sobbing and fist shaking.

"Lucy Locket, that's not fair. My Joshua here has always spoken of the family with the greatest regard. He's worked with the boys in Brighouse and Rastrick for nearly eight years and things are getting no more settled. We're good Methodists and take our duties seriously. But here in Halifax that's not enough. In South Australia we'll be part of running things so the poor don't go without, so the sick and the ill are supported, so slaves and convicts have their freedom. We've prayed about this for months. We've talked to Joshua's father and he's funding us to set up a grocer's store in Adelaide—everyone needs a grocery store. The Good Lord is guiding us. He will keep us safe. The Lord told his disciples to go out without their baggage, without their food—just with their staff—and God would take care. We are following in their footsteps."

Delia stood distractedly in the middle of the room, shouting and pointing at her sister. "Don't Lucy Locket me. That's a pet name for a baby and I'm neither a baby nor a pet. I stand on my own. And don't tell us that God is sending you away. He's not that cruel."

"Sorry Delia. You are not a baby, that's true. You are most dear to me. And I take this decision with a heavy heart. Joshua is ambitious and 'tis right that he should be. He will not be content unless he tries to make a better world, like the minister tells us. The Lord helps those who help themselves. I am excited: all those books I've read, all the stories I've heard about Captain Cook and his sailors. It'll be a big adventure but it will bring greater wealth and happiness. We must go."

Hannah spoke clearly and by the end, tears were rolling down Delia's cheeks. She heard the implacability of the decision. She knew there was no more arguing to be done. She felt abandoned and gulped back wracking sobs. "Mother, can I go with them? I can find a husband there."

"What nonsense. You would get yourself more than a husband,

young lady, more than you bargained for. It would be most improper without a chaperone." Peggy spoke with quiet fury.

The men drifted outside, avoiding the scene inside. They could not bear Delia's anguish. Thomas, with his head bowed, stood apart, stooped and leaning heavily on the gatepost. He could not see why anyone would want to leave Yorkshire. He could see no need to change—certainly not with this violence.

John Baines, the newcomer, part of his father's business and with younger half siblings to help, was dead against leaving Halifax. His father was a dominant presence in Halifax and the Baines family was widely integrated in the life of the town. Their cloth-dressing business occupied workshops in King Cross and in Paradise Row, employed people and traded steadily. There'd been Innkeeper Baines, there'd been hatter Baines, there'd been rebel Baines who'd died in the hulks. And now there was Reform Baines who was writing in his Leeds paper every week, writing against the parliament men, writing for the honest industrious class, writing to support Richard Oastler in his fight against long factory hours for children. The Baineses belonged in Halifax and it was unthinkable that John Baines would ever leave it. His life was there, and his battles at home; John Baines saw nothing of virtue in this mad idea and fell out of the discussion. He came in to find Harriet, who was quietly sitting in the corner of the parlour, herself not taking part in any of the arguments but looking strained and pale.

Delia was biting her lip, beseeching her eldest sister," Hansie, what about us? I can't live without my sister and her babies. Let me come too!"

"No Delia, no."

This time it was Harriet shaking her fist and spitting out tears.

"Hannah, you may change your life—if that's what you want to do—but you shan't change mine or anyone else's. If Delia is stupid enough to want to go with you then she too is lost to the family. Don't split us up even more with your hypocritical Methodist flummery. God doesn't tell us what to do; He doesn't know what's going to happen anymore than the rest of us, and despite all our prayers, He goes on letting awful things happen."

Hannah, who had foreseen sharp arguments, kept her calm, side-stepping Harriet's charge, and replying to Delia: "Delia, it's not for me—or for you—to make decisions like that. It's down to Papa and Mother."

Harriet was shaking with fury and burst out again.

"Hannah, it's unfair. John and I were going to speak about our wedding in the autumn at the parish church in Halifax and now you've spoilt everything. You won't come, it'll be horrid, and it's all your fault for doing what suits you and not the family."

At this Peggy drew in a sharp intake of breath, then moved her head as she caught the sound of baby Sarah crying in her crib in the front parlour.

"Hannah, should I attend to the child? You have much explaining to do, my girl. Why no talk before this with Papa and me? I'll get the baby—start explaining now."

Thomas came back in with John Baines and Richard Walker and his eyes followed his wife as she swept out of the room with her black skirts rustling indignantly behind her. He was utterly lost in this mayhem—his girls arguing violently was not his territory; he left that to Peggy. He sat in his chair, head in his hands, tapping his leg uncontrollably against the floor. Joshua Fisher and Joshua Turner stood awkwardly beyond the door shuffling from foot to foot. No one knew what to say.

Joe Mellor came back and, looking around the room, saw tears and shock in every face.

"I think we need time to take this in, time to consider. It's a tough call for everyone, even for Hannah and Joshua Fisher. But ...." And he looked at the floor as he tried to think of the best words to bring some kindness into the situation.

"Joshua told me and the lads here a few days ago," and he gestured towards Lizzie's husband, Richard Walker, and to Joshua Turner, Nancy's husband, "so we've had a moment or two to turn it all over. I didn't know that you, John Baines, were to be part of the family then, so we didn't talk to you. Perhaps it would have been better if we had. I'm glad you'll be taking care of our Harriet here. Yours is a good hardworking family, and those warehouses and workshops in Paradise Row seem a sound business, my friend, so congratulations to the pair of you."

Joe Mellor crossed the room to where John had stood himself besides Harriet. He held out his hand and said: "Welcome, John. I'm very happy for you two. Well done, Harriet—you will be happy with the Baines family—they are a hearty people."

Thomas raised his head and grunted out what might have been a word of welcome. So distressed was he by the news from Hannah and Joshua that he could not yet smile at this new alliance between his family and one of his best working acquaintances, an alliance for which he himself had been hoping this last few months. This was not the way things were supposed to be: he was the father and patriarch of the family, he should be telling them what was happening—not them telling him. Thomas felt belittled again, and useless.

Hannah came over to give her sister a hug, which was reluctantly received but the gesture broke the frozen feelings hanging in the air and helped the family shuffle in their seats and turn to Joshua Fisher for more information.

"I think we men need to talk this over. Father Thomas, sir, will you step outside into the yard and I can show you our thinking? Hannah, will you step into the parlour with your mother and sisters? It's a big step for us all and we want your blessing on our next lives." Joshua spoke calmly to the whole room.

"That's all I can do, it seems, step outside. I have no purpose now, no place in this family. Joe give me your hand." Dejected, Thomas stood looking at his son

In times of crisis he turned, as always, to his son. Since he had taken him down to the Savile Arms for that first meeting with creditors Thomas had seen his son as his righthand man. He knew Peggy kept the family with her food and household work but Yorkshire was a place for real men—he and his son were 'real men', just as he and his father, another Joseph Mellor, woolman of Elland had been before him. Now though, he could no longer count on being Yorkshire men anymore, no longer count on his family. He lumbered wearily outside.

Joe knew how hard this was for his father. He knew the pride he took in being a Yorkshire clothier. He knew he dreamed of being again a proper 'manufacturer'. He surmised that he would sign himself thus at Harriet and John's wedding in the autumn. He knew though that Thomas would never again be a 'manufacturer', unlike his relative Benjamin. Thomas had his workshop in Skircoat, a growing township, but weavers no longer brought pieces to his door for selling on in Halifax Piece Hall. Indeed the Piece Hall market was increasingly poorly attended; the biggest Cloth Hall in Europe was failing. The mills and manufactories had changed all that—and left Thomas Mellor behind. Joe knew this, as did his brothers-in-law, Joshua Fisher, Joshua Turner and Richard Walker. They were working together as joiners, wheelwrights, stone men, construction men. There was a market for machines but large mills were reducing the need for artisan craftsmen. The days of independent small clothier businesses were numbered.

Joe could see why Joshua Fisher had decided to set up business in Adelaide. He could also see how wounded were both his parents by the news. He had to work carefully to build them up again. Anxious little Delia he would have to leave to his eldest sister.

Peggy told Delia to take glasses of porter to the men in the yard. Discussions were thirsty work and the men had to make sense of this terrible news—as did she.

"Hannah, what's the thinking? What's the drive?" Peggy demanded of her eldest daughter.

"Mother, you know the business is not growing as Joshua would like. His father has contacts down in London and they say there's good business to be had in Australia. Theirs is a family of many contacts: tea is world-wide business. They expect a son of theirs to take risks and travel."

Delia muttered, not quite under her breath, "There you see. It's all Joshua's doing; he isn't satisfied with Yorkshire families."

"No, Lucy Locket," Hannah started to argue, but Delia interrupted angrily.

"Hannah, stop! All this is about you and nothing is about the family. I don't know how you can begin to think it right to leave here, to leave everyone who cares about you. What will we all do once you've gone? How can we bear never to see any of you again?"

Hannah turned away, crushed by the fury of her little sister.

The young men though were more open in their ideas. They had worked together in Rastrick and Brighouse for nearly eight years and had worked well. It had been fun. Their business had been doing fine, but now capital to take on bigger jobs was harder to find. They feared living narrow lives with little chance of growth.

Before his sudden death last year, Uncle Joseph Fox had been successful, as were the Thornton relatives with their fancy woollen business. But now neither family had enough spare to invest in bigger machines. Foxes and Thorntons were steady men around Rastrick but the canals (and soon the new railways) were changing all that. Brighouse, clean and smart, was now bigger than the older Rastrick. New traders came and took new business in the town, in the coal pits, in the stone quarries; old families were displaced. Old man Fox's widow had to manage the carpentry part of his business. His sons were uninterested in taking on the old business, or in letting their brother-in-law Joe move it forward. Joe Mellor, as ambitious as his father, knew the importance of capital and credit. As the son of an Insolvent, Joe found it hard to find credit. Like Delia, he was tempted to say; "Can we go too?"

Joe faced long conversations with his wife, Mary, a slender girl of firm views and strong will. Less personally ambitious, Joshua Turner and Richard Walker found their wives less forceful. Neither man drew on generations before them of higher standing across the moors and valleys. They were solid Yorkshire folk, independent minded, good chapel goers and 'industrious'. Turners and Walkers had worked in these valleys for centuries, never getting richer but not getting poorer either. If their quick-witted brother-in-law thought life might be better emigrating they were prepared to give him a chance to prove it, and their wives, Nancy and Lizzie, would follow their lead. This row changed much: opening opportunities which needed much debate and marshalling of facts, particularly facts around money.

That night Hannah cried herself to sleep. Despite her conviction that it was right to take the capital to emigrate, she feared the separation from her family, and the dangers of the voyage for her babies. Announcing the decision made those fears more real, the ambitions more febrile, less solid. She worried about Delia and her desperate outburst against Joshua. The girl was still a baby in so many ways but she was a sensitive baby, and needed help to toughen up. Life would throw unpleasant stuff at her and she needed help to withstand the 'slings and arrows of outrageous fortune'. After much head-wrangling and tossing and turning Hannah still found emigration to be good for her family. With the phrase from her reading ringing in her mind Hannah at last fell asleep, anxious but convinced they had made the right decision. The Lord would guide them and keep them.

In the midnight hours in Greetland, the idea of following Hannah and Joshua took root in Delia's mind. In the dark of their bedroom she talked it over with Momo, hoping to persuade her sister that it was a good idea: they would find husbands and have a better world to live in. Delia floated the idea that they did not have to become milliners and dressmakers to earn their living, perhaps their husbands would make enough money to keep them in clothes and good houses. The youngest girls knew better than to bounce these ideas round their father and mother. They kept silence while Thomas and Peggy moved, with strained faces and tired eyes around the normal family chores.

Papa needed time. He knew his place in the Yorkshire world and was intensely reluctant to let it go. Mother could contemplate changing things only if her babies were safe, only if her girls were content in their new adventures. She too needed time to work out her response to this dramatic announcement.

PART III—Chapter 28

Hannah Sails
May 1838

*99. Buffalo built 1813 in Calcutta sailed to Adelaide 1836.
Hannah and Joshua sailed in a ship like this called the Peston Bomanjee,
also built in Calcutta where the East India Company had big ship
building wharves. She sailed in 1838 from London to Adelaide.*

Delia was bewildered by the speed with which Hannah, Joshua and their three children, five-year-old Elizabeth, three-year-old Joseph and baby Sarah left their life in Halifax. All was bustle, all excitement and hurry—then suddenly—silence, gaps, loss.

Two months after the Great Meeting in February 1838, the house and shop in Brighouse were up to let; landlords given their quarter's notice. Delia minded the children while Hannah sold furniture and furnishings, gave away more, and selected a little to pack. Her quilt took pride of place in the chest she was taking from Joshua's family home. Half a ton of baggage allowed on board their ship the Peston Bomanjee included work tools and equipment. Clothes had to be sturdy to survive extreme heat and extreme cold—and get soaked in salt water. A cabin was too expensive. They lodged with 243 other passengers in the belly of the ship for five long months Governor Gawler with his large family, and twelve other passengers had cabins, as did the Captain, the doctor and other officers on the poop deck in the bows. Most passengers had makeshift hammocks: unstable, smelly and constantly noisy.

The presence of a doctor, employed by the South Australia Company, calmed Hannah's worst fears about the danger to her babies. Too many ships lost babies on every voyage. Storms and poor food added to the toll on weaker children. Hannah prayed fervently for a safe passage for her three.

In Brighouse and Halifax it was expected that Thomas Mellor's girl should do her duty by her neighbours. Delia saw very little of Hannah in this flurry of visiting although she kept her children busy at home. Preoccupied with complex business plans with his father John of Springvale, Joshua Fisher had no time for Mellor relatives. Father and son agreed which provisions should stock the new shop. They set up business links between London and the new province set up in 1834 by the South Australia Act. John Fisher's credit was good in Huddersfield and Halifax, but none knew whether that credit ran to goods destined for the other side of the world. Neither man had any idea of what Joshua faced; rumours flew that only tents met the new arrivals. The company promised a representative to welcome them off the boat and direct them to building lots in Adelaide, the freshly marked-out capital of South Australia. Colonial Government was proclaimed in December 1836 when members of the Council were sworn in near the Old Gum Tree. In March 1838 the Fisher family set up lines of credit, business contacts and introductions to notables in Adelaide. They planned their embarkation at Blackwall Dock for May. John Fisher wanted his son to ride in comfort to London as he feared the long road journey for his grandchildren. He ordered John Coachman to take the family in the slow lumbering carriage stored, mostly unused, in the family's stables at Springvale. They left on April 20th. On the coach roof were piled boxes of baggage, while inside sat Joshua, Hannah and the three children. It took two weeks to travel to Blackwall Dockyard on the Thames.

When Hannah and Joshua Fisher, Elizabeth, little Joseph, and baby Sarah left Springvale in the lumbering coach, luggage piled high and lashed onto the roof, Delia saw them off.

They left in the light of the early morning. Yorkshire looked its best: sharp, clear skies; birds singing their thrilling dawn chorus; dew glistening on each sharp blade of grass. Delia handed baby Sarah to her sister inside the coach once she was ready to hold the recalcitrant infant. Delia, staying overnight with the Fishers at Springvale, had woken the toddler, dressed her and played with her while her parents ran from task to task, demanding where things had been packed, and reminding the two older children to be quiet so they could think. She felt the warm round little body close up against hers and smelt the warmth in the back of her neck. She pushed away her desolation that she would not hold this child, no longer play with her, nor feed ducks in the pools of the little Blackbrook. It was incredible to her that Hannah, her best sister, would no longer be near, no longer give advice, share a meal, join their parties, their dancing, and their singing. Hannah hugged her before she climbed into the coach—but it was too quick, too encumbered by the toddler. Delia held tight. And gulped back her tears.

Delia raised her arm; she brought out her handkerchief so the children could see her as long as the coach was in sight. Then they were gone—the road was empty. Delia was left behind with a raw, gaping hole thumping in her chest wondering whether she would ever sing joyously again. Hannah had not died—like all those children at Rishworth last year—but to Delia, it felt the same. There was nothing now to plan for, nothing to do, just the dreadful grey of jagged emptiness and hollow loss.

Turning her back on the Huddersfield road from where her sister was travelling to faraway Sheffield, Nottingham, Leicester and the brilliant London, Delia turned back towards Longroyd Bridge. From there she went up the valley along Grimescar. Although it was a sad walk home as the late April bluebells wafted their heavy scent from beneath the bare beeches, her heart was lifted by the chattering of the birds in the canopy of trees. Rarely did she glimpse them but raised her eyes as they sang full throated among the mist of new leaves. Reaching the moor at Ainley Top she looked across to Banks House to the east, and leftwards to the West across the Black Brook valley to her own home in Greetland. By now the sun was high and she was hungry. Another hour and she stepped into her mother's kitchen.

At home her father existed thinly, detached and silent. Her mother struggled to keep the household going while noting increasing faults in her two remaining daughters. Delia and Mary found urgent business to keep them going down to Copley Bridge and up the hill to Halifax. They never now walked down-river to Brighouse: Hannah and Joshua's shop was shuttered and empty. Instead the girls climbed steeply to Elland Upper Edge past Banks House, their father's boyhood home, and from thence dropped into Rastrick, past the stone quarries fuelling the Fox family income. Everywhere they heard stories: riots in Wakefield, mass meetings at Steep Hill. Arguments raging about repealing the Corn Laws, a demand which Richard Oastler, the steward of nearby Fixby Hall, was repeatedly raising in parliament. In Halifax he belaboured mine and mill owners for employing children for over ten hours a day. No one was sure which side of the argument neighbours would take, and arguments were pursued with raised and anxious voices. Peggy pushed both girls out to work, Mary as a straw plaiter and Delia as a milliner, but they both also helped at home; Peggy needed them.

Hannah wrote from London telling the family of the famous sights they had seen. In their few days, Hannah wrote, they visited a theatre and Westminster Abbey and St. Paul's Cathedral; they shopped and finalised business details. She wrote of the noisy coachyards they'd passed through, of the crowds thronging Fleet Street. Her letter was hasty and short but Delia read every word with intense care and ran excitedly to share it with Momo. Their mother Peggy was less excitable and heard the news without comment.

After they slipped anchor on May 7th Hannah went below decks to write a longer letter home. She told of her reassurance that the family of the new governor, Colonel Gawler, was on board. They had stepped into a Thames lighter at Blackwall, and been taken out to the Peston Bomanjee. Anchor was weighed as the passengers stood on deck, watching the crew haul away on the ropes. With lines cast off, 250 passengers were confined to a forty-four metre length of ship by nine metres wide, powered by three sail-laden masts and surrounded by water—in which none of them could swim. Hannah waved through the greyness at the flat lands slipping away on either side and wondered what she was doing leaving everything she knew. The ship's captain promised that letters could be sent when they docked at Plymouth to take on board more passengers, including Governor Gawler. Hannah had her letter ready but it took six weeks to sail down the Channel from the Thames. Winds and tide ran strongly against them.

Governor Gawler embarked, and Hannah sent her letters back to Yorkshire. She did this again at Tenerife and at Rio de Janeiro. The family read and shared those letters around the district with intense speculation as to what it all meant.

The ship, Hannah wrote, is run very tightly. Everyone rises with the sun and immediately rolls up their bedding, stowing it on small shelves. Twice a week they take it on deck to shake out the dirt and bugs. Breakfast comes between eight and nine and every member of the table team must be ready, waiting for the men to bring it to their bench. Dinner is served at one and supper at six. All passengers, Hannah wrote, have to be in their berths by ten with matrons patrolling to ensure no young girls were left alone on any deck. (Peggy heard this with great approval. She constantly worried about her girls being unchaperoned and shuddered to think what would happen on a ship laden with lusty young men.) Teams of passengers had duties to sweep the decks after meals, clean up washing areas and tip the night's dirt overboard—with very strict instructions to tip it on the leeward side of the ship so the wind could not blow it back on board! It had only taken one ill-advised throw for everyone to realise the value of this instruction.

Delia read with relief that three lights were lit below decks but no naked flames allowed anywhere. Fire on board was deadly. Even a little light stilled her night frights. Hannah gave these details to help her youngest sister calm her anxiety. Ever resourceful, Hannah did not expect to find life on board easy. She had seen village women managing infants in tiny cottages with bare boards and damp stone walls; she could do the same. The ship though challenged all her ingenuity as she wrote to her family from Tenerife, particularly washing the children's clothes in their limited water—unless they collected more when tropical rain lashed down. Hannah told them it took half an hour to collect the water each week—five and quarter gallons per adult per week—and only 1 ¾ gallons for the infants. She had to dry their clothes—the most private ones included—on the main deck for all to see; no drying allowed below decks. Peggy wondered how any daughter of hers could be so common in her household management but kept the thought to herself.

Delia, after the privations of the Rishworth table, urged Hannah to tell her about eating on board ship. Food supplies, it turned out, were just sufficient but included no fruit nor vegetables. Surprisingly men and women were allocated an equal supply but, especially if the men had been helping the sailors on deck, Hannah gave a portion of her share to Joshua. Thankfully oatmeal was provided alongside potatoes and three quarters of a pound of rice a week. Hannah asked the ship's cooks to bake their homely oatcakes as the ovens cooled down. At the start, she wrote, they ate half a pound of beef a week and a pound of pork but later mostly bacon and ham; the children had milk from the sheep and goats on board, and an egg every other day from the ship's hen coops. During storms the cooped hens, she wrote, were battened down on deck as gallons of sea water rushed past from one side to the other. The hens refused to lay and the children lost their eggs. Delia, fascinated by these details of ship life, told her friends that her sister was living well. Not everyone believed her. They knew she was dreaming of persuading her family to join Hannah.

Hannah wrote to build her family's resolution to emigrate. She made them laugh at the story of a near drowning. On the way down the Thames, a passenger she was standing near was knocked overboard by a falling spar. He was a strong swimmer, but he and his hat were parted during the splash. He surfaced gasping but, instead of reaching back for the ship, he swam for his hat floating a distance away. Grabbing it, Hannah wrote, he turned back to the ship, which was now quite far off. Everyone gathered, peering over the ship's rail while the sailors cast lines and rings to assist the struggling swimmer. In the end he clutched a rope and was hauled safely back aboard where, instead of saying his thanks, he yelled:

"At least I've got my hat safe."

Hannah and Joshua were stunned by his irresponsibility. They were careful in everything they did, conscious of the utter dependence of their three children with no family nearby to help out.

Hannah's letters did not tell all. She did not write of her anxiety when faced by poor food, poor weather and poor health. She did say that supplies had run short, which was why they had put into Tenerife. In Rio de Janeiro, before they sailed onwards, she wrote, they met with an accident in the harbour from a heavily laden ship trying to slip along a crowded channel. It was smaller than the Peston Bomanjee, which was seriously damaged. Her masts were splintered in half. Because he'd been at fault the other master was quick to help repair decks and rigging. Three days later they left; but Hansie wrote, after their Australian landfall, that her heart was broken beneath the Sugar Loaf mountain in the beauty of Rio. Baby Sarah lost her battle to survive. Her death came while the men were banging in nails to repair the ship.

It was only in July, safely arrived in Australia, that Hannah had strength to write that Baby Sarah had been taken with a chest infection; after ten weeks at sea she had been too weak to resist.

Steeped in grey despair, Hannah sat for the rest of the voyage in the ships bowels as they sailed through the Roaring Forties; she wrote nothing of her desolation till they found dry land first on Kangaroo Island, and then later after disembarking at Holdfast Bay, south of Adelaide, five months after leaving Blackwall. Then she wrote to the family, posting the mails with the returning ship, mail which would not arrive till three or four months later. She could not speak well of their landing, she could not encourage them to come. Her babe was gone, her arms empty, bereft, aching. She turned to her two older children, bewildered and lost, and knew that for them, she had to wrench herself from this bleak despair. Joshua had little idea how to comfort her or his remaining children or himself. But as so many do, buried his agony in the endless tasks confronting him daily.

100. First settlement in Adelaide 1837 (South Australia Library)

As the family read this sad account, they felt ice clutch their hearts. Hannah's letter detailing the burial sickened Delia, imagining her dazed and deadened sister standing at the rail watching the black-coated captain read the burial service and the rough sailors dropping the tiny body overboard. That was the letter, short and smudged with tears, which shook Delia to her core.

On 31st October 1838 the passengers disembarked, unsteady on their feet. The company representative welcomed them with long words and pomposity and led Governor Gawler and his family to a wooden house further inland, leaving the bewildered immigrants marooned within a group of tents on a dry, rocky land. Their Australian life had begun.

101. Water colour by S.T.Gill of Beehive Corner on Hindley Street in 1845—Fisher's Grocery shop was on a corner where Morpeth Street crossed Hindley Street. The Fishers arrived in 1838 and buildings went up fast. In 1845 brick or stone buildings have already replaced Hannah's initial report of wooden ones. (Held in Museum of South Australia)

Later that year, institutions were set up to organise the new land. Governor Gawler took charge, and plots of land measured out in the capital of Adelaide, according to Colonel Light's grand plan. Houses were made of timber, Hannah wrote, and even the Governor's Residence was no grand stone mansion but small rooms in a wooden dwelling surrounded by a verandah. She and Joseph built their shop on the corner of Hindley and Morpeth street. She wrote dully and with a grey sense of despair haunting her words, trying to boost herself and those at home by telling how the children thrived, about Joshua's careful building of his grocery store, and of the goods arriving from England to sell to the growing population of Adelaide. The Wesleyan minister called and his talk eased both their aching hearts—they had found their community of worship.

Adelaide changed daily Hannah wrote. Buildings went up weekly, streets were marked out and horses provided transport through the plains and valleys surrounding the town. Adelaide, still new and raw, became the Fishers' home. They planned, they built, they traded. And slowly the letters home became more cheerful.

PART III—Chapter 29

Delia Proposes: God disposes
1839

*102. Chartist riots erupt in 1839. Large meeting at Steep Hill on
outskirts of Huddersfield
(WYAS)*

B ack in Yorkshire the talking did not stop. Now it was Joe Mellor in Rastrick driving forward the idea of family emigration. He saw the prosperity he craved eluding him in Yorkshire and he was fired up by his older sister's dream of growth and adventure. He, Richard Walker and Joshua Turner made a good team combining their skills and worksmanship. He began to persuade his wife Mary that they should emigrate, while Richard and Joshua repeated this story to their wives. Delia, already keen to go, insisted to sister Momo that they would have a better life. That left the question of money to afford the passage of such a big family, and more importantly the attitude of their parents.

Thomas and Peggy, at fifty-seven and fifty-four, were both unwilling to go on such a difficult voyage. They were horrified at leaving Harriet and John, particularly once they had enjoyed the wedding filled with Halifax people in the parish church in November. Here at the parish church, with his daughter marrying into a sound woollen cloth business, Thomas persuaded himself that he had fulfilled his father and grandfather's dream of handing on a thriving wool business. So much the harder to persuade him to move to the other side of the world—or so Joe found. Delia could not see how Papa could ever be persuaded that Australia was a good option.

Peggy cloaked her anxieties in concerns about the babies, and buried herself in the care of Lizzie's new baby, born soon after the Fishers left. Then she had John and Harriet's wedding to think about. With these distractions she obliterated the sadness of the gap at their family table. Other families had to deal with absences, so why not theirs. Delia and Momo knew not to raise any questions about their eldest sister. Peggy cleaned, tidied, washed, laundered and began to turn away old and valued customers. Delia wondered whether she was tiring or … changing her mind.

Joe took the papers about South Australian emigration to his brothers-in-law and together they pondered. Hannah sent letters, which arrived months after she had written them; it was clear that there were opportunities in Adelaide and that others were being attracted to those distant shores. Joe and Richard and Joshua Turner began to consider what tools they might take, what arrangements they could make for dependent family in Yorkshire. Foremost in their minds were any arrangements for Peggy and Thomas. Delia fretted about the older people constraining her chance of adventure.

Harriet however was busy with her new Baines family, surrounding her with demands and urgent business. Delia could see that she would keep the Mellors alive in Halifax and in the best of the wool traditions so important to their father. Delia noticed Peggy relaxing as Harriet grew busy and confident in her new life. The family saw the friendships she was building in the heart of Halifax town, and saw the warehouses and workshops in which the Baines family stored their pieces of wool. Harriet was thriving in Halifax, becoming part of the great industrial story of Northern England. Peggy's care eased and Delia breathed a sigh of relief.

Papa remained withdrawn and distant, especially from Joe. He saw his son as a traitor, a traitor to the family's traditions. Delia took home newspaper advertisements for him to pick up. She read out the stories in Hannah's letters. She brought home tales of the troubles of neighbours in Greetland and Elland. She tried coaxing her father out of his gloom with soft words and good cooking—with no success. She grieved for the small bodies she had minded these months past. She missed the warm body of Hansie's baby girl, as she still missed the chuckles of little Alan Howe.

Peggy, sick with anxiety as to how the dispute would resolve itself, kept herself busy in the house whilst waking sharply at night retreading the arguments in the darkness. She lost sleep and her face became tight and drawn. She urged Momo and Delia to improve their work as straw plaiters and milliners, and then worried about how she would find them good husbands.

Delia read and re-read Hannah's accounts. She shed tears of rage as well as anguish. How could God take away such a darling, such an innocent as Baby Sarah. She dreaded death. She could not face anymore. Surely God could not afflict his people so heavily. But she knew the opposite; cholera still stalked the land, starvation still gripped children's bellies. Men in rags hid in barns, women clutched wailing bundles to their breast pleading in Halifax town for crumbs of food. Yet in these Australian stories she heard of new people, wide skies and abundant opportunities. She had no pictures on which she could draw, not even from the library, but she imagined easy walks without windswept moors and steep, deep valleys, and she tried to imagine a climate with little mist and greater sun. Her desire to live in Australia was dampened only by her fear of the long sea voyage. Experienced as she was with small children, she feared cramped spaces for the toddlers—and saw herself being tasked with their entertainment. But she was young and enthusiastic. She dismissed fears, putting difficulties to the back of her mind. Her task that winter and spring was to persuade her parents that it was good to go to South Australia, to reunite the family even if bookish Harry really was staying behind.

One Wednesday after Hannah had sailed, Delia went into the Halifax lending library. She wanted to find out which port the Peston Bomanjee would be visiting next and how far they were from South Australia. She turned to her favourite book, an account of South Australia written in 1834, only five years ago. and published by the Society for the Diffusion of Useful Knowledge. What a wonderful name for a society, thought Delia. All knowledge was useful but for her, only information about Australia was important as it brought her closer to her departed sister. Every Australian fact blocked that hole in her life. By now, she thought, six weeks after Hansie had sailed from Blackwall, their ship might have crossed 'the Line'. (It hadn't; it was only at Plymouth picking up Governor Gawler.) Was there a signpost in the ocean to say the equator was crossed? How could people tell they were now in the southern part of the globe where summer was winter and winter was summer? Delia looked to find out these secrets of navigation but all she could find was a description of the ceremonies that ships observed as they 'crossed the line'. She wondered if the children enjoyed these ceremonies—and then she wondered whether they were still alive. She sighed and quickly snapped the pages shut. Time to be walking back home through Skircoat and over Copley Bridge. She must put a stop to these dreadful thoughts.

As she came in flushed from the speed with which she had climbed the hill, Peggy called, "I'm here in the housebody, dearest. I'm sorting through our linen. So many sheets are worn thin we must tear them in half and sew them back, middle to edges."

Delia groaned. She hated hemming weakened, threadbare centres of the sheets which then became the outside hems to eke out their use for another two or three years. Working with strong cloth with many threads to each inch was a pleasure—it pleated in her fingers and her

needle sang through wherever she placed it. Thin, frayed cloth meant a swaying needle and buckling thread. No neat edges to these refreshed sheets. And at night, she felt the line of the central seam irk her as she lay, trying to hold back her tears for Hannah and her babies.

103. Kings Dean Woods between Copley Bridge and Greetland (Author 2019)

It was, nonetheless, comforting to work alongside her mother. Peggy had never been able to talk much to her youngest child, the business of the household preventing chat. But now, with silence in the house around them, Delia found herself telling her mother about the children at Sunday school, about the manse at Rishworth with its stream of daily callers, even about sunny little Alan Howe. They avoided any talk of Australia or of Hannah but it was pleasant chatting about the girls learning to be milliners. From her millinery lessons in Elland Delia brought home ladies' magazines that her mistress took to keep herself up to date with London fashions. She had a good eye for balance and detail in dresses, as well as hats and skirts, and was becoming clever at weaving a pretty bonnet from the rolls of cloth and plaited straw stacked in the workshop. Peggy, who had no time for dressing fashionably, loved imagining these glamorous outfits, and the relationship between mother and daughter became closer.

Later in June Peggy became anxious about the great gatherings at Steep Hill over towards Huddersfield. She still remembered the terrifying time when Hannah and Joe and their friend Mary Walker had walked up with the crowds onto Greetland Moor. She worried about her girls getting caught up in riotous strife but Delia, pretty and lively, eager to join parties of other young people, laughed at her fears. As the baby of the family she was protected. Her elders remembered her nightmares with dread. She dismissed them airily. Peggy fretted about her insouciance and her apparent lack of forethought.

"Shh," her family would say with all talk of trouble. "We must watch out for Delia. We don't want to scare her." And so Delia, now fearing deaths of children, never talked of those fears, trying instead to save her elders anxiety by rejecting talk of violence with a toss of her head. That would never happen to her, she thought. Peggy wanted to prepare her youngest daughter to acknowledge danger so she could side-step trouble. No acknowledgement of danger meant no preparation; no preparation meant defeat. Peggy had faced too many troubles to take danger lightly

Delia judged it the moment to reassure her mother with positive talk about Australia. She began talking of the investment people in London were making in the new province. She listed people buying land and sending out favoured workers. She talked of the freedom of religion and of the lofty ideals being promoted in this new convict-free land. She had done her research carefully—Minister Tom's teaching had fallen on fertile ground. Surely she could convert her mother to her grand idea.

Peggy listened silently.

"Mother what do you think? Could we ever live there with Hansie and Joshua?"

Peggy drew her shoulders back and said, "We could but… there's no money to travel and Papa is adamant he won't leave Yorkshire. It's no use dreaming, my girl. Make the best of Halifax with all its arguments, all its disputes over factory children and working conditions. That's where our lives will always be."

"But Mother, can't we change, can't we follow our hopes?"

"Shhst, daughter. Even if Papa consented, there's no money, no rich merchant relatives behind us—and I wouldn't take their money even if there was. Not me, nor Papa would ever be beholden."

Peggy placed her arms across her chest and faced Delia defiantly.

"But Grandfather–" she started.

"That's different. He was my father and always stood behind his children whatever happened. And thank the Lord he did. If he'd abandoned us, I have no idea where we'd all be—no reputation that's for sure, and probably no house, perhaps even the workhouse. He's gone now to his rest, and his capital, such as it is, must stay in my brother's business." Peggy's face was stony and Delia knew she had pushed too hard.

"Never mind, Mother dearest. I'm glad he did stand behind us. Without him, Hansie could never have married into the Fisher family and, even though he's taken her away from us, they will be happy and I'm glad for them, I truly am, even though I miss them bitterly." Delia's face crumpled and she reached in her pocket for a handkerchief to hide the welling behind her eyes.

Peggy opened her arms for her youngest daughter and gave her a long hug as they stood together amidst the sprawling linen.

"Indeed, without Grandfather, Papa could not have rebuilt his reputation, nor his business, and without that, thy sister Harriet could not have married her John. His father Baines is a hard-nosed businessman needing his son's support as he raises that young family up in Paradise Row. We owe Grandfather a great deal; our survival was down to him. But that was then and this is now. Grandfather is gone and so is business here."

Delia choked out to her mother, "And to you, Mother. You kept going through all the arguments, all the demands. You showed us how to keep strong. I'm proud of you."

Peggy, secretly pleased at this affirmation of her own role during those difficult years, could not show her daughter this weakness, this appreciation of her strength. She shrugged and turned away, back to the pile of never-ending mending.

"Well, well," she said. "Fine words are dandy but they don't mend sheets, my girl. We'd better get on or else there'll be no end. And for that matter, we won't help Harriet fill her bottom drawer with linen for her wedding and that would be a great shame on the family. So keep working, my dearie, keep working."

That night Joe dropped by with a mended wheel for their father's cart. Joe was skilled at his wheels and Thomas appreciated his son's efficiency when his machinery broke down. However, he could not leave well alone and spoke roughly to his son.

"Thank 'ee, thank 'ee boy. It's good to have the wheel but t'would be better to have bales of wool to sell up in Piece Hall."

"Papa, you know my heart is not in wool and you know too that there is less money in wool than there used to be. 'Tis good for me and the brothers-in-law to be looking after our families with construction work. We work well together and we get commissions." Joe looked at Thomas, hoping that this time he would see the sense in the young people's shift into machinery. In his head though, Thomas heard only his own father's voice, telling him to follow the old ways and he set his face stonily against his son. Joe shrugged his shoulders and went back home.

But business was slowing down again with failing harvests and rising prices. No one wanted to invest in new machinery, which is where the profit was to be made. Instead everyone was getting things mended. This kept Joe's men employed but, not for enough time and not for enough money. Joe wondered how Hannah and her Joshua were managing in Australia.

In September Delia and Momo went up to Halifax to see if they could buy cloth for new dresses for Harriet's wedding. Thomas and his friend, Joseph Baines, were determined to see their children married in style. Notices were posted in the local papers; the banns were read three times in the big parish church. Both men knew their wives would be happier in the Square Chapel where so many families had attended over the years, but both men desired to make a statement. Both men wanted their places in the Halifax business community to be recognised. Both men had good reputations for judgment and the Baines family had many connections whom it was important to impress. The Anglican church was the church of the establishment. The Square Chapel had worthy members with plenty of money, such as banker Rawson, but the parish church was where the gentry were married and where Thomas and his Peggy had been married, so the parish church was where his Harriet would marry her John. As the girls came out of the draper's shop with a bundle of ribbons to dress their new outfits, a friend came up to Delia and showed her an advertisement on the front page of the Leeds Mercury.

"Here, Delia, look at this! You've been dreaming of Australia for so long and have wondered whether you could find money for the tickets. Well, look at this advertisement. I can't imagine why you would want to go but this might help."

The girl shoved the paper into Delia's outstretched hand and turned quickly away. "I've got to go. The paper comes from my brother and I don't want him to know I've given it to you. He guards his copies with care but I think he won't miss this—and it's of more interest to you, my friend."

Delia was left standing outside the shop and Momo looked at her queerly. "Have you been agitating with your friends about going to Australia? Papa would be so angry if he knew."

Deeply absorbed in reading the advertisement, Delia made no response.

"Tell me, Delia, tell me what it says," said her sister who would never suggest something if her father disapproved, but who was always ready to follow her more adventurous younger sister if fun seemed in the offing.

"The South Australia company want young men with certain skills—joinery, shepherding, and agricultural knowledge—and they're paying the passage. They don't want women by themselves but they can accompany their parents. Women need to be able to work with straw and as milliners—that's us, aint' it? They are even taking older people as long as they are under fifty. And all for free. There's no mention of any wool making skills so Papa couldn't go. But it's a dream come true if it could happen."

"Papa will never go. He's so stuck in his old ways," said Mary.

"I'm not so sure he's that set. He pretends he is, as he hates thinking he's failed as his father's son, Momo. But sometimes I see him looking at papers telling him about Australia and then declaiming it'll never last: that's leaving himself some wriggle room."

"Well I'd go," said Mary stoutly. "There's many, many young men as have gone—and not so many women. So we'd find husbands easy enough. And I'm not sure there's so many here for us in Halifax! Besides it would be good to be somewhere new, somewhere not so dogmatic about what we can and cannot do. The old biddies here keep us well under their thumbs."

Delia looked at her. She hadn't suspected that docile Mary chafed under the strict rules of chapel and village. She had a glimpse of hope that her persuasion was working throughout the family.

"Well, I'll keep this and give it to Joe. He can show the brothers-in-law and see what they think." Delia stuffed the newspaper into her bag and they both walked on down the hill back to Copley bridge.

"But no telling Papa nor Mother. First, we must hear Joe."

Companionably they walked back down the hill, arm in arm as they picked their way through the ruts along the road through Skircoat Green, which seemed to have more building going on every time they passed that way.

At Harriet's wedding that November, Thomas did indeed sign himself as a cloth manufacturer, just as Joe had predicted. Delia noticed he spent most of his time laughing heartily with other cloth merchants, cold shouldering his son and sons-in-law. They had no wool between their fingers. His fellow clothiers knew machinery was important but they considered the young owed them deference as, without wool, there was no need for machinery. They had little understanding that business as they knew it was fast disappearing.

Soon after the wedding, Joe broached Australia again. He told his father that there were prospects for himself and the brothers-in-law. He told him the two youngest girls would make good marriages in the new land. But Thomas spent his time with Baines family members. There were many Baines, and they all enjoyed drinking at the Black Bull where John's father had been publican long years ago. The Baines family were an intrinsic part of Halifax merchant society and Thomas felt his dream of being a rising cloth merchant was at last being answered. He gave his son a curt answer, saying he could never take advice from a machine man, a man with no feel for wool, no sense of business, no sense of tradition. Joe walked out of the inn, furious at his father's pig-headedness. He strode down the hill to Elland bridge and walked fast, up the steep climb to Rastrick and his wife Mary.

"I'm tempted to leave the old man behind, Wife. He's driving me mad, obsessing about wool and completely blind to the troubles all around, the riots and arguments, and news from Ireland and Scotland about hardship." Mary grunted back at him, noncommittally, and Joe left the subject. But it worried him that his father would not talk, that he didn't ask him in for a drink when he saw him passing the Skircoat workshop. When Joe went up to see his mother and sisters, his father stayed in his office room, the door firmly shut. Joe was no longer, it appeared, the apple of his father's eye, and it hurt everyone to feel the chill between the two men.

At Christmas the family was mournful: it was the first time Hannah, Joshua and the babies were absent. No one celebrated as usual. Never before had they raised a toast to 'Absent Friends' but this year they did. Cousin Thomas, the minister, came over at New Year and found the Mellors in great despondency.

He spoke to Delia—now his firm favourite—and begged to know what had happened to the once bubbling and noisy family.

"It's Hansie, Minister Tom. She's left for South Australia and the young men want to go with her. So do I but Mother and Papa cannot tear themselves from all they know. Papa wants to believe he is still a cloth manufacturer. He still goes across to Skircoat to do business, though what that business is no one knows. Joshua Turner's father Job works alongside him and the two of them keep reminding themselves how bad life is. Joe is beside himself with worry. He cannot see himself surviving in the bad times that look to be upon us. He's in a good business—building and machinery—but if the wheels don't turn in the mills then it's no good building more houses, more manufactories, and with rising prices how can we feed everyone. Anyhow we don't have the sort of capital that Joshua Fisher could raise from his father. None of us could afford the passage."

This was the longest thinking Delia had made to herself, let alone to anyone else, about the emigration issue that was splitting their family. Minister Tom was adept at getting people to talk and spell out loud their problems so they could see them more clearly. Then he would suggest, with a question, a possible solution. He could see how unhappy it was making his cousins and how the questions were revolving eternally in their minds without any solution being untangled or presented for them to consider.

His question to Delia caused her mouth to drop and her eyes to widen. "Has your father heard of the free passage being offered to honest craftsmen, true Britons of good character and great industriousness?

It was in the Bradford paper last week and I saw it again in a Sheffield paper this week."

"I have, Cousin Tom. It's no good for Papa. He's too old."

"Go into the library or the Assembly Rooms in Halifax this week and see what you can find. Then show your brother and talk to your mother, it might help. Your parents do not need to declare their true age. And I have heard that people give the best sounding occupation, by which I mean that agricultural labourer is more attractive in South Australia than wool manufacturer. It would help if your father thought about all that."

"So you don't mean to talk about duty, about respect for your elders? You don't mean to treat Father as the guide of our family?"

"Delia, I never talk about duty if there is no duty owed. Your brothers need to keep their families well and healthy. If they make decisions based on the best interests of those for whom they have a duty of care then the rest of you must honour and respect those decisions. I have great affection for your father and mother but they're living in the past. They've not noticed how much the world has changed. They are clinging to keeping it all the same but none of us can do that. And if the Good Lord opens a door, then we are beholden to take it. I will talk with your Mother and she, I'm sure, will talk to your father, as will your brother Joe. Now go, Delia. I will be sad to lose you—as will all at Rishworth—but things happen and we have to go to where the Lord leads us."

"Amen. Amen, Cousin Tom. You are a good and kind man and so is my dear Cousin Mary. Will you be well in Rishworth?"

"Indeed, my dear, we will, there is no other place for us. Our children are nearby and most importantly, the flock we've tended is there and needs us still. Our income is small but enough—and reliable. We will stay till the end and we will be buried in our little chapel graveyard—along with so many of our friends." He spoke calmly and with serenity. Death gave him no qualms; his service to his community and to his God gave him all he needed, and he would keep in harness until the day he died.

"I miss little Alan Howe," said Delia with a wistful sigh. The deaths of those seven babies during her time at Rishworth still haunted her. "I think perhaps Australia will be kinder to children than Yorkshire with its chills, mists and smoke." Her voice was full of hope and longing.

"It might be, oh hopeful one, but you will need all your nursing skills to keep the little ones safe on the sea voyage. May the Lord go with you, my dearest Delia."

"And also with thee, cousin Tom!"

The following week Delia went up to Halifax, to the lending library and found several copies of the Leeds Mercury, the Bradford Observer and the Leeds Intelligencer. It was true; there were advertisements for men of good character, under 50, and possessing certain skills, particularly in building, horticulture, and farming, and welcoming women skilled in dressmaking and straw plaiting. She copied them and took them home. She showed Mary but hid them from her parents until Joe came over. Impressed by Delia's perseverance, he turned thoughtful and muttered, "But how, how persuade Papa that this isn't charity. He so hates being dependent and beholden. How can we persuade him?"

> IN MEMORY of
>
> THOMAS MELLOR
> Pastor of this Church died
> April 12th 1852 in the 81st year of his age
>
> "Happy if with my latest breath
> I may but speak his name
> Preach Him to all and on my death
> Behold, behold the lamb"
>
> Also MARY beloved wife of the above named
> who departed this life December 25th 1857
> aged 86 years
> Also MARY beloved wife of BENJAMIN MELLOR
> son of the above who departed this life
> April 19th 1866 aged 57 years
> Also of the above BENJAMIN MELLOR who
> departed this life June 11th 1881 aged 72 years
> Also MARTHA daughter of the above BENJAMIN
> MELLOR who died January 15th 1885 aged 41 years
>
> Rishworth Roadside Baptist Church
> 1992

104. Words engraved on Revd. Thomas Mellor's tombstone, Rishworth Roadside Chapel burial ground. (Held in Chester Library and in Elland Library)

That week, when he and his brothers-in-law gathered for a drink in the Brighouse pub, he showed them the advertisements and they pondered the possibilities. Something profound shifted. The time of contemplating options was done. Joe Mellor, Richard Walker and Joshua Turner began making arrangements for a new life in South Australia.

Foremost in their minds were the arrangements for Peggy and Thomas themselves. Minister Tom had been as good as his word and had spoken briefly to Peggy, deeming her too proud and too competent to waste time indulging in idle argument. He simply told her that God works in mysterious ways and that sometimes the most dangerous course is the one that leads to greatest content. It is not our place in this world of toil, he said, to demand an easy passage, but to accept the prayer for 'strength to live our lives courageously'. He left her—in her piles of washing and cooking—as he had done so many times before—to turn over his words in her own good time.

In her prayers at home and in Upper Elland Chapel, Peggy told the Lord many times that she had no more strength, that all her strength was spent, that it was wrong at her time of life to demand more strength. But Delia could tell her chin was steadying. Her lips were pursing and her hands more forceful; they fidgeted less in her lap as she listened to her family. Over the months, Peggy found the way to accept the new path shown by the Lord. She was desolate at leaving behind Harriet, but of all her girls, Harriet had always been the one most connected to the friends around her.

Now Harriet was cleaving to her new family, who surrounded her with affection and demands. Her baby was on the way and they would thrive, while the rest of the family would grow strong in Australia. The Mellors would thrive wherever they were—or so Peggy told herself every night as she said her prayers. "Trust in the Lord," she prayed.

Papa remained withdrawn and distant from everyone—but especially from Joe. Delia re-established her Australia campaign with Hannah's stories and neighbours' difficulties. In the end though, what turned him towards Australia was not her words but his disgust, disgust at riotous, foul-mouthed rebels who gathered at the pub near his workshop.

One day he was passing the Waggoners on his way down from Halifax where he had been doing business with Harriet's John and his father, Joseph Baines. It was a warm day and Thomas had watched as bales of wool were shifted by men with sinews starting and sweat pouring; those heavy bales were moved from the front to the back of the wool shop where John was supervising the process of finishing a piece of wool. It was skilled work and made a big difference to the eventual price of the cloth. Thomas knew how much effort it took to produce such quality work. As he turned into the lane beside his workshop thinking of all the work he'd just seen, a gang of louts spilled out of the Waggoners, full of drink and hot air—as Thomas and Job Turner termed it.

They yelled, "Down with the employers." "Fair wages for all," they chanted and also, "Give us a fair day's pay for a fair day's work." They followed this by calling on the merchants of Halifax to cede a proper respect for the labouring classes.

105. Old Postcard of Waggoners Inn, Skircoat
(WYAS)

Thomas raised his fist at them and bawled, "If you do a fair day's work, then you'll get a fair day's pay but you lot don't know what work is. You bring this country to rack and ruin. I'm sick of your wingeing rants. Get your fingers out and do proper work."

Fortunately, Job Turner, hearing the noise, came out at that moment and hauled an angry and noisy Thomas into the safety of his workshop. But Thomas did not let his complaints go. He took them home to Peggy and he told her in very round terms, "I'm fed up with this land. It's full of vagrants, varmints and those who take what they will and give nothing back. I'm joining with Joe and the family and I'm leaving with them. Where's them papers they keep talking about?"

Peggy, who had been sick with anxiety as to how the family dispute would resolve itself, sat down suddenly on her kitchen stool.

"Months thou tellest me how stupid they all are, how thee and me are sticking here and now thou shoutest the odds about them vagabonds outside the pub and tellest me we're going. I've been married to thee for 35 years and still tha' flabbergast me. Hast thou told Joe what thee intends?"

"No, I haven't and I won't. He kept me guessing about what he was doing so now I'll keep him guessing."

"No no, not so, Husband, or I'll leave thee behind. That Joe has been nothing but a saint. He's given us every which way to turn. He's laid out the facts so carefully and all thou hast done is sit in shop and mutter, mutter away with old man Turner, the pair of you together, grumbling about how badly the world's treating you. Thou mun' go to Joe this Sabbath and take him out for a walk, then tell him thy decision."

"He's not been that careful, Wife."

Thomas began to bluster but Peggy silenced him with a stern face.

"Thou hast made it damnably difficult for him so far. Now thou mun' make it easy—and start by telling him he's been kindness itself."

"That's not true, Wife, and I won't do that. But," Thomas added after a short moment of reflection, "I will ease it for him."

Content with this grudging acknowledgement, Peggy went cautiously to work, spreading the news that Thomas would be going to

South Australia after all. Only two hurdles remained. Joe had to persuade both his parents to bring their ages down below fifty—otherwise they would not be accepted—and Thomas had to change, in writing, his dearly cherished status as a 'clothier and manufacturer'. South Australia at this stage had no need of cloth manufacturers and his application termed thus would have been discarded quickly. Thomas was nearly as stubborn about this detail as he had been about deciding to go, but Joe and Peggy quietly warned him that he would destroy the whole family if he did not write 'agricultural labourer'. In all honesty he had extensive agricultural knowledge from his work in the closes but to call himself a labourer when all his life he had employed others, when he had been independent and his own maister: this was a bitter pill. After he'd done the signing, Joe took him out to Halifax to show him how much interest his family's application was causing. He puffed his chest out and took the compliments of being brave and adventurous "like a true Yorkshireman," Thomas called back. And he pushed to the back of his mind the humiliation of calling himself an agricultural labourer. He hoped that life in South Australia would be worth all this fuss.

Peggy, Delia and Mary heaved a sigh of relief. Now they could attend to the family's bags and to weighing out everything they packed. The men had to take tools and work equipment. Joe was pleased skilled workmen were welcomed, particularly his engineering skills with agricultural machines. His ambition was turned in the best direction. Delia released from her scheming was now torn between the excitement of packing and the sadness of walking round with Momo to say goodbye to all their friends.

Delia wrote to Hannah that Papa had relented. Months later she received a reply enthusiastically welcoming the family's decision. Hannah sent a list of things she wanted her mother to bring and a set of instructions that clothes should not be fancy: the voyage would veer from very hot at the Equator, to freezing cold in the Forties. Storms would be uncomfortable with passengers being sick and unable to stand on deck. When it was hot the sailors would lash a canvas cover over the decks and fill buckets with sea water which the passengers could splash over themselves to cool down. Peggy wondered how their clothes coped with this dampness but kept her doubts to herself. Hannah urged her father to bring saddles and bridles with him as horses were available and useful in covering the greater distances in this new country, but not many saddlers were working in Adelaide. If anyone wanted to change their occupations, wrote Hannah, it was hard to find good bakers, an option Joshua Turner seriously considered until Joe and Richard said they needed good workmen to develop their machinery business, and that it was one for all and all for one in this new land.

"We don't really know what it'll be like," Thomas told Peggy on their last night, as they sat over the coal fire to keep themselves warm in late March 1840. "Will there be coal? What about kindling and wood? Will we be warm enough in the winter? And what can it be like to have Christmas in the summer. I can't believe it but Hannah says that spring is in October and Autumn in March. How will that be—I can't see it myself—it's unnatural, surely."

"Well, it's unnatural here, that's true, but then how do we know what's natural there? I'm sure I don't know." And then Peggy voiced her concern. "And will we see the same birds or do birds just stay in England?"

"I don't know, my dearie. It's a big jump into the unknown—especially for us—but it'll be good for the young and that's why we're doing it."

"I know, Husband, I know, but it's a big step and I'm a bit afraid."

"True, Wife. But though I say it as is against the preachifying tribe, the Lord will guide us and keep us, we will learn new ways and help our family learn new ways too."

Peggy looked around their kitchen, bewildered by the echo of their voices in their now bare kitchen.

"Tomorrow we'll be gone from here. This place will be as though we've never been and we'll be on the road to London town. I'm looking forward to seeing those sights and to boarding our ship, Fairlie. I grieve for Nancy and her lost little 'un, the last Mellor of ours to be buried in

Halifax. Perhaps it was tempting fate to call him Thomas Fairlie but it seemed good at the time: such a sad little scrap he was. Delia was very upset when he took ill."

Thomas had seen his youngest daughter crying up on Greetland Moor when she heard of Nancy's babe dying two weeks ago. "She's been worried about little 'uns since she lost so many at Rishworth that year of the cholera. It's one of the reasons she wants to go to the new land: no more cholera she says."

Thomas knocked his pipe out on the fender as he said this deciding it was time for bed—their last in this house, the home of their family. Still no good thinking such thoughts, he told himself.

"Come on, woman. Time to go to the new land. We need our sleep."

PART III—Chapter 30

The Voyage
April-July 7ᵗʰ 1840

*106. Ships lying at anchor in Port Adelaide during nineteenth century
National Library of Australia*

That last night, Delia slept scarcely a wink. Her parents, less excitable, raked the cinders in the kitchen fire retiring to bed to take sleep despite the enormity of the change in front of them. Delia and Mary lay awake wondering what the stagecoach would be like, what they would see in London and how it would feel to be on a ship taking them to the other side of the world. An hour before daybreak they finally fell asleep, only for their mother to wake them with her lantern flickering in the morning greyness.

"My darlings, time to wake."

Delia reached out and fumbled with the clothes she had laid beside her bed the night before.

Quicker than her sister, Momo was soon dressed and kneeling beside her bed to ask God's blessing on their journey. Delia hurriedly joined her, ashamed that she had been slow to think of her duty to God. Sister Harriet was coming over later in the day to take their bedding and last pieces of furniture to the storehouses in Paradise Row. Downstairs, no one spoke loudly. It seemed disrespectful to their now empty home. Peggy filled four bowls with oat gruel soaked overnight. Thomas sat to eat, but she and her daughters ate quickly, standing around the family table, now scrubbed white. Delia saw a cat looking out from the barn and her heart missed a beat. Never again would she tempt her cats with milk in their saucers, never again try to stroke the purring moggie who was winding round her legs. The magnitude of the day left her winded.

The Turners and the Walkers were leaving by coach for London a week or so later as they were going straight to Blackwall. Joe and Mary with their little Tommie Mellor were accompanying his parents and two youngest sisters on the stage-coach to London to spend a week in London seeing the sights. This last morning in Yorkshire, Joe brought a cart up to Greetland to carry the family and their bags to the White Swan in Halifax Cross street. Chests and trunks had been packed and sent by carrier to Blackwall Dock four weeks previously. Today each passenger carried a carpet bag, about eighteen inches long by fourteen inches wide and twenty inches deep. That held all they needed until they were allowed to open their cabin trunks on board the Fairlie, fourteen days after they'd set sail.

Delia wondered what her parents were thinking as they rumbled down the hill past the Rose and Crown, across Elland Bridge and up Salterhebble Hill to the centre of Halifax. Too early for many to be about they were saved last minute goodbyes, and tearful embraces. The coach would leave the White Swan at seven in the morning and travel for twenty-five hours until they reached London. Papa proposed stopping overnight at Leicester but Joe and Mary thought it better to keep moving, and then to rest little Tommie in London. Remembering his time in London 15 years before, Thomas wondered if anyone could rest in that clamour of street sellers, touts and shouting neighbours. The noise and shouting continued day and night in every London street. Joe and Mary were adamant though about the need to keep going for Tommie, and the others acquiesced. As Joe drove the cart into the Inn yard, John Baines stepped out from the shadows to take the horse's head.

*107 White Swan Inn Halifax from where London coaches departed.
(Calderdale Library, Halifax)*

"Good morning, travellers," John said. "It's soon the stagecoach will be going. Time for ye to be climbing aboard. Keep the child inside with Mother and Mary. Papa, Joe and the girls must climb to the roof."

He helped each one out of the cart. Delia was last and she straightened her skirt with care as she stood up and was handed down onto the cobbles. The stage coach stood opposite, empty of passengers and waiting with its impatient guard. Harriet, with her baby Thomas in her arms, came into the yard just at that moment.

"As always Delia, attending to your dress," she whispered to her youngest sister. And the two smiled wistfully at each other, knowing too well that this would be the last time they'd share gentle teasing.

It was Harriet's turn to wave family off. And she liked it as little as Delia had done two years earlier. Both Delia and Momo had vowed not to cry, but neither could manage. Each girl brought out their handkerchiefs to cover their faces as they clambered onto the coach roof. Peggy and Thomas, more aware than the young of how long forever was, were more stoic.

108. Last look at Elland
(From Lucy Hammerton's Book of Olde Elland, held in Elland Libary.)

Peggy gave Harriet a long embrace while the baby squawked in his father's arms. Thomas shook John's arm up and down, and up and down. At the last moment, solicitor Cadney appeared in the yard and he too shook Thomas very cordially by the hand. Joseph Baines brought his men in and they stood stiffly around the yard while the horses were put to. The horns sounded, men shouted, the girls waved handkerchiefs and within seconds they roared out of the yard, back down Salterhebble to Elland bridge and thence onto the Huddersfield Road.

Inside the coach Tommie was solemnly quiet. On the roof the girls were weeping long slow tears, and the two men were staring wordlessly over the familiar hillsides. Delia stared dumbly through the veil of water in her eyes, unable to grasp that this was truly for the 'last time' but unable to do anything other than swallow hard. Sick to the bottom of her stomach, she stuffed her handkerchief into her mouth to stop the lump in her throat. At Huddersfield they would pick up four more passengers but for now the Mellors had their journey to themselves, and they rode in damp-eyed silence.

109. The state of main roads between London and Halifax in 1840
(WYAS)

Leaving Huddersfield, the girls looked at unfamiliar landscapes and exclaimed as they saw a new mill or a new bridge. The further they went the quieter they became. They marvelled at the speed of the change of their four horses in each inn, but then so quick were the halts that they became discontented when the broth offered up to them as the horses were changed was not only thin and unappetizing but also snatched away before they could finish. By the time they reached Nottingham four hours later they wondered how they could bear any longer the shaking and rattling as the coach lurched on over ruts, cobbles and uneven stones. Delia drifted in and out of sleep. At least on the open roof seats neither she nor Mary felt queasy. That was not the case for poor little Tommie inside with his mother and grandmother. He had his head near the window so he could gulp down fresh air as they galloped through the landscape. Mary held a paperbag close to her child's face for the moments his stomach revolted against the violent movements.

Twenty-five hours later, the family were jolted awake as they turned into London's Black Bull Inn, near St. Martin the Grand. They staggered out of the coach in a daze. Porters threw their bags into a pile under the grimy small paned window of the public bar. They stood bemused, in a tight huddle, while people rushed every which way brushing past them in a most impertinent manner, according to Peggy. Joe and Mary guarded the luggage while Delia managed an exhausted and limp Tommie. Thomas went into the public bar and bespoke the family two large rooms. Dazed by the noise and bustle, they followed him upstairs, along the balcony running in front of the rooms and fell onto their beds in their travel-stained clothes. They slept for two hours until another coaching horn in the yard below shattered their troubled sleep. Thomas urged the girls to freshen up and to step outside into the Strand. He was eager to show them the sights. He was finding that he was coping better with London than he thought he would, and better than the rest of the family. His bitter experiences with his London prison was, for once, serving him well.

Daily during the following week Mary took her boy to St. James's Park and from there to Green Park, where he loved watching the sheep grazing and the cattle being driven to milking each evening. The rest of the family wandered the streets looking at shops, visiting St. Paul's Cathedral in the City and the Abbey at Westminster. One evening they went to a play at the nearby Haymarket Theatre. They went to London Zoo in Regent's Park, and wondered what birds and animals they would see in South Australia. Joe and Thomas visited their shipping agent and urgently checked that their luggage had arrived at Blackwall. By the end of the week on April 3rd, they'd had enough sightseeing and were keen to take themselves and their bags by horse omnibus down the Thames to Blackwall Dock in the East End, just as Hannah had done two years earlier.

The Fairlie lay riding at anchor in the Thames. The activity on board looked impressive. But to Peggy's frightened eyes the vessel seemed too small for the 266 passengers standing on the quayside. Delia and Momo ran to the wharfside to get a better view, and sister-in-law Mary shouted after them, "Take care, you could fall in." She held Tommie tightly, despite his vigorous protests.

110. Crowded quayside for emigrant departures from Blackwall Dock

Joe returned from the agent's office with papers clutched in his hand.

"Look," he said. "There be our bags and chests swinging onto the lighter to be boarded onto the ship." All of them stood, open mouthed, while their worldly possessions waved in the air and were lowered, too fast they feared, onto the already overloaded barge beside the dock. Four hefty dockers stood on the deck guiding the huge crates into the cavernous hold, then cast off from the dockside and pulled out to the ship on the lines connecting the Fairlie to the dockside. Their luggage was thrown up amidships.

Delia said to her sister, "What would happen if they dropped it into the river?"

"They wouldn't," said Momo, but unconvincingly.

Peggy refused even think about boarding until she knew the Turners and Walkers were in the Emigration Yard. Fortunately, before their own number was called, she saw them. Nancy's older girl, Margaret, ran up to tell her they were number 4469 and that the Walkers were 4462. Peggy sighed with relief now all were gathered close. Her face relaxed its grim guardian look as she noticed Lizzie, pale with anxiety, and Nancy, looking disapprovingly at that scamp William Walker, whose hand she was holding so firmly; no chance of him jumping off into any enticing puddles. She saw Momo and Delia being silly, giggling as they whispered together about the groups of young men waiting alongside them. Her daughter-in-law Mary, calm and preoccupied with her darling Tommie, allowed Joe to command the papers and encourage the family to keep in ordered places. He was as masterful as his father had ever been, she thought, her eyes crinkling with pride. With all the papers sorted, all the family together, all the movement solidifying in one direction towards the boats, Thomas stopped fretting about the indignity of the jostling crowd, and took his place alongside Peggy. Each family clustered tightly holding their embarkation tickets overhead. Lizzie looked backwards and waved at a small woman standing on the wharf side. Peggy wondered who she was, and Lizzie told her she'd helped her find the way through the shipyard. The family started to embark.

Each man had his embarkation number and his wife and children were counted with him on the same number; Delia and Mary, as spinsters, had their own numbers.

First on was Thomas and his wife at embarkation number 4424. Fitting, thought Thomas to himself, that he should lead his family to a new world. Next came Joseph and his family number 4425, Delia was 4426 and Momo 4427. Confident that all her family were with her Peggy trod gingerly into the barge and was pulled over to the Fairlie. Hands pulled her up the side of the boat and she stood nervously on the gently moving deck. The others followed. Once aboard, the young men disappeared to explore below decks.

Soon they returned and urged everyone to go below, to find a place in which they could berth themselves every night for the next three or four months. Delia and Momo were delighted by the little gangways and ladders up and down the decks, but the young mothers were full of foreboding for the safety of their children. Peggy helped them spread their bedding in hammocks while the men pulled out their mess utensils and went to find a narrow table with nailed down benches that they could claim as their own, even if they had to share it with another family at different times of eating. Delia wondered aloud, "Why on earth do they nail down these benches?" No one could answer; ten days later everyone knew.

At six, the men queued at the cook's hatch for the family's dinner; when finished everyone scraped their tin utensils noisily into a bigger bowl in preparation for washing-up. It took half an hour to queue for food, which was tasteless and thin. No vegetables, no fruit but some meat, which prompted Peggy to wonder as to its freshness. The ship rose and fell slightly to a small swell.

That night, with the damp smell of the Thames filling their nostrils and the creaking of the ship cracking their ears, the family eventually settled, the girls in a female-only area with five others, and each couple in their own quarters. Delia and Mary had a good laugh as they tried to climb into their hammocks, falling out spectacularly before they mastered the art of climbing into a swinging bed. Peggy grumbled rather more and found it more challenging with her less agile bones. The canvas partitions between the sleepers made every sound audible to all. Delia was distressed by the snoring coming from the other girls—and from the men the other side of the gangway. Despite this initial revulsion it was a sound she grew to ignore. Long into that first night aboard, Delia heard men calling from the loading barges as the hulls strained through the lapping tide and black, glassy depths swarmed endlessly past, taking everything down to the distant sea.

At one in the afternoon of the next day, sitting in the river on a rising tide, they saw the ball of Greenwich Observatory, high up on its hill above the river, drop abruptly, telling all shipping the state of the tide for slipping their moorings. An hour later, with everyone crowded on deck, the sailors threw lines to the two tugboats, the Samson and the London, and cast off lines holding them to the mooring buoys. The tugs tooted, funnels belched smoke and the Fairlie slipped easily into their wake as they busily towed her down the river to Gravesend. At twilight the sailors anchored and lit the riding lights at her stern and on both beams.

All afternoon, Delia had stood on deck watching the same grey flats that Hannah had seen from her ship, the Peston Bomanjee, two years earlier. Her head turned to watch each passing craft. The river was never still, always running. Barges were tied four deep to dark, damp wharves lining both banks. Hulls of ships being built towered over flat marshes and alongside mast ponds, copper workshops, grim faced cliff-high warehouses; the sound of calling men carried over the still water. Hammering, caulking, and cranking in the warren of ship-building industry on the banks of the Thames echoed across the river. Men sculled ferries over to secret stairs beneath the ancient inns on either side. Houses, smoke, warehouses and factories lay stretched on both banks before falling away into desolate marshes. Delia could scarce believe how endless it was. London lay before her: an enormity of smoke, action and soot. Was it right to leave all this behind? It was the first doubt that she had ever entertained—and she repressed it speedily.

The next day they were towed into Margate Roads, a safe anchorage off the coast of Kent. But the following morning, the tugs tooted as they chuffed back up river, the sailors set full sail and three days later the ship sailed magnificently down the Channel passing the Lizard and out into the ocean. They ran into storms, which frightened many, especially when a jib boom was carried away. With every lurch and roll of the ship all things loose slid fast across the decks: food, chests, cooking utensils, bags and boots. Delia felt better for their benches being nailed down. She sat, knowing she could hold tight and be safe. This was their first taste of rough waters and most people took ill. Few were immune. Thomas was one. He had to carry buckets to the side of the ship for everyone else. Gradually Delia and Sister Mary found their sea legs and stood on deck gulping fresh lungfuls of sea air, calming their heaving stomachs. It took longer for Joe's wife, Mary, and for Nancy to recover. Peggy and Lizzie never found their sea legs in big storms. The children fortunately were fine, even Tommie who had suffered so badly in the lurching coach that had brought them to London.

111. On board a sailing ship taking emigrants to their new lands
(National Maritime Museum, Greenwich)

The routine of life aboard engaged everyone in its detail. Everyone asked whether the barometer was rising or falling. Everyone asked the sailors how many knots they were achieving that day. And everyone rejoiced when they crossed the Line on May 17th. As Delia's book had told her, there was much merriment and some confusion. Unexpectedly, a medicine chest was upset and for some moments people were terrified that a fire had been started as smoke billowed out from the chemicals combining within the chest. Later at Evening Prayers led by the Captain, they thanked God for their safe deliverance. In June, foolish youths cut down hammocks at night with their sleeping burdens oblivious to any trouble. Passengers were incensed when they fell out of their sleep. The youths deemed it very funny—until the captain ordered their punishment: tied to the masts on deck with no food for the day.

Daily, the captain at his morning prayers, encouraged people to move or work at sewing or tell stories to each other or keep the decks clean and clear. Boredom and sitting still was not good for morale, he boomed at them. A marathon of a mile around the decks was set and a guinea reward entered on the log for the best time. This was won by a sailor in nine minutes thirteen seconds as he had to climb and descend many a ladder and circle much baggage. A few days later this record was equalled but never bettered.

Delia spent hours on the deck, pacing up and down, round and round. She met up with two courteous young men called James Bowley and George Pike. Both were bound for Adelaide and both were recording their impressions of the voyage. Delia liked to chat with them and to find out what was happening. James found it easy to chat to the sailors who often explained what was happening and where they were. Delia then re-told these stories to her family at dinner time.

But three weeks into the voyage, a child died of measles. Dr. Ware and his son were powerless to prevent a further twenty-three children from dying. James Bowley recorded each death, but Delia only cared for three, her three: baby Sarah Walker went first, soon followed by her brother William and then three year old Hannah Turner. Delia stuffed her mouth as each little body was buried at sea. Her sister Lizzie, losing her two children, became mute and wan. Nothing could coax her to talk. Delia walked away from her hovering misery. In her own grief Nancy still had a child to care for and smiled and joked to keep Margaret from seeing her in tears. Peggy was gruff, unresponsive to the moods of either of her unmarried girls. They retreated into each other's company, staring out for long hours into the receding wake of their ship. None of the men knew how to warm the cold dread in their wives, nor did they know how to soothe their own desolation. It was a sad ship that sailed across the seas.

In early June the ship was struck by a thunderbolt temporarily blinding the helm at the wheel. As the ship rolled, waves broke across the decks, sea water foamed across the ship and poured out of the gunnels; the passengers were confined below decks. Anything loose was hurled across the deck while below, belongings slid wildly with people frantic to retrieve them. No one wanted food. But still men queued at the hatches bringing it to the mess tables. With mainsail furled and bare spars the ship ran before the wind. Water sloshed on every deck sucking in the bilges. Even Delia, carefree in most of the storms, found the creaking, the groans from the beams, the cracks from the rigging, the banging of the spars, the slapping of the ropes and the rush of water around her feet quite terrifying. Peggy nursed her own terror in silence, desperate not to pass it on to her family. She clung to any bench or bar that she could hold, urging her surviving grandchildren, Tommie Fisher and Margaret Turner, to sit with her and hold very tight.

A month later in early July, Captain Edward Garret called the ship's company together at the weekly Sabbath service amidships and told them they were only days out from Port Adelaide. Gasps of excitement rustled round the ship as neighbours passed the news to those who had not heard over the wind. Delia packed, considering carefully which of the three dresses she had made on board would suit best for her entrance into Adelaide, and into her future.

Tuesday July 6th dawned bright. Passengers crowded on deck to catch their first glimpse of their new home. The sailors set anchor in

Holdfast bay and the next day sailed the ship up to Port Adelaide. It looked nothing like Blackwall Dock in London's River but more like a little wharf beside their own canal in Salterhebble, only without the surrounding hills and heavily wooded valleys. Two or three ships were lying up against the wharves and smaller boats were swimming around them loaded with crates. They could see a small rise in the land behind the ships, and one or two huts dotted on the shore.

112. Besides a South Australian river, possibly the Sturt where Thomas later farmed 85 acres (National Archives South Australia)

Delia was shocked to discover that she was expected to land by being carried on a sailor's back through the brackish water to the landing jetty. The young men carried their wives and children, Thomas waded with his trousers rolled up, and Peggy, Delia and Momo were carried by a sailor. Once landed they were expected to make their own way up the rise behind the landing place to Emigration Square. Here thirty-two weather-boarded cottages were laid out in a square with two water closets at each corner of the square, each cabin or cottage measuring twelve by twelve feet. Water and wood stored half a mile away was collected by each family. The ship disembarked the passengers, many of whom had nowhere other than these cabins for shelter. Delia's friend, George Pike, placed his family of eleven in one cabin, only to find a further five people lodged with them the following day. It was, he said, too close for any comfort although dry and the ground firm, unlike their quarters of the last three months. Delia wondered how she would miss her ship companions; four months of confinement had brought strangers very close. But irresistibly her thoughts were turning to her beloved Hansie and the children. With some fear, alongside butterflies of excitement, she prayed that all was well.

Anxiously she scanned the little rise for a view of Hannah and Joshua but with little expectation of seeing them as she thought they would have no knowledge of their arrival. She did not then know that news of ships arriving swept through the new township within moments. Adelaide took a huge interest in all ships landing in their port, carrying news and people from all over the British Empire. Sailors brought it up from the Port; small boats in the gulf of St. Vincent reported every sighting of inward bound ships. Government House, shopkeepers, workmen, traders, all passed on the news immediately they heard it. A ship was come from London it was told. People rushed eagerly for letters, for parcels and baggage, all sent from 'Home'. They extravagantly welcomed friends from neighbouring parts of the England, Ireland or Scotland that they'd left behind. Employers rushed to Emigration Square, eager to pick the best of the new workers.

Delia looked up at the rise and shouted that she could see the children. Even after two years, and much growing, the figures tumbling towards them were instantly familiar. Joseph Fisher, a sturdy six-year-old with white-blond curls falling over his face almost felled Delia, so excited was he to see her again. Eight-year-old Elizabeth, quieter than she had been and rather taller, came up more slowly, less certain of her welcome; Hannah and Joshua followed steadily. After long and fervent embraces and much exclamation about how brown and healthy everyone looked, the Fishers told them that, up behind the rise, they had one of the few drays with which they could take their boxes, chests and bags back to Adelaide. The family chatted and laughed together without drawing breath whilst the sailors unloaded skiffs full of crates from the Fairlee, setting the cargo in piles along the shore, just above the sea line. The travellers enlisted Joshua Fisher to help them locate their luggage and then he brought close the dray he had brought up from Hindley street.

Watching so many of their ship friends struggling to carry boxes and bags along a dusty track the Mellors were deeply relieved. Not for them the cottages on Embarkation Square. They would be housed with Hannah and Joshua in their shop on the corner of Hindley and Morpeth streets. While the horse-and-dray took the luggage up to the shop, the family struggled to walk and talk together. Conversations were started and left unfinished; questions asked and left unanswered. One companion gave way to another. Hannah was taking great care of her parents; she had not forgotten how badly they had felt when emigration was first broached, and wanted them to see how glad she was that they had come. Delia was talking to Elizabeth and Joe Fisher, scarcely believing that two years and two journeys halfway round the world had separated them. She found them as exciting, curious and friendly as they'd always been. She ran and jumped with them, chasing her nephew Joe when he teased her by hiding in the dunes around them.

After so long at sea, Mellors, Turners and Walkers were rolling in their walk. Death haunted them. The Fisher children laughed at their unsteady mariner's gait. Delia, surrounded by the children she had waved off two years before, walked ahead of her mother and sisters. In front of her she saw small hills, scrubby trees, dry stones and little low wooden houses. Surrounded by the eleven other adults in her family and four little ones, she struggled with relief at the end of the journey. She had arrived. Joy at reunion with her sister battled with the searing, persistent ache of devastating loss; so many babies had gone. She breathed in the warm air, imagined the pudgy and absent little hands of Sarah Fisher, Hannah Turner, and William and baby Sarah Walker, and the skeletal little Thomas Fairlie Turner left behind in his Halifax graveyard, and Alan Howe in Rishworth, and simultaneously caught with delight the stream of talk from eight-year-old Elizabeth and six-year-old-Joe Fisher. Tears rose to her eyes as she thought of those last cuddles with the warm babe, remembering the smell from the back of her neck. She felt the chill on the ship of the stiffening babies as each child lost their fight against the measles. Delia mourned those small lives, their gurgles and their soft touches. She heard the horror of the splash as the crew threw their tiny bodies into the sea and rebelled against the easy turning away made by so many onlookers.

But she also recalled Minister Tom saying at Christmas tide back in Greetland, it was time to take care of the new and the young, time to take the chances God laid out before them. Time to move away from old ways, old goals. Her journey had cost so much, all their journeys had cost the whole family, and her father's journey had cost Thomas and Peggy throughout their partnership. They all had paid, in their own way, the cost of their earth.

Those costs brought their family to this new land. They stood at the threshold of a new reality; her beloved Hansie, and her parents reunited, the wallabies and the kookaburra, the airy eucalyptus trees, and the green slopes breathing new hope, new opportunities. Content that the hard journey from the old was through, she trod upwards into her new life in South Australia. Her heart lifted and a smile played in the corner of her mouth. Delia was beginning anew. She had her life to live and her joy to pass on.

I, and her many descendants, stand today because she sailed that ocean, toiled that journey around 200 years ago. We thank you, Delia, and welcome the words your husband Daniel Brock, the godly grandson of a Particular Baptist Minister in Devon wrote about you while he was exploring your new land under the leadership of Captain Sturt on his 1844/46 expedition into the interior.

23rd January 1845

"I believe this is the anniversary of my marriage. It would be better for my whole history to be blotted from my mind, save and except that which is identified with high and heavenly principles, than I should forget the boon I was put in possession of when I was united to Delia— if anyone being has reason to be proud of his wife more than another it is myself. Not withstanding all the many disadvantages she lived under in her earlier years, she is a most desirable worthy woman. I count my union with her the greatest temporal mercy I have ever received. May our reunion be sanctified, that we may promote one another's well being, leading and urging one another on towards the high mark of our calling—May God bless her."

In March 1845-

"My beloved Delia—thinking of her sometimes interrupts that full resignation which is so desirable. She is very often the subject of my hopes and fears."

Loose Ends

113. Hindley Street, Adelaide 1845 by S. Gill—where the Fishers had their shop on the corner with Morphett Street by when Delia and Mary were both married and Hannah widowed (1844).
(SA archives.)

Adelaide grew remarkably quickly. People varied their professional careers and became involved in building a new state as port officials, as information collectors, as farmers and builders, as magistrates and government legislators—as well as explorers, gold diggers and manufacturers. This did not stop an exodus of emigrants in the early 1840s due to colonists facing economic distress. Daniel George Brock, Delia's husband, a gunsmith from Devon became first a collector of Information on colonial settlement for the newspaper The South Australian

Register and then an explorer for Captain Sturt's final exploration expedition to find the inland sea and after that a shipping agent. The tents and wooden buildings that Hannah saw in the early days were replaced ten years later by brick and stone buildings. The family continued to hold a 'holiday' hut in the hills for years—which my grandmother claimed fifty years later was an early home—and which she loved.

Personal stories and photographs after 1840

HARRISON.   (Copyright)   LEEDS

114. Early photograph of Thomas Mellor taken in Leeds indicating that he returned for a visit to England before his death in 1855 in Adelaide where he is buried besides his wife Peggy in West Terrace Cemetery. On his father's death certificate Joe recorded Thomas as aged 73, a 'woollen cloth manufacturer' and the son of Joseph Mellor. These early photographs are held by family members and shared by descendants of the Mellors on Ancestry.

In South Australia Thomas Mellor collaborated with another man and together they farmed some eighty-nine acres during the 1840s and early 50s. The fact that Peggy was well dressed if rather tired in her photo, and that it seems he travelled back to Leeds in England before his death in 1855 (perhaps after hers in 1853 in Adelaide) indicates that the family fortunes were improving.

115. Margaret (Peggy) Mellor nee Thornton (jonathanpaullambert shared this on 17 Jan 2012 on ancestry) Photograph of Peggy Thornton possibly nearing her end. It may be taken in Adelaide, Australia where she died in 1853. She looks drawn and pale. Her dress is detailed and heavy indicating that their money was not too restricted. She is buried besides her husband in the Pioneer Cemetery of West Terrace, alongside both her baby grandson Ernest and her son Joseph in the same tomb. (Family)

116. Hannah (Hansie) Johns (nee Mellor) after her second marriage in 1851 to William Johns, a widower from Cornwall with adult children. (Family)

Hannah died on September 23rd 1880 while walking with her sister Nancy Turner to an anniversary celebration of the founding of Port Adelaide. She was hit by a train near Semaphore. It is possible that she did not hear the approaching train. This was three months after she was widowed for the second time. Her obituary stated that she had been a consistent and long serving upright member of the Wesleyan Methodist Church throughout her life in South Australia.

Joshua Fisher, Hannah's husband, (1810-1843) died on 3.9.1843 at his residence in Hindley Street, after a protracted illness but aged only 32 and deeply regretted by all who knew him—according to his death notice. His widow, Hannah (Hansie) did not remarry for many years. Her son's education was assisted by a friend of Joshua's who owned the Register, an early newspaper.

117 Joseph (Joe) Fisher, Hansie's son. Courtesy of State Library of South Australia

"Few men are better known or more highly respected in business circles in Adelaide than Mr. Joseph Fisher, whose latest liberal benefactions are announced above, and whose kindly disposition and bluff, but genial, manners have won for their possessor troops of friends. Mr. Fisher has spent practically all his life in South Australia; but, unlike most of the pioneer colonists, he has never left the original settlement for more than brief intervals, and he can claim the distinction of having been engaged in business in Adelaide almost continuously since he ended his school days, about 57 years ago." (From a newspaper article)

Joseph (Joe) Fisher (1834-1880), was Hannah and Joshua's only son. His father's early death in 1844 left him aged ten, and his sister Elizabeth aged fourteen, with no further siblings. Supported by one of his father's friends through his later schooling, the proprietor of the South Australian Gazette, Joe Fisher not only became a newspaper proprietor himself but also an MP for South Australia. He visited England on several occasions.

His sister **Elizabeth Fisher,** aged seventeen, married William Garsed in 1849. That family came from Golcar, near Slaithwaite where William's brothers ran a big woollen manufacturing business handed on from their father. They were probably known by the Mellors from their own time in Greetland and Elland.

118. Joseph Mellor, a Pioneer photographed at the Anniversary Banquet of 28.12.1871 given by Edward Solomon to honour the Pioneers who landed before 1841 Chris Baker shared this on 24 Apr 2009 on Ancestry

119 Joseph Mellor, proprietor of Mellor Bros (shared by Cathy McKay 04 Jun 2016 on ancestry)

Joseph (Joe) Mellor (1809-1880) and his brothers-in-law set up a business making farm machinery called Mellor Bros. They employed significant numbers of workers. In 1861 he sent a machine to an international London exhibition and was awarded a silver medal. He handed the business onto his sons. It flourished until an economic depression in the late 1880s. He built a large house for his family in Mellor Park. Joe and his wife Mary both returned to England on visits—as did their sons. After Mary died in 1875 Joe remarried, a woman call Margaret Taylor. He is buried in West Terrace Cemetery alongside his first wife Mary, their infant daughter Mary Eva and their four sons.

Thomas Fox Mellor, their eldest son born in Halifax in 1836, died in 1891.

120. Mary Fox Mellor, Joe Mellor's first wife, 1809-1875 (photo taken from composite portraits of Pioneers at 1871 anniversary banquet put on by Edward Solomon for Pioneer Colonists who arrived before 1841 (shared by Chris Baker on 24 Apr 2009 on Ancestry and also by Sue Ouzounis on 31.7.2018).

Mary Fox nee Mellor 1809-1873. In England she had one child, a son, **Thomas (Tommie)** born in Halifax in 1836 who died 1898. In Australia she had three more sons who all carried her maiden name Fox—James (1841-1914), Benjamin (1843-1916), John (1845-1913). In 1854 she had a baby daughter, Mary Eva Fox who died the same year. She was buried in the pioneer cemetery of West Terrace, Adelaide with her husband and baby daughter.

Elizabeth (Lizzie) Mellor (1812-1884) and her husband **Richard Walker** had more children while he worked in partnership with Joe Mellor. Later the partnership was dissolved. One son, also called William was born in 1844 and died that same year. A further William John was born in 1848 and had descendants alive in 2011. Lizzie spent time in hospital with mental distress and in their old age Richard joined her there predeceasing her in 1892. She died at the same hospital, Park Hospital in 1894. She was visited by her sister Hannah the most, but also by Nancy and Delia less frequently, according to the visitor's book for the hospital. I have found no pictures of either Lizzie or Richard Walker, nor of their son William. Although the records of their emigration on the Fairlie indicate that they boarded with 2 year old William and baby Sarah there is no evidence of them surviving in Australia—and the birth of another William in 1844 suggests that his older brother was no longer living. It is possible that the records reflect the passengers that boarded rather than those who disembarked at Port Adelaide. We know that twenty-three children died on board the Fairlie of measles.

Nancy (Nance) Mellor (1813-1894) and her husband **Joshua Turner** recorded their family dates in a big family Bible. In modern times the Turner Mob is well recorded on their own ancestry website which is private. I have been unable to contact them. The family hold several photographs of her all well dressed and turned out in different and stylish outfits.

Harriet Mellor (1815-1882) and her husband **John Baines** (1812-1869) were engaged in the Halifax cloth business till John Baines died in 1861. She kept lodgers, one of whom was a young apprentice cloth worker from South Australia. Her son Joseph Thomas Baines did well, marrying twice. His children lived near Cheltenham and his grandsons served in the Great War, one of them being killed in action. Her father-in-law Joseph Baines lived until he was ninety having married three times. His last wife outlived him. A son by his second wife moved to London's Hyde Park area suggesting successful business management. I have no pictures of Harriet nor of her husband John.

Strangely in 1873 probate was granted on both Peggy's and Thomas Mellor's wills. They each left £200 to their daughter Harriet Baines of Halifax although they died in Australia twenty and eighteen years prior to the proving of their wills in London. No one else received any other portion. It is possible that her husband's early death in 1869 had left her in reduced circumstances and her brother and sisters managed to pass on this money discretely so she should not be embarrassed by 'charity' from them.

121. Linked to Sidney Malin in 1877, the son of Mary Mellor and Job Gould Malin at Lipson Street, Port Adelaide (shared by sue ouzounis on 28.9.2017 on ancestry.)

Mary Mellor (1817-1904) married twice—Job Gould Malin who died in 1856 leaving three children, then John Lavin by whom she appears to have no further children—I have found no pictures.

122. Delia "Lucy" Brock nee Mellor, the youngest of the six Mellor girls, in a posed photograph. I imagine the stern face is due to the great length of time sitters had to keep still while the exposure ran for long minutes. (Family)

Delia "Lucy" Mellor (1820-1886) married Daniel Brock (1811-1867) in January 1842. Daniel was a gunsmith, explorer, recorder and shipping agent. They had three girls and one surviving son. This son, Thomas Alsop Brock, became a shipping agent and fathered seven sons and four girls, the third of whom was my grandmother Delia Brock born in 1890, seventy years after Delia was born in Greetland and fifty years after she arrived in Australia. My grandmother related to me that her father said her grandmother Delia—after whom she was named—was one of the strongest of women.

123. Daniel George Brock and his dog at Poole's Grave.

124. Daniel George Brock (shared by Vicki burns 2.9.2014 on ancestry)

On 24th January 1842 **Delia** married **Daniel George Brock**, formerly of Honiton, Devon, England who had emigrated in the Royal Admiral in 1838. Their first son, William, was born in May 1843 but died while his father was on the 1844 exploration with Captain Sturt seeking Australia's 'inland sea'. He wrote his accounts of two Australian expeditions for his mother Anne Alsop who lived with her second husband and third son, both called James Bridle, gunsmiths in Barnstaple. It was noted that he enclosed a lock of hair from her grandson's 'bonny poll'. These papers were sent to Daniel's older brother, Reverend William Brock in Norwich. Later William was called by the Baptist Congregation in Bloomsbury Chapel, London and led that chapel for twenty years, generously supported by the architect and property developer, Samuel Morton Peto who designed and built Lowestoft Railway Station. Bloomsbury Chapel in North London matched the Elephant and Castle chapel in South London under the leadership of Spurgeon, the great Baptist revivalist. William Brock served until his wife's death in 1871 and died in Eastbourne two years later.

Daniel kept journals of his expeditions two of which have survived, Recollections of DGB 1843 and To the Desert with Sturt. The exploration party left Adelaide in June 1844 and returned 28th January 1846.

During this expedition he recorded the third anniversary of his wedding. Both the books were published by the Royal Agricultural Society of South Australia.

In April 1845 Daniel records his thoughts turning to his dear Delia at this time hoping she is well (probably near the date of delivery of their second child). He then records that on 19th January 1846 the party were about sixty miles from the Darling River exhausted and short of water. The next day they received contact with a party from Adelaide and he heard that his son William had died, but that his wife and baby daughter (called Kitty) were well. HOME on 28th January 1846, he wrote.

Daniel did no more expeditions but became a shipping agent. Delia and he had two more girls, Mary, Delia Ann, and a son, Thomas Alsop Brock (born 1849). Daniel died in 1867 and Delia died in 1886 both in Adelaide. Their son, Thomas, lived in one of three bungalows in Semaphore beside the sea, with his own large family. His sisters—Kitty Gardiner and Delia Annie Bayley lived in the other two with their families. Both are buried in West Cemetery, Adelaide. Mary married a Tapley and moved to the South Island in New Zealand where she is buried in Dunedin.

125. Thomas Alsop Brock photographed in Adelaide with his wife and first four children (family)

126. Later in life, Thomas with his two sisters, Kitty Gardiner and Delia Ann Bayly, who lived beside him in a trio of bungalows in Semaphore. His third sister Mary married a Tapley and later moved to South Island, New Zealand. The one Gardiner girl, plus the eleven Brock children, grew up alongside the seven Bayly brothers and their one sister Nor-Nor who mothered them when her mother died aged 46 in 1898. (Family)

Thomas Alsop Brock (1849-1933) Delia Mellor's only surviving son, father to Delia Gladys Brock, my grandmother with his wife Hannah Bonnar and their first four children. The second daughter, Hazeldine died aged two of diphtheria and Alsop, the second son died aged sixteen of consumption. The youngest daughter, Madge Brock, died in England of an asthma attack in 1937 aged forty-five. Halcombe and George were killed in the Great War. The remaining six lived to their three score years and ten—or longer. Thomas was proud of being TAB and was widely called Uncle Tom—as reported by his English granddaughter, Jocelyn Delia Harvie Bennett.

127. George Brock, (1888-1818) artillery man, Australian forces, gassed on the Somme in June 1918. He was the second son of Thomas Alsop Brock to be killed in the Great War.

Halcombe Brock (1886-1915) died at Gallipoli in 1915. George was the next brother up from my grandmother, and Halcombe the next one again. Delia Gladys Brock, kept these pictures in her desk for the rest of her life. Her father, TAB or Thomas Alsop Brock, wrote to her in July 1918 to tell her of her mother's distress at George's death and to share her relief that her own husband, Dr. Frank Bennett was found to be a prisoner of war in Poland, not as feared 'missing presumed dead'.

128. Delia Gladys Brock on her 18th birthday in Adelaide - around the time she met her future husband, a ship's doctor on a vessel sailing from Fremantle in Western Australia to Adelaide. Delia Gladys was the author's much loved grandmother. (family)

Delia Gladys Brock (1890-1974), TAB's daughter, and the second surviving sister of George and Halcombe, was eighteen when she first met her future husband, Dr. Frank Harvie Bennett on board ship between Freemantle and Adelaide. They married in England in Southampton in July 1911 after he had returned to England to secure himself a medical practice in Walton-on-Thames rather than continue as a serving ship's doctor. Her younger sister Madge accompanied Delia as did her mother Dottie on the voyage to Southampton in 1911. The Great War then intervened and Delia did not see her parents again till they visited England for the last time in 1922—and gave their grand-daughter Jocelyn Delia a dog.

129. Jocelyn Delia Harvie Russell (nee Bennett) and author's mother - aged 101 in 2015 with her grand-daughter Esme Mary Delia and two of her great-grandchildren on the day the Duchess of Cornwall met her while opening the New Village Hall in Stourpaine, Dorset. In 2017 the children's second cousin, Cora Delia was born, the great-great-great-great grand daughter of Delia Mellor, 6th and last daughter of Thomas and Peggy Mellor born in Greetland, West Yorkshire in 1820. (Author)

Jocelyn Delia Harvie Russell (nee Bennett) 1914-2015. She was born in Walton-on-Thames, Surrey where her father had bought a medical practice after serving in a psychiatric hospital in Tooting and as a ship's doctor after his early graduation from St. Mary's Hospital London. Her older brother Nigel, named after her mother's elder brother, was two when she was born. When their father was called up as a medic in 1916 they moved with their mother to rented accommodation in Bognor. The locum doctor who took the practice during her father's war service kept for himself many of her father's former patients. During the twenties her father suffered poor health from his wartime trench fever. Her mother's Australian family visited and the carpets were rolled up for dancing. She had a wide and varied career during the 30s and 40s and travelled widely including a visit to Australia. After raising her family in London she moved with her husband first to Hertfordshire and later to a village in Dorset where she served the community competently, assiduously and conscientiously for forty years. Her grand-daughter named Esme Mary Delia in honour of Delia Gladys Brock lived nearby in Southampton and attended the opening of the Village Hall with these two great-grandchildren. In 2010 aged ninety-six, Jocelyn published her memoir, *Child of the British Empire*. This books tells the story of her predecessors travelling into her story as Empire Builders and Colonists—not always a good story but a human story of struggle and survival which has shaped so much of today's world.

LOSSES

At least eight of the great-grandsons of Thomas and Peggy whether in England or Australia, served in the Empire forces and lost their lives due to action in France and Gallipoli between 1914-1918. This story honours their loss and their fight. May it remind future generations that war is a deadly and hugely costly outcome for any family or community.

130. Proclamation Day, 28ᵗʰ December, 1836 at the Old Gum Tree, Glenelg, Adelaide.
Colony of South Australia established in Australia and by Act of Parliament in Westminster showing first Governor Hindmarsh and first settlers 21 months before Hannah and Joshua Fisher landed.
(Australian national library archives.)

Author's Descent from Delia Mellor

FIRST GENERATION
Thomas 1782-1855   married   Peggy Thornton 1785-1853

SECOND GENERATION
Their seventh child and sixth daughter
Delia 'Lucy' Mellor 1820-1886   married   Daniel George Brock 1811-1876

THIRD GENERATION - SISTER DELIA ANN BROCK
Their only son and his middle sister Delia Ann Tapley
Thomas Alsop Brock 1849-1933   married   Hannah Dottie Bonnar 1855-1929

FOURTH GENERATION - GREAT WAR CASUALTIES
Their eighth child and third daughter
Delia Gladys Brock 1890-1974   married   Frank Harvie Bennett 1881-1960

FIFTH GENERATION
Their second child and only daughter
Jocelyn Delia Harvie Bennett 1914-2015   married   George 'Charles' Russell 1899-1971

SIXTH GENERATION
Their first child and daughter
Caroline Susan Russell b 1947   married   David John Clark 1947-2020

SEVENTH GENERATION
Their second child and daughter
Esme Mary Delia Clark b 1978   married   Angus Ferguson

SIXTH GENERATION
Only son of fifth generation
Charles Harvie Russell b. 1951   married   Gillie Smith

SEVENTH GENERATION
Their only daughter
Alice Russell b. 1982   married   Alex

EIGHTH GENERATION
Their first daughter
Cora Delia b. 2017

Eight generations after Peggy and Thomas Thornton
Six generations of Delia's name—only one absence in eight generations

Acknowledgements

Information: I have been blessed with access to impressive libraries both in person and on line. It is wonderful to find places where one can check factual detail of the time with confidence—Calderdale Library and Archives, Halifax and Elland branches of that library, Huddersfield Library and Huddersfield University Archives and Library—all their librarians were kind, helpful and encouraging. They deserve great thanks as the life of research is lonely and their support drives improved accuracy and depth. On line I am very grateful for the historical records and pictures held by both The National library of Australia and the South Australia Archives. The records they hold of the life of emigrants and their ships are extensive and illuminating. They are hugely helpful in trying to explain the story of migrants. Contemporary prints and pictures held by local libraries run by Kirklees and Calderdale Authorities illuminate both the similarities and differences between life in 1820 and 2020 while modern photographs indicate what those same places look like today.

In addition the archives and libraries of local historical societies are impressive and helpful and the people tending them kind and informative about their areas. In particular the kindness and information from members of the Huddersfield Family History Society at Holmfirth—and the encouragement from a member of the Halifax Historical Association—kept me going through the quagmire of Mellors and clothiers so abundant in Calderdale.

Friends and supporters—In writing up this work I have had tremendous support from Katie Isbester at Claret Press. Not only has she carefully led me through the complexity of publishing today, edited my work checking out detals of grammar, punctuation, clarity and expressiveness but she pruned and rearranged where necessary. Most crucially however she set my guiding star helping to bring this complex story spread over 40 years, with a cast of nine people in one family, into a coherent story. She told me to set its purpose into one sentence of what it was about. Every time I struggled to weave consistency and coherence through this tangled web I returned to that star and found detail and character falling into place.

Clapham Writers' Group has been a source of strong and expert guidance in phrasing my words, in developing the necessary points of view, and in articulating each character. It has been, even throughout the dramas of our Covid years, a source of support, encouragement and friendship. I recommend any aspiring writer to find such a kind and thoughtful group to support them.

My dearest daughters-in-law have both read parts of this work and both have given me great encouragement and confidence to continue. Their validation, and the interest of my sons-in-law have accorded me much strength to persevere; as has the kindness and interest of my friends, Charlotte Robinson and Julia Jama. My children have listened patiently to the regular updates about how the story is going with attentiveness and kindness and I have drawn much needed support from their interest—even when the great business of family living leaves little time for delving into the world of 200 years ago. Many insights expressed in the book lie in the care and comfort the whole family gives each other week in and week out, in trouble and in fun. I am so grateful for this loyalty and enthusiasm.

And lastly, I must mention my enquiring and curious grandchildren. I wanted to pass on history to them. I had no idea how important would be their questions about what was happening where, their interest in what I was doing and their confidence that it was all worth doing. Their voices kept me going and gave me direction. I have dedicated the book to them and to my dynamic, enterprising and intelligent mother, their great-grandmother Jocelyn Delia Russell who lived vigorously until her end aged 101, always interested in what the future would hold for the great-grandchildren she loved. It is they who can now hold in respect the lives led by her ancestors as they struggled with difficulties and persisted in expanding their horizons right across the world. I trust their example will inspire these children of the 21st century to change their worlds just as their ancestors changed theirs in the early 19th century.

While records show that this family existed, there is nothing that showed me their thinking or their characters. I have deduced these from my wider reading and knowledge and from my observance of people throughout my life. This story is fictional though set in real places, in a real period, with real people at precise and accurate times. No one of the characters mentioned describes any single person of my acquaintance. Any inaccuracies are entirely mine—and inevitable in telling a story so distant in time and circumstances. I have done my best to make it realistic and comprehensible for today's readers by bridging the gap between my historical knowledge and my current understanding of life. It is my best effort to provide a narrative of one emigrating family's endeavours—and if I fail in this it is my fault alone. I trust I succeed.

Clapham
22.7.22

Sources

ancestry.co.uk—This well-known and invaluable charging site recording public records, family information and connecting them through family trees enabled my research hugely by finding odd connections and cross checking their reliability. It can become a rabbit hole of information—and may have some bearing on the length of time this book and its research have taken me—but I could not have achieved the level of accurate information without this tool.

Once on the internet I wandered from site to site discovering information from South Australia Archives and Australia National Library about the early emigrants and the ships in which they sailed. This underpinned the final chapter about the voyage in the Fairlie. I did not follow up stories about life in Australia, fascinating though it was—that was just too much additional and distracting information.

Personal papers—not many of these but some work done by a Brock neighbour of my grandmother's in 1930s Walton-on-Thames to see if there was a family connection (there wasn't but it meant the family tree was traced back to Daniel Brock's birth in Honiton in 1811). Ancestry site confirmed these links.

Two published books written by Daniel Brock, my great-great grandfather who married Delia Mellor in January 1842 and joined Captain Sturt's exploratory expedition in 1843, returning in 1844 having failed to discover the hoped for 'inland sea'. The first was

An Account of Australia about his expedition to gather information about the early settlers for the Australian Register, and the second *Dan-*

iel Brock, Traveller written as an account for his mother and not published until 1947.

In addition I found a typed foolscap in my grandmother's papers referring to Joseph Mellor's antecedents. Included in these papers were copies of original photos from the mid-nineteenth century, mostly from Solomon's studio in Rundle Street, Adelaide.

Snippets of chat passed on by my mother and my grandmother—gave me glimpses of a different life in South Australia—milking cows, chapel attendance rather than anglican, possible shop run by our ancestors.

Research in Yorkshire—I visited Halifax Library, Elland Library, Huddersfield Library, and the University of Huddersfield Library. I found copies of the 1860s book of illustrations of Yorkshire life, another book of drawings of local houses from early nineteenth century West Riding, Lucy Hammerton's 1890s printed copy of her memoir of Elland life in 1820s. I found newspaper accounts and council publications from 2012 explaining the Luddite murder of William Horsfall. Accounts of church and chapel centenaries gave wonderful pictures of past members and information about their communal activities and development. All these libraries were courteous, helpful and fascinating sources of information about their areas in the 1800s. They also held deep reserves of writing about the crafts, industries and industrial development of the West Riding.

Local books about the area and its history—Huddersfield and Halifax both have good informative photographs in books about their history and geography. I used a CD of Watson's History of Halifax Antiquities written from the Vicarage in 1785 and bought copies of histories by current local historians.

I joined the Huddersfield Family History Association and found their library in Holmfirth a haven of knowledgeable and helpful people.

I met with a learned member of Halifax Historical Society and, in an illuminating chat in her car, she reinforced my enquiries about Minister Thomas Mellor of the Roadside Chapel in Rishworth.

I watched episodes of BBC's Gentleman Jack whose story took place at Shibden Hall, Halifax at the same time as my Mellor story—and read excerpts from modern books about her life—focusing on the relationships between her family as landlords and their tenants—and her battle with the local banker Rawson over coal mining interests.

Importantly, I visited the area and walked vigorously over the hills, across stone bridges, up cobbled paths, past stone cottages and farms, through enchanted woods, and into churches and chapels. As a southerner living in low rise London I realised that no work would be accurate if it failed to mention the steep hills—and the canopy of woodland trees lining so many valleys. I walked down from Halifax through Skircoat and across the river Calder up the other side to Greetland. Another day took me over Ainley Top and down to Huddersfield. Then in the rain, I explored Rishworth and Ripponden.

The most exhilarating and exciting building I encountered was the magnificent Halifax Piece Hall—where I found the painting of merchants assembling to trade pieces of cloth. St. John's Halifax was a refreshing setting for a modern concert one evening and I discovered the Square Chapel closely connected with the new Calderdale Library. I even found Gaol Street in Halifax, with the Gaol recently demolished. Huddersfield and Halifax both had shopping areas redolent of their past and gave me delicious meals after my research was done.

I walked up the old Marsden Road to the site of William Horsfall's murder and from there down to Dungeon Bottom and to Dungeon Mill following the leaflet explaining the walk.

Lastly, and critically, I visited the Weaver's House in Golcar, in the Colne Valley. This is a house lovingly preserved by local people and presented with great accuracy as to living and working conditions for wool people of the mid-nineteenth century. It shows how life was lived in the West Riding woollen industry of the nineteenth century and is a privilege and joy to visit.

Contemporary writing—I read excerpts from Daniel Defoe's Journeys round Britain (1724), Charlotte Bronte's Shirley (1848) about the Luddite Risings in 1812. In the past I read works by Mrs. Gaskell, Charles Dickens, George Eliot, and John Bunyan's Pilgrim's Progress— all of which informed my historical understanding and sensitivity.

Current Historical work—I found a wealth of work covering this fascinating period of huge change wrought by the Industrial Revolution. These new books deepened the understanding I had acquired at the University of Kent at Canterbury in 1966-1969. I owe an interest in this period to my tutor J. Oxborrow who set me my first essay in Economic History as a question as to whether or not the standard of living rose or fell in 1820s England. My answer then was that largely it depends on who you were and where you lived. I don't think the answer today is substantially different but expanded attitudes and views which have developed over the last 50 years give much more detail, and much more nuance. Authors in particular who stand out are Jenny Uglow, Keith Thomas and Judith Flanders. I list the books in my bibliography including some work on the challenging history of debt at the time.

Photographs—Counter to common practice I have mixed modern photographs of actual places around Halifax and Huddersfield with contemporary prints, pictures and maps which I found in Calderdale Libraries. I have sourced old family photos revealing some of the characters in this book in studio photos. South Australia Libraries and Australian National Archives hold some of the prints by S. Gill and others of early days in Adelaide—and of the early ships that took so many emigrants to new lands from old Europe during the nineteenth century. Not all of the photos have modern standards of pixels but I hope the pictures I have chosen add to my book's revelation of the differences and similarities in family lives two centuries apart.

Bibliography

General

Iron, Steam and Money: The Making of the Industrial Revolution (2014) Roger Osborne

The Forging of the Modern State, 1783-1870 (1983, 1986) Eric J Evans

The Making of Home: The 500 Year Story of How Our Houses Became Homes (2014) Judith Flanders

Eavesdropping on Jane Austen's England: How Our Ancestors Lived Two Centuries Ago (2013) Roy and Lesley Adkins

The Character of Credit: Personal Debt in English Culture 1740-1914 (2003) Margot C Finn

Behind Closed Doors: At Home in Georgian England (2009) Amanda Vickery

The Worst Poverty: A History of Debt and Debtors (1991) Hugh Barty King

In Pursuit of Civility: Manners and Civilisation in Early Modern England (2018) Keith Thomas

Family Fortunes: Men and Women of the English Middle Class 1780-1850 (1987) Davidoff and Hall

In These Times: Living in Britain through Napoleon's Wars 1793-1815: (2014) J. Uglow

The World of Defoe (1976) Peter Earle

The Peterloo Massacre (1989) Robert Reid

George III: Majesty and Madness (2020) Jeremy Black

Local

Halifax 1842: A Year of Crisis (2014) Catherine Howe

Huddersfield in the 1820s (2009) Edward J Law

Halifax Through Time (2010) Stephen Gee

Laithes and Looms, Cows and Combstocks: Living and Dying in Marsden 1655-1855 (2013) H. Seidel

The Huddersfield Narrow Canal: Two Hundred Years in the life of a Pennine Waterway (2010) Keith Gibson and David Finnis

History of the Huddersfield Woollen Industry (1988) W. B.Crump and G. Ghorbal

Liberty or Death: Radicals, Republicans and Luddites 1793-1823 (2012) A. Brooke and L. Kipling

Under the Canopy of Heaven: A Luddite Novel (2018) Georgina Hutchison

Shirley (1849) Charlotte Bronte

Female Fortune: Land, Gender and Authority—The Anne Lister Diaries and Other Writings 1833-36 (1998) Jill Liddington

Marsden, A Journey through Time (2014-2016) J. Thorpe and M. Pinder

ancestry.co.uk. Parish records of birth, deaths, marriage and census returns—among other records

A History of Olde Elland (1901) Lucy Hammerton

Milton Keynes UK
Ingram Content Group UK Ltd.
UKHW021113180124
436199UK00007B/21